THE
MITOCHONDRION

THE
MITOCHONDRION
Molecular Basis of Structure and Function

ALBERT L. LEHNINGER

Department of Physiological Chemistry

The Johns Hopkins University School of Medicine

W. A. BENJAMIN, INC.

New York   Amsterdam

1964

THE MITOCHONDRION
Molecular Basis of Structure and Function

Library of Congress Catalog Card Number 64–13923
Manufactured in the United States of America

*The manuscript was put into production on 10 October 1963;
this volume was published on 28 April 1964*

*The publisher is pleased to acknowledge the assistance of
Galen H. Fleck, who copyedited the manuscript, and
William Prokos, who designed the book and dust
jacket, and produced the illustrations*

W. A. BENJAMIN, INC.
2465 Broadway, New York 10025

EDITOR'S FOREWORD

This book is the first to appear in a Series of Monographs in Microbial and Molecular Biology. The purpose of this series is to encourage and sponsor the publication of carefully selected and edited short monographs, of approximately 150 pages, on topics in the forefront of research in these fields.

Each book in the series will present a more comprehensive review of its topic, and a broader perspective, than is ordinarily possible in a review article. The presentations are intended to be sufficiently detailed, and thoroughly enough documented and illustrated, so that the advanced student will be able to obtain a comprehensive and up-to-date grasp of an actively developing area without having to refer extensively to original papers. To facilitate access to especially important experimental detail or theoretical development, reprints of key papers will at times be included.

These volumes are not primarily reference works, and they will differ from the traditional monograph in not necessarily covering every relevant reference. The rapid proliferation of the scientific literature makes it increasingly difficult for the experienced investigator, let alone the graduate student, to rely on his coverage of original articles to keep him informed of important advances across the general field of microbial and molecular biology. Hence the editor and the publisher believe that appropriate re-

v

views are of increasing value; and for this purpose it seems to us more important that the reviews be critical and lucid than that they be exhaustive. Accordingly, we encourage the authors to be selective, to speculate on immediate problems and on directions of future advance, and to editorialize in much the same way as they would in lecturing to their own students. The present, first volume, however, deals with a rather larger topic than most volumes in the series, and so the coverage has necessarily been less detailed.

I hope that this series of volumes will be of value to the scientific community. Criticisms and suggestions will be welcomed.

BERNARD D. DAVIS

Boston, Massachusetts
March 1964

PREFACE

It is now some fifteen years since the mitochondria were first recognized to be the "power plants" of aerobic cells, in which the energy freed in oxidation of cellular foodstuffs is converted into the phosphate bond energy of adenosine triphosphate. In this period enzymologists have studied the reaction patterns of biological oxidations and phosphorylation of mitochondria. Electron microscopists have analyzed their conformation, structure, and distribution. Cell physiologists have measured their capacity for ion transport, and the geneticists have reviewed their role in evolution of cellular organization.

From these efforts, the outlines of an edifice of knowledge are beginning to arise. It is now a good time to stand back and contemplate this structure, perhaps in the terms used by Lewis and Randall many years ago in describing the evolution of thermodynamics as a science. They likened thermodynamics to an ancient cathedral and said:

"The labor of generations of architects and artisans has been forgotten, the scaffolding erected for their toil has long since been removed, their mistakes have been erased, or have become hidden by the dust of centuries. . . .

"But sometimes we enter such an edifice that is still partly under construction; then the sound of hammers, the reek of tobacco, the trivial jests bandied from workman to workman, enable us to realize that these great structures are but the result of giving to ordinary human effort a direction and a purpose."

Current research on the mitochondrion may very aptly be pictured as a busy scene of construction, where the rising structure is still hidden by scaffolding. Here artisans of many guilds ply their traditional skills, each group intent on its specific task. There is a great sound of hammers and the shouts of the workmen are often strident. To formulate an impression of this new edifice, we must tour the site of construction, peer behind the scaffolding, gather reports from the architects and artisans, and then retreat out of earshot to reflect on the purpose and direction of this effort.

The aim of this book, then, is to collect and interpret the rapidly growing experimental information on the mitochondrion, not only the basic enzymology of the biological oxidations and phosphorylations which appear to constitute the major activities of the mitochondrion, but also many other aspects, such as ion transport, membrane contractile phenomena, control and integration mechanisms, the molecular structure of the mitochondrial membrane, and the origin and biogenesis of these structures. It seems most timely to attempt such an integration of information and ideas on the mitochondrion at this stage of development. The experimental literature on electron transport, oxidative phosphorylation, and the dynamics of mitochondrial reactions has been growing enormously in both volume and complexity, as this field attracts increasing numbers of investigators. It is becoming more and more difficult for the non-expert to grasp the essence of the major developments, which are sometimes obscured by vigorous controversies and by laboratory jargon. More than this, there is now a rapidly growing body of information relating the purely enzymatic aspects of electron transport and oxidative phosphorylation with active transport of ions by mitochondria, with cycles of volume and shape changes, and most significantly, with the molecular and geometric organization of mitochondrial structure. These interrelationships deserve to be more widely appreciated and understood, not only by students but also by active investigators in the field. But most important is the fact that the molecular structure and the dynamic function of the mitochondrion are now beginning to illuminate and define each other, in the finest sense implied by the term *molecular biology*. Thus, in the mechanism of energy-coupled respiration may lie the secret of the ultrastructure of the mitochondrion, and, conversely, in the molecular organization of the mitochondrion may lie the secret of electron transport and oxidative phosphorylation. Since there are available no recent monographs or reviews of research on the mitochondrion written from this broader point of view, it is hoped that this effort will be found to fill a unique need.

This book is intended not only for research workers and students interested in the enzymology of respiration and oxidative phosphorylation and other aspects of mitochondrial activity, but also for graduate and undergraduate students in the fields of biochemistry, cytology, cell physiology, and molecular biology. It was the intent to provide an easily read interpretative account of the contributions of many laboratories and many points of view. In addition, however, the book provides a key to the entire literature of the mitochondrion, which is so necessary for the research worker in this field.

The actual form of bibliographic reference requires special comment. To preserve maximum readability, it was decided not to interrupt the text with frequent citations of references and footnotes, and with the inevitably minute weighings of pros and cons so characteristic of the traditional monograph. Rather each chapter is provided with a carefully chosen list of review articles, which provide the full historical background. These are supplemented by a list of recent research articles which are discussed in the text and which are representative of what the author considers to be the most significant current experimental developments. Both reviews and research articles are listed with full titles. It is believed that the experimental basis for any fact mentioned in the text can be found in the literature on brief perusal of the bibliography cited. Thus it is hoped the book will be useful to the active investigator and at the same time readable for the student.

A book which purports to interpret existing knowledge to a non-expert audience must of course clearly separate fact from speculation. But if it is to make any impact on future research, it must also glimpse ahead to the horizons of the problem, and attempt to formulate hypotheses and predictions and to engender a receptive outlook toward future developments. It is hoped that some of the ideas offered may be found of interest.

ALBERT L. LEHNINGER

Baltimore, Maryland
February, 1964

ACKNOWLEDGMENTS

The author is greatly indebted to some of his colleagues in the Department of Physiological Chemistry, The Johns Hopkins University School of Medicine, for criticism and advice. He is also grateful to Dr. George E. Palade and especially Dr. Bernard Davis, who read the entire manuscript carefully and provided numerous helpful suggestions. However, the author must bear sole responsibility for all shortcomings.

The author's most heartfelt acknowledgment is to his wife and children, who cheerfully encouraged this effort.

A. L. L.

CONTENTS

9 ENERGY-COUPLED CHANGES OF VOLUME AND STRUCTURE

10 THE ULTRASTRUCTURE OF THE MITOCHONDRIAL MEMBRANE AND THE RESPIRATORY ASSEMBLY

ABBREVIATIONS

A minimum number of abbreviations have been employed to preserve readability; the following have been used because of their familiarity.

ATP	adenosine 5'-triphosphate
ADP	adenosine 5'-diphosphate
AMP	adenosine 5'-monophosphate

Similarly, GTP, ITP, and CTP for the corresponding guanosine, inosine, and cytidine 5'-triphosphates.

P_i	inorganic phosphate
$\sim$	high-energy bond
NAD^+, NADH	oxidized and reduced forms of nicotinamide adenine dinucleotide, according to recommendations of Enzyme Commission of the International Union of Biochemistry. These are equivalent to DPN^+ and DPNH, respectively.
$NADP^+$, NADPH	oxidized and reduced form of nicotinamide adenine nucleotide monophosphate (equivalent to TPN^+ and TPNH, respectively).
FAD	flavin adenine dinucleotide
FMN	flavin mononucleotide
CoA	coenzyme A

GSH, GSSG	reduced and oxidized glutathione, respectively
FP	flavoprotein
FP_1	NADH dehydrogenase
FP_2	succinate dehydrogenase

THE
MITOCHONDRION

1

HISTORY AND SCOPE

Since the early 1950s, biochemical studies of the enzymatic mechanisms of the oxidative cycles, electron transport, and oxidative phosphorylation have proceeded in confluence with studies of the structure and cell biology of the mitochondrion. The fruits of this confluence will be considered in detail in the following chapters. Here we shall first consider the major historical developments in each of these two mainstreams of biological research, their coming together, and the scope of the discussion to follow.

THE HISTORY OF THE MITOCHONDRION
AS A CYTOPLASMIC STRUCTURE

It is not possible to specify who first discovered the mitochondria as distinctive cytoplasmic organelles. Actually, in the years 1850–1890 many cytologists observed granular elements and inclusions in the cytoplasm of different cells, some undoubtedly artifacts, to which they assigned many names and functions. Perhaps Kölliker deserves particular mention, since he was among the first to describe characteristically arranged granules in the sarcoplasm of striated muscle and to study them systematically over a period of years beginning about 1850. These granules, which were later to be called *sarcosomes* by Retzius in 1890, were at first thought to be present only in muscle, but today we recognize the sarcosomes as the mitochondria of muscle tissue. Kölliker should also be credited with the first separation of mitochondria from cell structure. In 1888 he teased these granules from insect muscle, in which they are very profuse, found them to swell in water, and showed them to possess a membrane.

In the 1880s Flemming recognized characteristic filamentous structures in the cytoplasm of many cells. He termed these structures *fila,* and today we can recognize them with certainty to be mitochondria. It was not until 1890, however, that Altmann developed a greatly superior stain that was relatively specific for the granules and made possible systematic observations on granule occurrence. Altmann wrote a somewhat visionary and highly speculative book, entitled *Elementarorganismen,* in which he suggested that these structures were autonomous, elemental living units, which he called *bioblasts,* and he postulated them to be the ultimate "elementary living particles" of cellular life. He visualized bioblasts to be similar to bacteria and capable of living independently or in colonies in the cytoplasm of the host cell. Altmann also speculated broadly on the genetic and metabolic implications of such self-contained "elementary organisms."

The next significant advances came ten years later. In 1898 Benda introduced crystal violet as a stain for mitochondria and Michaelis introduced the principle of *supravital staining* of mitochondria with Janus green. The work of Michaelis is particularly significant, since it showed that mitochondria in living cells could bring about oxidation-reduction changes in a dye. It was Benda who first coined the name *mitochondrion,* derived from the Greek *mitos,* a thread, and *chondros,* a grain. However this term was not immediately accepted; it was but one of a welter of names that had been applied to the granules by various investigators in this early period. Cowdry has listed some of them: blepharoblasts, chondriokonts, chondriomites, chondrioplasts, chondriosomes, chondriospheres, fila, fuchsinophilic granules, interstitial bodies, körner, fädenkörner, mitogel, parabasal bodies, plasmasomes, plastochondria, plastosomes, spheroplasts, and vermicules, among others. Of all these terms, perhaps only the name *chondriosome* deserves preservation, along with *mitochondrion,* as being both apt and euphonious.

Meves and other investigators in the early decades of the twentieth century did much to stimulate study of mitochondria, although Meves' expansive theories on the role of mitochondria in cellular differentiation and as bearers of hereditary characteristics, published in 1918, were quite erroneous. Actually, the speculations of most early cytologists centered on a genetic role. It was not until 1912 that Kingsbury called attention to the possibility that the mitochondria were the sites of cellular oxidations. He considered the mitochondria to be the "structural expression of reducing substances in cell respiration." It is interesting that in 1913 Warburg found respiration to be associated with granular, insoluble elements of cell structure, which he recovered by filtration of tissue dispersions, but the significance of his observation was not developed further by cytologists of the day.

Regaud, in 1908, was the first to conclude that mitochondria contain phospholipid and protein, on the basis of their response to specific stains. These techniques provided a sounder basis for the chemical similarity of mitochondria in different types of cells and made possible differentiation of mitochondria from other granular inclusions of the cytoplasm. The development of better fixing and staining methods in this period was followed by extensive and systematic observations of the number, size, orientation, and distribution of mitochondria in many different cell types that finally established the mitochondrion as a universally occurring component of aerobic cells. Cowdry's important review of the early literature on mitochondria, published in 1918, summarizes this work in great detail.

A new approach of major significance emerged in the work of Lewis and Lewis beginning in 1914. They painstakingly studied the behavior of individual mitochondria in living cells in tissue culture and found them to undergo changes with time in their shape, size, and location. These observations suggested that mitochondria play a dynamic role and possess plasticity of structure; they were forerunners of modern exploration of mitochondria in living cells with phase-contrast optics and time-lapse movies. These and other observations indicated that the number, size, and location of the mitochondria in the cell were often expressions of the cell's nutritional or endocrine state. A metabolic or respiratory function for the mitochondrion was increasingly favored, and less attention was placed on a primarily genetic role.

The beginning of a new era of cytological research on mitochondria was signaled by the important exploratory work of Bensley in the early 1930s on the attempted isolation of mitochondria from broken-cell dispersions of liver tissue by means of differential centrifugation. Although Bensley's efforts failed to yield intact mitochondria, for lack of appropriate suspending media and centrifugation procedures, he was fully aware of the potential value of having relatively large amounts of isolated mitochondria available for direct biochemical analysis. It was Bensley's pioneering work that presaged the confluence of cytological work on mitochondria with biochemical research on respiration.

HISTORY OF RESEARCH ON RESPIRATION

The study of animal respiration has an ancient and noble lineage as a scientific problem, and it has had a fundamental impact on some of the most crucial developments in the history of chemistry, physics, and biology over the past two centuries. Lavoisier's experiments in 1780 on the requirement of oxygen by living things aided the demise of the phlogiston theory and other superstitions of the age of alchemy. That event was followed, in the early and middle nineteenth century, by a series of major scientific discoveries in which the study of respiration played an important role. The work of Liebig and others on animal respiration and metabolism aided in the development of the laws of chemical stoichiometry. Berzelius's work on kinetics and catalysis was also profoundly influenced by the early investigations of respiration, as were the ideas of Mayer and Helmholtz when they enunciated the laws of conservation of energy and matter. Similarly, the study of oxygen, its allotropic forms, and its reaction with organic and inorganic compounds was greatly stimulated by study of respiration.

The modern era of research on respiration may be said to begin at the turn of the twentieth century, which brought the discovery of dye-reducing dehydrogenases in cell-free extracts of tissues by Batelli and Stern, by Schardinger, and by Thunberg. The unifying chemical basis for biological dehydrogenation reactions came somewhat later with the work of Wieland,

in the period 1912–1922. On the other hand, the importance of
the attack of oxygen in cellular respiration was also brought to
the fore in this period, which saw the beginnings of Warburg's
lifetime of research on respiration. Starting with Claude Bernard's observations in 1857–1865 on the inhibition of animal
respiration by cyanide, Warburg developed the concept that
most, if not all, utilization of oxygen by cells takes place through
intervention of an iron-containing catalyst, the *Atmungsferment*, that could be inhibited by cyanide and by carbon monoxide. Warburg showed the chemical soundness of this concept
by demonstrating the nonenzymatic catalysis of oxidation of
thiols and other compounds by iron and its inhibition by cyanide
and other agents capable of combining with iron. This view was
supported by concurrent work of Keilin, who rediscovered the
cytochromes in 1923 and showed them to undergo characteristic changes in oxidation state in intact insect muscles.

These first explorations were then followed in the period
1928–1933 by the classical and powerful work of Warburg on
the effect of light of different wavelengths on the relief of the
inhibition of cellular respiration by carbon monoxide. This
work led, via photochemical theory, to the construction of the
absorption spectrum of the CO complex of the *Atmungsferment*, clearly that of an iron-porphyrin compound.

The two lines of investigation on enzymatic activation of
substrates by dehydrogenases and activation of oxygen by *Atmungsferment* came together in the 1930s. The isolation and determination of structure of the pyridine nucleotides, as well as
the principles of their action with dehydrogenases, were initiated
by Euler and carried to a new stage of understanding by Warburg. At this time also came the discovery of the flavin nucleotides and flavoproteins by Warburg and Theorell, which led
finally to the concept that the flavoproteins are mediators between the pyridine nucleotides and the cytochrome system. In
this illuminating period, Keilin isolated cytochrome *c* and per-
formed his first reconstructions of electron transport with heart
particles. From these events, the basic form of the respiratory
chain as the sequence

$$\text{dehydrogenases} \rightarrow \text{flavoproteins} \rightarrow \text{cytochromes} \rightarrow O_2$$

began to take shape, a concept that was also supported by work
of Szent-Györgyi.

Following Szent-Györgyi's discovery of the catalytic effect of the four-carbon dicarboxylic acids on respiration, Krebs, on the basis of simple but penetrating experiments on the respiration of muscle suspensions, postulated the citric acid cycle as the primary cellular mechanism for the oxidation of carbohydrate. This imaginative concept of a cyclic multienzyme system for stepwise oxidative degradation of the carbon skeleton of pyruvate had a profound impact on both experimentation and thought in biological oxidations. Some years were to elapse before isotopic tracer experiments convinced the remaining skeptics; but once the citric acid cycle was accepted, it was then shown also to be the pathway for oxidation of two-carbon units from fatty acids by Lehninger and from the ketone bodies by Breusch and others.

The luxurious flowering of research on biological oxidations in the 1930s occurred with relatively little attention to the mechanism of energy recovery during respiration, although it had long been appreciated from physiological and calorimetric studies that combustion of carbohydrate produced, ultimately, large amounts of heat. ATP was discovered in 1931 by Lohmann, but it was at first considered to be peculiar to muscle. Its real significance in cellular energy transformation was not appreciated until the important demonstration of Warburg in 1937–1938 of the formation of ATP coupled to enzymatic oxidation of glyceraldehyde phosphate and the work of Meyerhof on the formation of ATP from phosphopyruvate. Finally, in the period 1937–1941, Kalckar first described aerobic or oxidative phosphorylation coupled specifically to respiration, which Belitser soon postulated on theoretical grounds to be associated with electron transport from substrate to oxygen via flavoprotein and cytochromes.

These were the major events just preceding the confluence of the biochemical and cytological research on mitochondria. Actually, very few biochemists concerned themselves with the possible importance of the fact that respiratory enzymes were found to be associated with particulate matter of cells and tissues. It was a part of the biochemical *Zeitgeist* that particles were a nuisance and stood in the way of purification of the respiratory enzymes. Yet it almost seems paradoxical that it was two biochemists who had many years earlier made important discoveries on the occurrence of biological oxidation-reduction mechanisms in granular elements of the cell. Michaelis had

shown in 1898 that mitochondria of unfixed cells reduced oxidation-reduction indicators such as Janus green, and Warburg
had shown in 1913 that the capacity to consume oxygen resided
in the particulate elements of the cell.

THE CONFLUENCE

In 1940 at the Rockefeller Institute, Claude began his systematic investigations of the structure, behavior, and chemical
composition of "large granules" (mitochondria) and "small
granules" (microsomes) isolated by differential centrifugation
of liver homogenates. The earlier approaches of Bensley and his
colleagues were very greatly refined, and the problem was approached with a high degree of biochemical sophistication. It
was this work that crystallized development of the great school
of cytology at the Rockefeller Institute that has had such a
profound influence for more than twenty years. Claude and his
colleagues noted the microscopic appearance, size, and osmotic
sensitivity of the isolated large granules of liver and also carried out chemical analysis of the fractions. Soon electron micrographs of isolated large granules were made, several years before perfection of modern thin-sectioning and fixation methods.
It is now known that the large granules isolated by Claude's
early procedures were rather badly damaged and impure;
nevertheless, such fractions were found to have significant cytochrome oxidase and succinoxidase activity, whereas the micro-
some fraction possessed none.

It is an especially happy turn of events that the work on
mitochondria in the Rockefeller Institute interested not only
cytologists such as Claude, Porter, and Palade but also biochemists and enzymologists of the Institute, among them Hogeboom, Hotchkiss, and Schneider. The goal of isolating intact
mitochondria was pursued further, and in 1948 it was reported
by Hogeboom, Schneider, and Palade that when a medium of
0.88 M sucrose is used for dispersion of rat liver cells, the
nuclei, mitochondria, and microsomes are easily separable by
differential centrifugation. Most importantly, the liver mitochondria could be recovered in the elongated form characteristically seen in intact liver cells, and they were stained by
Janus green and other specific agents. On the other hand, preparations obtained from saline media or from media containing
lower sucrose concentrations were spherical and swollen. It was

of the greatest significance that such preparations of intact mitochondria contained most of the cytochrome oxidase activity of the whole liver homogenate from which they were isolated, since cytochrome oxidase is the final common pathway of most biological oxidations.

The full significance of the role of the mitochondria in respiration was not revealed by these experiments, however, and its realization came from an independent direction: the study of the biochemical properties of the multienzyme system of liver that catalyzes oxidation of fatty acids. Early observations of Leloir and Munoz and of Lehninger in the period 1943–1947 had indicated that the activity of this complex system was critically dependent on the structure of some easily damaged particulate element in liver homogenates. Later, Lehninger and Kennedy showed the activity of this system to have a bell-shaped dependence on the concentration of certain organic and inorganic solutes in the medium, which indicated that the activity was present in some osmotically active structure.

While their work was under way, the first description of Hogeboom, Schneider, and Palade of the isolation of intact mitochondria from 0.88 M sucrose medium appeared. Kennedy and Lehninger immediately applied the new method, and in a short time they reported that rat liver mitochondria isolated by the new procedure contained considerable fatty acid oxidase activity, which was easily sufficient to account for the activity of the intact liver cell. Microsomes, cell nuclei, and the "soluble fraction" of rat liver prepared by the new method failed to oxidize fatty acids. Moreover, the isolated mitochondria also were found by Kennedy and Lehninger to carry out the oxidation of all the Krebs citric acid cycle intermediates at a rate compatible with that of the intact liver, and, most importantly, oxidative phosphorylation accompanied these organized oxidations. On the other hand, the isolated mitochondria failed to catalyze the reactions of glycolysis, indicating the specificity of respiratory enzyme localization in mitochondria. Some months later Schneider and Potter reported independently that isolated rat liver mitochondria contain most of the *oxalacetic oxidase* activity of rat liver, presumably a reflection of the action of part or all of the Krebs citric acid cycle.

These observations were soon confirmed by others. Green and his colleagues showed in 1951 that their so-called *cyclophorase system,* a particulate preparation from kidney and liver that catalyzed fatty acid and Krebs cycle oxidations, was a reflection of mitochondrial activity. Isolated mitochondria have since become the standard starting preparation for examination of electron transport and oxidative phosphorylation in animal tissues. Furthermore, it also became clear from over a decade of work that these complex respiratory systems are characteristic of the mitochondria of all cell types examined, whether of animal or plant origin. Firm justification was thus provided for Claude's apt designation of the mitochondrion as the "power plant" of the cell and for the metabolic individuality of the mitochondrion.

Further evidence for the individuality of mitochondrial structure and function also came from new developments in the field of electron microscopy. Palade greatly refined the use of osmium tetroxide as a fixative to visualize the characteristic electron-opaque images of the membrane systems and the granules of cells. Porter, at the Rockefeller Institute, and Sjöstrand, in Stockholm, perfected new thin-sectioning methods. In 1952 and 1953 Sjöstrand and Palade independently published the first high-resolution images of mitochondria in thin-sectioned tissues and described the major features of mitochondrial structure. The mitochondria have since been amply demonstrated to have characteristic individuality of structure as well as of function.

Whereas these developments are completely accepted today, it must be pointed out that when these correlations were first being made, there was significant uncertainty and question as to the structural and enzymatic homogeneity of mitochondria. In fact, subfractionation of isolated mitochondria by Chantrenne, Novikoff, and others appeared to indicate qualitative as well as quantitative heterogeneity. Furthermore, it was found that certain enzymes associated with the Krebs cycle are not exclusively located in mitochondria, among them being isocitrate dehydrogenase and malate dehydrogenase, which are also present in large amounts in the soluble cytoplasm.

Today these questions are largely resolved through the painstaking efforts of such workers as DeDuve, Schneider, and Novikoff. The centrifugal methods for isolation of mitochondria have been greatly refined, the distribution of individual enzymes in different subcellular fractions carefully catalogued, and the question of mitochondrial heterogeneity resolved in part, at least, by the discovery that mitochondrial preparations also contain the lysosomes. Today also we are more aware of the morphological and biochemical compartmentation of enzymatic events in the intact cell. Although a given type of enzyme known to participate in the Krebs cycle may be present in both mitochondria and the soluble cytoplasmic matrix, it may have quite different metabolic functions in the two compartments.

The major lines of investigation on mitochondria that have developed during the 1950s and early 1960s will now be sketched briefly to indicate the scope of the research to be described in following chapters.

ENZYMATIC ORGANIZATION OF MITOCHONDRIA

The central objectives in attaining a molecular description of the mitochondrion are the isolation of the enzymatic components of the oxidative cycles, definition of their molecular structure and action, analysis of their participation in the multienzyme systems in the mitochondria, and mapping of their location in the mitochondrial structure. The enzymes of the respiratory chain actually comprise some 25 per cent or more of the proteins of the mitochondrial membranes, a fact that focuses attention on these enzymes as units not only of function but also of mitochondrial structure.

The physical and chemical forces involved in maintaining the characteristic arrangement of the electron carrier molecules in "respiratory assemblies" and the molecular engineering problem of reconstructing such multienzyme complexes and assemblies in vitro from isolated and purified components are now under intense study. New methods of dislodging such enzymes from mitochondrial structure and of purifying them are being perfected and new criteria of purity and "nativeness" of enzyme molecules may have to be developed for the case of "structured" enzyme systems. These problems are especially prominent in current investigations on the reconstitution of oxidative phosphorylation and the definition of its mechanism, in which experimental progress has been painfully slow and hard-won.

Another characteristic of mitochondrial enzymology is the phenomenon of crypticity and compartmentation of enzymes and substrates in the mitochondrial structure. These features are intricately involved in the control and channeling of enzymatic pathways within the mitochondrion and in its metabolic interactions with the surrounding cytoplasmic matrix.

The Krebs citric acid cycle and the fatty acid oxidation cycle, as they operate in intact mitochondria, are also endowed with self-regulating properties through feedback inhibition and other principles that utilize the characteristic affinities of the individual enzymes of the cycles for substrates, products, coenzymes, and metal ions as elements in control mechanisms. The integration of the action of the fifty or more enzymes involved in the operation of the major oxidative cycles of the mitochondrion into a smoothly running, tightly controlled system that feeds electrons into the respiratory chain, also a self-adjusting system, is now looming as a complex problem in molecular cybernetics.

ION TRANSLOCATION IN MITOCHONDRIA

Not long after the discovery that isolated mitochondria catalyze the oxidative cycles and phosphorylation, it was found by several groups that mitochondria are also capable of maintaining gradients of certain cations and anions during respiration; among the ions were K^+, Mg^{++}, and phosphate. Although many studies since have confirmed the occurrence of active ion accumulation in isolated mitochondria, there was no inkling until recently as to the magnitude of the ion fluxes or of their quantitative relationship to the stoichiometry of electron transport and oxidative phosphorylation. However, new illumination has come in the finding that Ca^{++} ions may be accumulated during respiration in relatively enormous amounts by isolated mitochondria, together with inorganic phosphate. For each atom of oxygen taken up, three or more Ca^{++} ions are accumulated. The recent work on active translocation of Ca^{++}, Mg^{++}, and Mn^{++} by mitochondria indicates that these activities are integral with and are driven by the energy-conserving sites in the respiratory chain.

MECHANOCHEMICAL ACTIVITIES
OF THE MITOCHONDRIAL MEMBRANE

Changes of mitochondrial shape and volume have recently been found to be coupled to the energy-conserving mechanisms of the respiratory chain. When isolated mitochondria respire in the absence of phosphate acceptor, they undergo swelling, with uptake of water (and solutes) from the medium. On the other hand, when respiration is poisoned or the mitochondria are kept anaerobic, they do not swell. The reverse process, the shrinkage or contraction of mitochondria, with extrusion of water, may be brought about by instituting phosphorylating respiration or by the direct action of ATP. Recently a number of specific enzymes and biochemical factors involved in the mechanism of mitochondrial contraction have been isolated and identified. Increasing interest now attaches to contractile and mechanochemical phenomena in mitochondria, particularly since recent work has revealed a number of highly significant common denominators of mechanism and properties in the ATPase activities of the mitochondrion and of the myofibril.

MEMBRANE STRUCTURE

One of the most significant developments in recent years is the recognition that cellular membranes are not simply inert skins but may contain macromolecular assemblies of characteristic enzymes. Study of the mitochondrial membrane has been most prominent in constructing this picture. New techniques of sample preparation and observation in the electron microscope, such as the negative-staining method, have added new information on membrane structure. The physical principles stabilizing the structure of natural membranes are also of much interest, and significant efforts are now underway on the in vitro construction of phospholipid bilayer systems of known composition as "cores" of natural membranes. The chemical and physical analysis of such bilayers emphasizes the importance of the electrical charge and the space-filling characteristics of the different lipid building blocks. The lipid bilayer may be regarded as a specific mosaic of various types of lipids, each of which, like the 20 amino acid building blocks of proteins, may contribute a special quality to the membrane.

BIOSYNTHETIC ACTIVITIES OF MITOCHONDRIA
AND THE BIOGENESIS OF MITOCHONDRIAL STRUCTURE

Many speculations have been made over the years concerning the biogenesis of mitochondria in the intact cell. At one time or another they have been postulated to arise from the plasma membrane, the nuclear membrane, the endoplasmic reticulum, and the cytoplasmic matrix or by the simple division of preexisting mitochondria. Recent biochemical studies suggest that at least some of the mitochondrial components are synthesized by enzyme systems present in the mitochondrion itself. The available evidence indicates that specific mitochondrial enzymes, such as the cytochromes and dehydrogenases, are not synthesized in the mitochondrion.

On the other hand, isolated mitochondria readily incorporate labeled amino acids into the insoluble proteins of the membrane structure. It is possible, therefore, that biosynthesis of mitochondrial membrane proteins may differ qualitatively in mechanism or dynamics from the biosynthesis of soluble proteins or specific enzymes.

Mitochondria also contain the complete enzymatic apparatus for biosynthesis of fatty acids, but it is curious that they do not contain all the enzymes required for assembly of the complex phosphatides, which are such characteristic and important components of the mitochondrial membrane. Thus, the biochemical evidence suggests that at least some of the macromolecular components of mitochondrial structure are preassembled in other parts of the cell. The correlation of biochemical observations, such as these, with observations on the origin of mitochondria made by microscopic examination may one day lead to in vitro study of mitochondrial morphogenesis in the test tube.

REFERENCES

Reviews

Conn, E. E., "Comparative biochemistry of electron transport and oxidative phosphorylation," in M. Florkin and H. S. Mason (eds.), *Comparative Biochemistry*, Academic, New York, 1960, Vol. I, p. 441.

Cowdry, E. V., "The mitochondrial constituents of protoplasm," *Contrib. Embryol.*, **8**, 39 (1918).

DeDuve, C., J. Berthet and H. Beaufay, "Gradient centrifugation of cell particles," *Progr. Biophys. Biophys. Chem.*, **9**, 326 (1959).

———, R. Wattiaux, and P. Baudhuin, "Distribution of enzymes between subcellular fractions in animal tissues," *Advan. Enzymol.*, **24**, 291 (1962).

Ernster, L., and O. Lindberg, "Animal mitochondria," *Ann. Rev. Physiol.*, **20**, 13 (1958).

Green, D. E., "Studies in organized enzyme systems," *Harvey Lectures, Ser.* 52 (**1956–1957**), 177 (1958).

Krebs, H. A., and H. L. Kornberg, "Energy transformations in living matter," *Ergeb. Physiol.*, **49**, 212 (1957). Also published as a monograph, Springer, Berlin, 1957.

Lehninger, A. L., "The organized respiratory activity of isolated rat liver mitochondria," in J. T. Edsall (ed.), *Enzymes and Enzyme Systems*, Harvard, Cambridge, 1951, p. 1.

————, "Oxidative phosphorylation," *Harvey Lectures, Ser.* 49 (**1953–1954**), 176 (1955).

————, "Physiology of mitochondria," in O. H. Gaebler (ed.), *Enzymes: Units of Biological Structure and Function*, Academic, New York, 1956, p. 217.

Novikoff, A. B., "Mitochondria (chondriosomes)," in J. Brachet and A. E. Mirsky (eds.), *The Cell*, Academic, New York, 1961, Vol. II, p. 299. Important review of both biological and biochemical aspects.

Palade, G. E., "Electron microscopy of cytoplasmic structures," in O. H. Gaebler (ed.), *Enzymes: Units of Biological Structure and Function*, Academic, New York, 1956, p. 185.

Schneider, W. D., "Mitochondrial metabolism," *Advan. Enzymol.*, **21**, 1 (1959).

Warburg, O., *Heavy Metals, Prosthetic Groups, and Enzyme Action* (transl. A. Lawson), Oxford, London, 1949.

Research papers

The following list, arranged chronologically, provides some historical landmarks in the identification of mitochondria as elements in cellular respiration and active transport:

1913   O. Warburg, "Über sauerstoffatmende Körnchen aus Leberzellen und über Sauerstoffatmung in Berkfeld-Filtraten wässriger Leberextrackte," *Arch. Ges. Physiol.*, **154**, 599.

1934   R. R. Bensley and N. Hoerr, "Studies on cell structure by the freezing-drying method. VI. The preparation and properties of mitochondria," *Anat. Record*, **60**, 449.

1940   D. Keilin, and E. F. Hartree, "Succinic dehydrogenase-cytochrome system of cells. Intracellular respiratory system catalyzing aerobic oxidation of succinic acid," *Proc. Roy. Soc. (London)*, **B129**, 277.

1946   A. Claude, "Fractionation of mammalian liver cells by differential centrifugation," *J. Exptl. Med.*, **84**, 51, 61.

1946   G. H. Hogeboom, A. Claude, and R. D. Hotchkiss, "The distribution of cytochrome oxidase and succinoxidase in the cytoplasm of the mammalian liver cell," *J. Biol. Chem.*, **165**, 615.

1948 G. H. Hogeboom, W. C. Schneider, and G. H. Palade, "Isolation of intact mitochondria from rat liver; some biochemical properties of mitochondria and submicroscopic particulate material," *J. Biol. Chem.*, **172**, 619.

1948 D. E. Green, W. F. Loomis, and V. H. Auerbach, "Studies on the cyclophorase system I." *J. Biol. Chem.*, **172**, 389.

1948 E. P. Kennedy, and A. L. Lehninger, "Intracellular structures and the fatty acid oxidase system of rat liver," *J. Biol. Chem.*, **172**, 847.

1948 W. C. Schneider, and V. R. Potter, "The distribution of oxalacetic oxidase activity in rat liver and rat kidney fractions," *J. Biol. Chem.*, **177**, 893.

1949 E. P. Kennedy, and A. L. Lehninger, "Oxidation of fatty acids and tricarboxylic acid cycle intermediates by isolated rat liver mitochondria," *J. Biol. Chem.*, **179**, 957.

1953 J. Raaflaub, "Die Schwellung isolierter Leberzell Mitochondrien und ihre physikalisch-chemische Beeinflussbarkeit; über den Wirkungsmechanismus von Adenosintriphosphat als Cofaktor isolierter Mitochondrien," *Helv. Physiol. Pharmacol. Acta*, **11**, 142.

1953 M. G. MacFarlane, and A. G. Spencer, "Changes in the water, sodium, and potassium content of rat-liver mitochondria during metabolism," *Biochem. J.*, **54**, 569.

1954 W. Bartley, and R. E. Davies, "Active transport of ions by subcellular particles," *Biochem. J.*, **57**, 39.

1955 B. Chance, and G. R. Williams, "Respiratory enzymes in oxidative phosphorylation, I-V," *J. Biol. Chem.*, **217**, 383ff.

1959 A. L. Lehninger, "Reversal of various types of mitochondrial swelling by adenosine triphosphate," *J. Biol. Chem.*, **234**, 2465.

2

MITOCHONDRIA

IN THE INTACT CELL

First let us consider animal mitochondria in their natural habitat, the cytoplasm of the cell, as a framework of reference for the more detailed consideration we shall give to mitochondrial structure and function in the chapters to come. For both the biochemist and the cell biologist it may be instructive to contemplate the wide range of variations in size, form, number, and location of mitochondria in different kinds of cells. However, these factors should be considered in the context of the metabolic functions of mitochondria and their biochemical interplay with their surroundings in the cytoplasm. Mitochondria require a fuel supply in the form of fatty acids, pyruvate, or amino acids; they also require ADP and phosphate for maximal respiration. Conversely, the ATP produced by mitochondria is utilized at specific sites in the cell, such as the cell membrane, the ribosomes, or the contractile bands of myofibrils.

Two other major properties must be recognized in analyzing the location and behavior of mitochondria in cells. Mitochondria are able to accumulate certain ions such as K^+, Ca^{++}, Mg^{++}, Mn^{++}, and $HPO_4^{=}$ by active transport mechanisms;

they may be looked upon as intracytoplasmic islands that participate in homeostatic regulation of the ionic composition of the hyaloplasm. Mitochondria may also undergo very substantial changes in shape and volume through respiration-dependent contractile mechanisms that are presumably responsible for moving water and changing the permeability toward substrates.

GENERAL ASPECTS OF STRUCTURE

Beginning with the pioneering electron microscope investigations of Sjöstrand and of Palade on thin sections of intact tissues, much information has become available with respect to the detailed internal structure of mitochondria. In Figure 2–1 is shown a model of a liver mitochondrion as revealed by osmium-fixed thin sections of liver. This model shows the common pattern of organization that characterizes mitochondria in

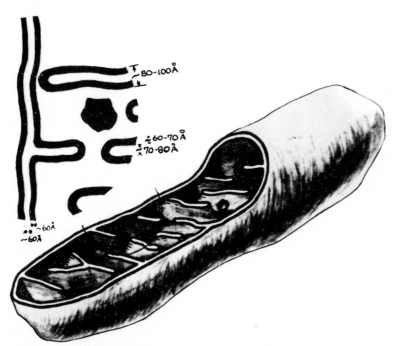

Figure 2–1 Schematic representation of osmium-fixed liver mitochondrion. [Original drawing courtesy of G. E. Palade; published in A. L. Lehninger, *Pediatrics*, **26**, Part I, 469 (1960).]

all known cell types. Later we shall consider the biological variations in shape, size, and arrangement of substructures such as the cristae. Surrounding the mitochondrial lumen are two continuous membrane systems, each comprising a closed sac, so arranged that the mitochondrial structure may be represented as a sac within a sac. The lumen of the inner sac does not communicate with the space between the two membranes. The outer membrane is smooth, whereas the inner membrane has many infoldings that in the simplest case have the form of septa but may assume extremely complex conformations. These infoldings were termed the *cristae mitochondriales* by Palade. Both membrane systems stain characteristically with osmium tetroxide or with permanganate; the details of mitochondrial membrane structure and composition will be described in a later chapter.

Another recognized component of mitochondrial structure is the *matrix*, which fills the lumen of the inner membrane system. The matrix may be continuous throughout the lumen in some mitochondria but perhaps not in all. The matrix has significant electron density and fine granularity and is known to contain considerable protein and some lipid; it is presumably organized and is a semirigid rather than a dilute fluid. Lastly, osmium-fixed mitochondria often contain in the matrix a number of small granules (diameter ~ 250 Å) of exceedingly high electron density. These intramitochondrial granules undergo changes in number, diameter, and electron-opacity depending on the metabolic state of the tissue.

The membrane systems of the mitochondrion are characterized by a rather constant thickness and spacing in all cell types studied, when stained under given conditions with osmium or permanganate. With osmium each of the dense lines is approximately 60 to 70 Å thick, and the lines are separated by an electron-lucid space of some 60 to 80 Å. When carefully stained, each dense line can be seen to have substructure.

SIZE AND SHAPE

The apparent size and shape of mitochondria will depend to some extent on the methods used to fix and stain the material, the nature of the optical system employed, whether the mitochondria are examined in isolated form or in situ, the point in time at which the material is fixed (since some mitochondria undergo rapid changes in shape and volume in situ), and the cell type. In the cell types in which they are relatively free in the cytoplasm, such as liver, kidney, and pancreatic cells, mitochondria usually have an elongated conformation; their long dimension is of the order of 3 μ and their width is of the order of 0.5 to1.0 μ. Rat liver mitochondria are perhaps typical of the middle of the spectrum of size and shape. When isolated from sucrose-polyvinylpyrrolidone homogenates, they are approximate ellipsoids of revolution and average 3.3 μ in length and a little less than 1.0 μ in width, as visualized in the electron microscope. In other cell types the mitochondria may be extremely elongated rods or filaments that reach a length of 10 μ in pancreas exocrine cells, for example.

Early work with the light microscope and classical staining methods indicated mitochondria to have surprisingly constant thickness but considerable variation in length, an observation that suggested that mitochondria add (or lose) substance at their extremities. End-to-end fusion or contact of mitochondria, as contrasted with side-to-side fusion, is very common in different cell types. Spherical mitochondria are often seen to aggregate into elongated strands. Closed circular loops of mitochondria have also been observed to form by end-to-end fusion or contact. The tendency to undergo such end-to-end fusion or aggregation is at its most spectacular in the development of the helical mitochondrial sheaths around the midpiece of the spermatozoon. The chemical or physical basis for the apparent polarity of the ends of mitochondria deserves investigation.

Recent work of Bahr and Zeitler on rat liver mitochondria isolated from 0.3 M sucrose homogenates shows that the weight distribution curve for the whole mitochondrial population is remarkably similar from animal to animal. The median dry weight is about 1.1×10^{-13} g per mitochondrion; 68 per cent of the mitochondria have a dry weight in the range 0.68 to 1.78 $\times 10^{-13}$g. Bahr and Zeitler also showed that liver mitochondria isolated under these conditions occur in two geometric forms of almost equal occurrence, one spherical and the other oblong. The smaller axis of the oblong mitochondria is approximately equal to the diameter of the spherical mitochondria; the oblong forms have 1.6 times the mass of the spheres.

Independent evidence for two different classes of mitochondria (apart from the lysosomes) has also come from differential centrifugation procedures and from enzyme tests. Bahr and

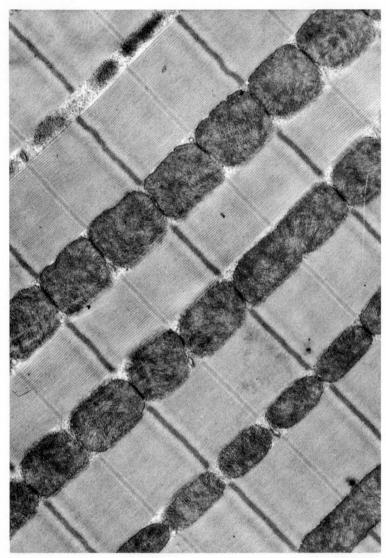

Figure 2–2 Longitudinal section of wasp flight muscle, showing regular arrangement of mitochondria in relation to cross striations ($\times$ 20,-000). [From D. S. Smith, *J. Biophys. Biochem. Cytol.*, **Suppl. 11,** 125 (1961).]

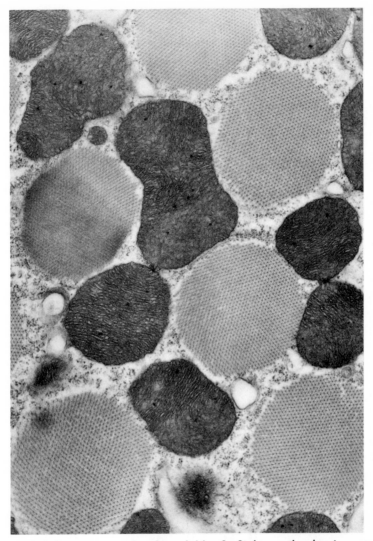

Figure 2–3 Transverse section through blowfly flight muscle, showing regularity of packing arrangement of mitochondria around myofibrils ($\times$ 40,000). [From D. S. Smith, *J. Biophys. Biochem. Cytol.*, **19**, 120 (1963).]

Zeitler have shown that 8 per cent of the oblong mitochondria are dumbbell-shaped, 5 per cent consist of two closely connected spherical particles, and 7 per cent of an association of one round and one oblong mitochondrion; the ratios of these shapes were not influenced by tonicity of the media. However, in 0.88 M sucrose most of the mitochondria were oblong. Bahr and Zeitler suggest that the round and oblong mitochondria may be elements in mitochondrial division (or fusion).

The filamentous or elongated conformation of mitochondria

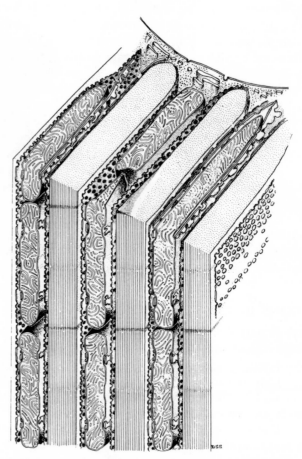

Figure 2–4 Slab-like mitochondria of flight muscle of dragonfly, showing profuse cristae. [Original in D. S. Smith, *J. Biophys. Biochem. Cytol.*, **11**, 119 (1961).]

is by no means universal. Actually, in some tissues, such as striated muscle, the mitochondria may assume extremely complex conformations. Figures 2–2 and 2–3 show the shape and arrangement of mitochondria in two types of insect muscle, which has very high demands on respiratory energy, as recorded by D. S. Smith in his penetrating and fascinating studies. Figure 2–2 is from a section of wasp muscle cut in the axis of the myofibrils, showing the regular arrangement of mitochondria in relation to the cross striations. Figure 2–3 is from a transverse section of blowfly muscle, showing the packing arrangement of the mitochondria and myofibrils.

In flight muscle of the dragonfly (Figure 2–4) Smith has found the mitochondria to be enormous slablike structures some 8μ in length and width and with a relatively large volume; they alternate regularly with the myofibrils and possess immensely profuse cristae. In other types of muscle, less dependent on such a high flux of respiratory energy, mitochondria may be ring-like in conformation and completely surround the I bands of the myofibrils. Palade has found that when leg muscle of the rat is sectioned transversely at the I-band level, the mitochondria appear to be highly branched around and among the I bands of several neighboring myofibrils. Stellate conformations of mitochondria are also observed.

In pancreatic cells of fasted animals Palade has shown that the mitochondria often surround lipid droplets in a concentric conformation, an arrangement that provides intimate physical contact with a fuel supply. We shall see later that mitochondria may also exist in helical conformations.

VARIATIONS IN CONFORMATION OF CRISTAE

Rather remarkable variations occur in the conformation of the *cristae mitochondriales*, which are best revealed by close scrutiny of serial sections of mitochondria. In mitochondria of rat hepatocytes as indicated in the model of Figure 2–1, the cristae are relatively sparse and irregular in occurrence; they are usually transverse to the long axis, and the infoldings involve a rather extended arc around the body of the mitochondria to form septum-like structures. Since continuity of the inner membrane and the cristae is frequently seen in sections of liver mitochondria, as shown in the diagram, it has been concluded by Palade that the folds of the inner membrane that

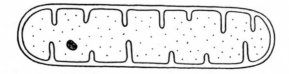

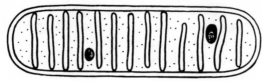

Figure 2–5 Schematic comparison of cristae in liver (above) and kidney (below) mitochondria.

form the cristae may be rather broad, resembling the pleats of an accordion. However, this conformation is not completely typical.

In kidney mitochondria the cristae are very profuse and regularly oriented in a transverse manner, like a stack of coins. It is only rarely that a section through a kidney mitochondrion shows an actual point of continuity between the membrane of a crista and the inner element of the two surrounding membranes. Sjöstrand has therefore suggested that if the cristae in kidney and other mitochondria are continuous with the inner element of the surrounding membrane, the connection must be through a very narrow neck or stem. He has stressed the view that the cristae in most mitochondria are much more complex than the simple pleated conformation proposed by Palade. The conformations of cristae of liver and kidney are contrasted schematically in Figure 2–5.

The great complexity of the cristae in other types of cells is illustrated by a reconstruction of a mitochondrion in a neuron of a motor end plate that Anderssen-Cedergren has prepared from serial sections (Figure 2–6). This shows yet another conformation of the cristae, namely, tube-like or finger-like invaginations of the inner membrane system that may branch and anastomose. It is interesting that in most mitochondria the cristae are transverse to the long axis. However, in mitochondria

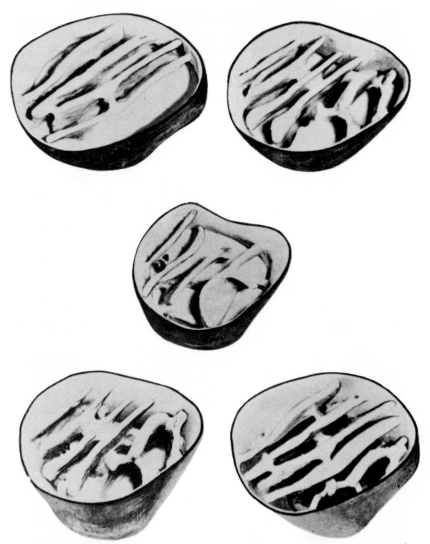

Figure 2–6 Conformation of cristae in mitochondria of neuron, as deduced from serial sections. [From E. Anderssen-Cedergren, *J. Ultrastructure Res.*, **Suppl. 1**, 124 (1959); courtesy of Academic Press.]

of mammalian neurons in the central nervous system the cristae are often longitudinal in arrangement, parallel to the long axis. Furthermore, within a single mitochondrion of flight muscle (Figure 2–4) the profuse cristae may be transverse, longitudinal, or oblique and may also branch and anastomose.

D. S. Smith has prepared three-dimensional representations of the cristae in mitochondria in the flight muscle of the blow-

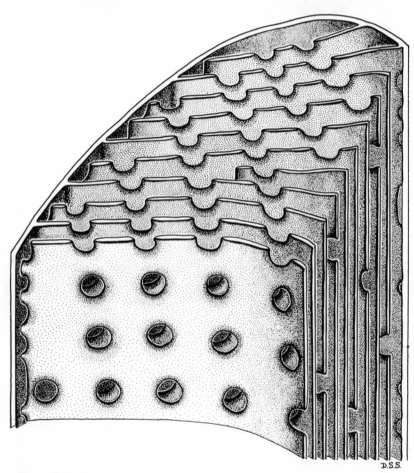

D.S.S.

Figure 2–7 Diagrammatic representation of portion of mitochondrion in blowfly flight muscle, showing cristae with regular fenestrations. The distance between the cristae is exaggerated. [D. S. Smith, *J. Cell. Biol.*, **19**, 136 (1963).]

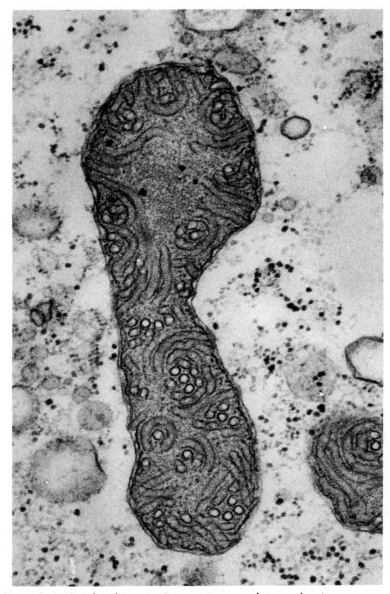

Figure 2–8 Mitochondrion in *Paramecium caudatum,* showing arrangement of cristae. (J. André.)

fly; they show a remarkable arrangement of regularly fenes-
trated, sheet-like cristae (Figure 2–7). In mitochondria of some
protozoa, the cristae closely resemble villi (cf. Figure 2–8).
A particularly striking arrangement of cristae has been found
by Revel and his colleagues in muscle mitochondria of the bat.
Here the transverse cristae assume an extremely regular saw-
tooth arrangement that is highly suggestive of the molecular
regularity of crystal structure. Serial sections at different angles
show that these mitochondria also contain an amazingly regular
and exact array of three-sided, longitudinally arranged, tube-
like cristae, shown in Figure 2–9. The molecular basis for the
characteristic form and dimensions of these structures is a
matter of the greatest interest. Finally, another singular type
of structure is shown in Figure 2–10, namely, a so-called *yolk*

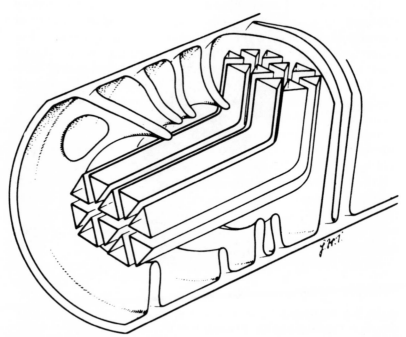

Figure 2–9 Schematic representation of mitochondrion of cricothyroid
muscle of bat, showing regularly arranged, three-sided pris-
matic cristae. [J. P. Revel, D. W. Fawcett, and C. W. Philpott,
J. Cell. Biol., **16**, 192 (1963).]

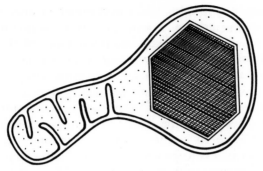

Figure 2–10 Diagram showing a yolk crystal within a mitochondrion in an oöcyte of *Rana pipiens*. (After R. T. Ward, 1959.)

crystal, possibly of ferritin, within a mitochondrion of a frog oöcyte.

The geometrical arrangement of cristae in the mitochondrial structure appears to be a major determinant of the ability of mitochondria to swell and contract and to change shape. For example, liver and kidney mitochondria readily swell and contract in respiration-dependent cycles, but mitochondria from the brain do not swell significantly, even in very hypotonic media, presumably because their cristae provide structural constraints. The arrangement of cristae often undergoes pronounced alterations as a function of developmental changes, nutritional state, and endocrine manipulations; some examples will be described later.

Mitochondria isolated by centrifugal methods from homogenates often show aberrations in the structure of the cristae that are dependent on the tonicity of the medium; the cristae tend to "inflate," thereby exposing more surface area, and the matrix becomes less dense.

SURFACE AREA

As Palade pointed out, the cristae undoubtedly represent a device for increasing the surface area of the mitochondrial membranes. Since the assemblies of enzymes of electron transport and oxidative phosphorylation are embedded in the membranes of the cristae, it is significant that heart mitochondria, with profuse cristae, have a much higher content of these enzymes and a higher rate of respiration than liver mitochondria, which have relatively sparse cristae. The large surface area presented by the cristae may also be related to the activity of the ion-transport mechanisms of the mitochondrial membrane.

It may be instructive to make an approximate calculation of the surface area of the mitochondria of a liver cell in relation to the surface area of the cell membrane. It is assumed for the sake of simplicity that the liver cell is a smooth sphere with a diameter of 30 μ. Its surface area ($4\pi r^2$) is thus about 3000 μ^2. A single liver cell is assumed to contain 1000 cylindrical mitochondria of average dimensions 3.5 by 1.0 μ. Since each has an outer surface of about 13 μ^2, the total mitochondrial outer surface area in one cell is 13,000 μ^2, or more than 4 times the surface of the liver cell plasma membrane. However, if each mitochondrion of the liver cell has 10 cristae, each in turn having an area equal to the base of the mitochondrial cylinder, which is a reasonable approximation, then the cristae of a single liver mitochondrion have a surface area of about 16 μ^2 and the total cristal area in one cell is thus about 16,000 μ^2. The total mitochondrial membrane surface in one cell is thus of the order of 29,000 μ^2, whereas the cell membrane surface is only about 3000 μ^2. In kidney and muscle mitochondria the cristae are far more profuse and thus contribute a very much larger membrane area.

PLASTICITY OF FORM

Although electron micrographs have been most revealing of mitochondrial structure and its variations, they tend to leave a static impression of rigidity of structure. An entirely different dimension of mitochondrial structure is revealed by study of intact cells with the light microscope. As early as 1914, Lewis and Lewis described motion of mitochondria in the cytoplasm, increases and decreases in their size, their fission and fusion, and the fact that their shape might change as often as 15 to 20 times in a 10-min period. The effects of heat, CO_2, acids, osmotic pressure, and organic solvents on mitochondrial structure were also examined. More recent work with phase-contrast optics and time-lapse cinematography, particularly by Chevremont, Frederic, and by Gey, has been very revealing of the dynamics of form in mitochondria of living cells. In Figure 2–11 are shown the conformational changes at 60-sec intervals of a

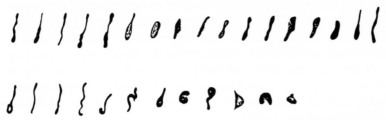

Figure 2–11 Shape changes in single mitochondria in a fibroblast at 60-sec intervals. [J. Frederic, Arch. Biol. (Liège), **LXIX**, 2, 198 (1958).]

single mitochondrion in a fibroblast recorded by Frederic. He also showed that 2,4-dinitrophenol, urethane, ATP, and versene cause pronounced changes in mitochondrial form and movements, as does anaerobiosis, indicating that the shape and volume of mitochondria in situ are linked to respiration and phosphorylation. It will be seen later that changes in mitochondrial volume and shape can also be studied in vitro.

Mitochondria in cells like fibroblasts and hepatocytes are relatively free-swimming, that is, they may move about in the cytoplasm, largely by passive movement during cyclosis or streaming of the cytoplasm. Under these conditions mitochondria seem to have the greatest plasticity of form. On the other hand, in skeletal muscle cells the mitochondria remain fixed and sessile near the contractile portions of the myofibrils, and they do not tend to undergo such striking changes in form or volume.

NUMBER OF MITOCHONDRIA PER CELL

In general, two types of approach to counting mitochondria have been used: scanning and statistical analysis of serial sections of cells and determination of the ratio of mitochondria to nuclei by direct count in stained homogenates of tissues. Rat hepatocytes have been variously reported to have anywhere from 500 to 2500 mitochondria; the best measurements suggest an average of about 800 per cell. The renal tubule cells of mammals contain some 300 mitochondria. Sperm cells contain relatively few mitochondria; in some cases only 20 to 24 per cell. At the other extreme, Anderssen found up to 500,000 mitochondria in the giant amoeba *Chaos chaos*. In the egg cell of the sea urchin *Strongylocentrotus purpuratus* about 14,000 are present. Much remains to be done with regard to mitochondrial counts in different cells. It will be interesting to see what quantitative relationships may develop between cell size, surface area, and rate of respiration on the one hand and the number of mitochondria on the other. In fact, R. E. Smith has already shown that a quantitative relationship exists between total body weight, liver mitochondrial mass, and oxygen utilization in a series of mammals.

Mitochondria may make up a significantly large fraction of the cytoplasmic mass and volume. In rat liver cells, mitochondria contain from 15 to 23 per cent of the total nitrogen of the cell. Recent measurements on low-power electron micrographs by Loud show that the mitochondria of the rat liver cell occupy on the average 18.6 per cent of the total volume of the cell and some 22 per cent of the total cytoplasmic volume.

INTRACELLULAR LOCATION

Cowdry, in his excellent review in 1918, recorded the location and orientation of mitochondria in many different cell types. One of the earliest generalizations made by Cowdry and later reaffirmed by electron microscope invesigations was that in epithelial cells the mitochondria are often polarized, that is, their long axes are often disposed in the direction of the active secretion or transport process characteristic of the cell. This is beautifully shown in the tubule cells of the kidney, where the mitochondria are aligned in the axis between the blood and the lumen of the tubule. As will be developed later, this finding is consistent with a secretory or transcellular active transport function of mitochondria.

A second generalization is that mitochondria are frequently located near a supply of substrate. Thus, in the pancreatic acinar cell, mitochondria are often found wrapped around a lipid droplet so completely that they have a concentric conformation, particularly after the animal is fasted. Novikoff has noted that in the interior cells of solid hepatomas the mitochondria are oriented perpendicular to the cell membrane and are near it, whereas in the free or ascitic form of this tumor cell, which is presumably more efficiently supplied with nutrients from the ascitic fluid bathing it, the mitochondria tend to group closely and laterally around the nucleus.

A third generalization concerning disposition of mitochondria in the cytoplasm may be enunciated: frequently they are found near points in the cytoplasm known to require ATP generated by the mitochondria. Most conspicuous is the location of mitochondria in skeletal muscle, where they frequently are in contact with the contractile portion of the myofibril so that the mitochondria and myofibrils are organized in a regular three-dimensional array. This is particularly true in the flight muscle of insects, where there is close juxtaposition of ATP-forming and ATP-utilizing structures, as seen in Figures 2–2 and 2–3.

Mitochondria are also often arranged in helical sheaths surrounding the midpiece of the spermatozoon; presumably, this permits ATP to be utilized for motility of the tail through a very short diffusion path. Similarly, mitochondria are found immediately below the cell membrane near the base of the cilia in protozoa and other ciliated cells; again these are ATP-requiring structures. Mitochondria are also concentrated near synaptic junctions of axons, where energy exchanges take place during impulse transmission. They are concentrated just below the surface of the Schwann cell, which in essence is an ATP-requiring factory for making large expanses of cell membrane, which in turn winds around the axon to constitute the myelin sheath. In pancreas exocrine cells, which synthesize and secrete large amounts of the digestive enzymes, mitochondria are intimately associated with the rough-surfaced endoplasmic reticulum; presumably, they provide the ATP for amino acid activation and protein synthesis in the ribosome. Mitochondria are often located adjacent to or are attached to the perinuclear membrane, but the significance of this finding is not clear.

MITOCHONDRIA IN MICROORGANISMS

Although mitochondria have been found to occur in aerobic yeast cells, as well as in other microorganisms of relatively large cell size such as amoebae, paramecia, trypanosomes, and sporozoa and in molds such as *Neurospora crassa,* there has been some controversy as to whether they exist in the bacteria. A number of workers have reported centrifugal isolation of respiratory particles from disrupted bacterial cells and have sometimes claimed them to be mitochondria; actually, electron microscopy of bacteria has revealed little indication of the occurrence of true mitochondria. Mitchell has made the following succinct remarks:

Although most bacteria are relatively small they are not built of correspondingly small molecules. Since bacteria of normal size are linearly only about a hundred times longer (ca. 1 μ) than the polymers (proteins, nucleic acids, polysaccharides, lipids) of which they are made (ca. 10 mμ), it would be as impossible for them to contain scale-model subcellular organelles (such as endoplasmic reticulum and mitochondria), corresponding closely to those of animals and plants, as it would be for the rooms of a doll's house to be built of full-size bricks and boards.

Largely through the work of Weibull and of Mitchell, it is now clear that the respiratory chain enzymes of bacteria are located in the protoplast membrane, which in fact has many of the properties of the mitochondrial membrane and can be regarded as its counterpart in size, architecture, and enzymatic capabilities. Nevertheless, it appears likely that some bacteria contain cytoplasmic organelles with respiratory activity that may arise from infoldings of the plasma membrane, such as the *mesosomes* recently described by Vanderwinkel and Murray.

↗ CHANGES DURING CELL DIVISION

In general it has been believed by cytologists that the mitochondria remain fairly constant in number in any one cell; however, more reliable and quantitative measurements are required to prove this important proposition. Although division or fission of mitochondria has been observed by many investigators, it is most certain that mitochondrial division does not usually occur in massed synchrony with cell division. Frederic has made very careful observations of division of mitochondria in living fibroblasts during mitosis. He found that the total volume of mitochondrial material decreases and active movement of the mitochondria slows down in prophase; the mitochondria become thinner and less refractile, and some break down into spheres.

As the daughter cells begin to form, the mitochondria, now evenly but passively distributed in the two halves of the cell, begin to increase in length, apparently by fusion, and become optically more dense. There is an impression that material is taken up by the mitochondria from the hyaloplasm. Some time after cell division is complete, the number of mitochondria in the daughter cells becomes approximately equal to the number in the original parent cell; however, reconstitution of the mitochondrial number is much slower than nuclear reconstitution.

More exact information is available about mitochondrial

changes in meiosis, the division of germ cells, which has been studied by a number of investigators. In the spermatocyte of the snail *Viviparus*, Kaye has shown there are between 20 and 26 mitochondria. These undergo end-to-end fusion in threes to form eight or nine long mitochondrial rods before the first meiotic division takes place; these long mitochondria align themselves in the axis between the daughter cells. Following division, the daughter cells each receive four to five long mitochondria. At the second meiotic division these fused mitochondria divide transversely and equally so that each daughter of the second division (that is, the spermatid) has four or five short mitochondria. These are the precursors of the nebenkern of the spermatid.

CHANGES DURING DEVELOPMENT

In the development of the spermatid into the spermatozoon virtually all the mitochondria of the cell cluster and aggregate into a large spherical body called the *nebenkern* or *chondriosphere*. The nebenkern often retains outlines of structure of the individual mitochondria. The evolution of the chondriosphere in the spermatid and its development into the helical nebenkern of the mature spermatozoon during spermiogenesis have been described in detail by Kaye and particularly well in a beautiful study by Andre. As the mature spermatozoon of certain species develops, the spherical nebenkern begins to elongate and a helical ribbon of long mitochondria fused end-to-end develops. This becomes wound around the axial filament of the developing spermatozoon. Concurrently with this process, the cristae become highly regular and densely packed and the mitochondrial helix becomes tighter and tighter around the mid-piece. Finally, in the mature spermatozoon, very little extra-mitochondrial cytoplasm is left and the nebenkern consist of four long mitochondria tightly wound in a helix around the axial filament, with extremely regular cristae.

Chance and Thorell have studied changes in oxidation state of pyridine nucleotides in the nebenkern of intact grasshopper spermatids by using microfluorometric methods. They were able to observe that the mitochondrial pyridine nucleotides and those of the hyaloplasm responded independently to respiratory changes. The fusion of mitochondria into filaments, into the chondriosphere, and into the helical nebenkern during spermiogenesis may be devices to permit geometric spacing and concentration of the energy-generating systems near energy-requiring structures and possibly to adjust or minimize the length of the diffusion paths for oxygen, substrates, ADP, and phosphate (see diagram of spermatozoon, Figure 2–12).

A number of significant findings have also been made concerning the role of mitochondria in developing sea urchin eggs. In the unfertilized egg, which in some species has a very low rate of respiration, the mitochondria are aggregated into bundles containing up to 60 individual mitochondria. Presum-

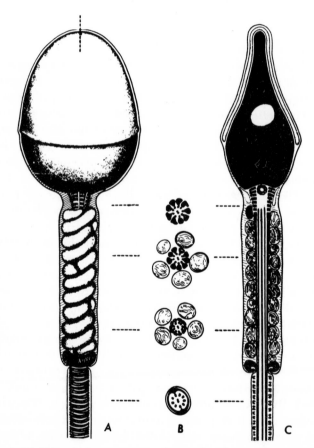

Figure 2–12 Helical arrangement of mitochondria around midpiece of spermatozoon. [D. W. Fawcett, *Intern. Rev. Cytol.,* **VII,** 208 (1958).]

ably, in the aggregated state the rate of respiration is limited by the rate of diffusion of oxygen or substrates into the interior mitochondria of the bundle. After fertilization, there is a dramatic disaggregation of the bundles into single, discrete mitochondria and there is a concomitant large increase in the rate of respiration.

CHANGES IN SOME PHYSIOLOGICAL AND PATHOLOGICAL STATES

Characteristic changes may occur in the shape and disposition of liver mitochondria as a function of nutritional state; similarly, dehydration and alterations in salt intake cause dramatic changes in conformation of kidney mitochondria. The number and shape of mitochondria may also be under endocrine control. Work in Lehninger's laboratory has shown the swelling action of thyroxine on liver mitochondria in vitro. Changes in thyroid state also alter mitochondria in vivo; Greenawalt and Foster have shown that treatment of rats with excess thyroxine causes some 10 per cent of the liver mitochondria to assume bizarre, elongated forms with apparently concentric longitudinal cristae. These often have a dumbbell shape suggestive of incipient division. Excess cortisone administration causes liver mitochondria to swell. As will be seen later, the peptide hormones oxytocin, vasopressin, insulin, and growth hormone are also mitochondrial swelling agents.

Swelling, loss of matrix, and dramatic changes in membrane lipids occur in mitochondria of animals receiving total body X irradiation. In fact, enspherulation and swelling of mitochondria is a rather common sign of cell damage. These changes, together with changes in the endoplasmic reticulum, have been termed *cloudy swelling* by the pathologist.

The possible relationship of mitochondria to carcinogenesis and to the malignant state has been a lively topic since Warburg first postulated that injury to respiration is the primary cause of the malignant transformation. Mitochondria in tumor cells may differ from those in parent normal cells in size, shape, and number; but it is perhaps dangerous to generalize these changes, since there are many individual variations. Other aspects of the properties of tumor mitochondria will be considered in a later chapter.

The effect of drugs and therapeutic agents on mitochondria

in vitro or in vivo offers an increasing fertile field for pharma-codynamic study because of the increasing recognition of the importance of membranes in determining the distribution and specificity of drugs. Some instances of interesting drug effects will be detailed in the following chapters.

A new milestone in the study of clinical pathology has appeared in recent investigations by Luft and his colleagues, namely, the concept of *mitochondrial disease*. These investigators made a combined clinical-morphological-biochemical study of a patient suffering from a very severe hypermetabolism that was shown not to be of thyroid origin. Isolation of the mitochondria from skeletal muscle biopsy specimens revealed that the mitochondria possessed a normal efficiency of oxidative phosphorylation but virtually no dependence of respiratory rate on ADP acceptor, that is, respiration was *loosely coupled* (see Chapter 7). The muscle tissue showed a very large increase in numbers of mitochondria. They were found to have many densely packed cristae that showed aberrations of structure, as well as concentric surrounding sheaths consisting of many layers of membrane. This is apparently the first recorded instance of an endogenous defect in mitochondria, presumably of genetic origin, in which the functional organization of the respiratory enzymes is significantly altered.

The concept of mitochondrial disease has been discussed at some length by Hoch, who has summarized the evidence for the view that clinical thyrotoxicosis, which we have seen causes formation of bizarre mitochondria in the liver, is essentially a mitochondrial disease. The opportunity for correlating ultrastructure, clinical findings, and biochemical observations should open other metabolic and endocrine disturbances of mitochondria to investigation.

REFERENCES

Reviews

Cowdry, E. V., "The mitochondrial constituents of protoplasm," *Contrib. Embryol.*, 8, 39 (1918).

Ernster, L., and O. Lindberg, "Animal mitochondria," *Ann. Rev. Physiol.*, 20, 13 (1958).

Hoch, F. L., "Thyrotoxicosis as a disease of mitochondria," *New Engl. J. Med.*, **266**, 446, 498 (1962).

Lehninger, A. L., "Water uptake and extrusion by mitochondria in relation to oxidative phosphorylation," *Physiol. Rev.*, **42**, 467 (1962).

Mitchell, P., "Biochemical cytology of microorganisms," *Am. Rev. Microbiol.*, **13**, 407 (1959).

Novikoff, A. B., "Mitochondria (chondriosomes)," in J. Brachet and A. E. Mirsky (eds.), *The Cell*, Academic, New York, 1961, Vol. II, p. 299.

Rouiller, C., "Physiological and pathological changes in mitochondrial morphology," *Intern. Rev. Cytol.*, **9**, 227 (1960). A valuable and comprehensive review.

Sjöstrand, F. S., "Ultrastructure of cells as revealed by the electron microscope," *Intern. Rev. Cytol.*, **5**, 455 (1956).

Research papers

Anderssen-Cedergren, E., "Ultrastructure of motor end-plate and sarcoplasmic components of mouse skeletal muscle fiber," *J. Ultrastruct. Res., Suppl.* **1**, 191 (1959).

André, J., "Contribution á la connaissance du chondriome. Étude de ses modifications ultrastructurales pendant la spermatogenese," *J. Ultrastruct. Res., Suppl.* 3 (1962).

Bahr, G. F., and E. Zeitler, "Study of mitochondria in rat liver. Quantitative electron microscopy," *J. Cell Biol.*, **15**, 489 (1962).

Frederic, J., "Recherches cytologiques sur le chondriome normal ou soumis à l'experimentation dans des cellules vivantes cultivees in vitro," *Arch. Biol. (Liège)*, **69**, 167 (1958).

Loud, A. V., "A method for quantitative estimation of cytoplasmic structures," *J. Cell Biol.*, **15**, 481 (1962).

Luft, R., D. Ikkos, G. Palmieri, L. Ernster, and B. Afzelius, "A case of severe hypermetabolism of non-thyroid origin with a defect in the maintenance of mitochondrial respiratory control: A correlated clinical, biochemical, and morphological study," *J. Clin. Invest.*, **41**, 1776 (1962).

Palade, G. E., "Electron microscopy of cytoplasmic structures," in O. H. Gaebler (ed.), *Enzymes: Units of Biological Structure and Function*, Academic, New York, 1956, Chap. 9.

Perry, R. P., B. Thorell, L. Akerman, and B. Chance, "Localization and assay of respiratory enzymes in single living cells," *Nature*, **184**, 929, 931 (1959).

Revel, J. P., D. W. Fawcett, and C. W. Philpott, "Observations on mitochondrial structure. Angular configurations of the cristae," *J. Cell Biol.*, **16**, 187 (1963).

Rhodin, J., "Correlation of ultrastructural organization and function in normal and experimentally changed proximal convoluted tubule cells of the mouse kidney," *Aktiebolaget Godvil*, Stockholm, 1954.

Smith, D. S., "The structure of insect fibrillar flight muscle," *J. Biophys. Biochem. Cytol., Suppl.* **10,** 123 (1961).

——, "The organization of the flight muscle in a dragonfly, *Aeshna sp. (Odonata)*," *J. Biophys. Biochem. Cytol.*, **11,** 119 (1961).

——, "The structure of flight muscle sarcosomes in the blowfly *Calliphora erythrocephala (Diptera)*," *J. Cell. Biol.*, **19,** 115 (1963).

Smith, R. E., "Quantitative relations between liver mitochondria metabolism and total body weight in mammals," *Ann. N. Y. Acad. Sci.*, **62,** 403 (1956).

Vanderwinkel, E., and R. G. E. Murray, "Organelles intracytoplasmiques bacteriens et site d'activité oxydo-réductive," *J. Ultrastruct. Res.*, **7,** 185 (1962).

3

THE OXIDATION CYCLES
AND THE RESPIRATORY CHAIN

It is the purpose of this chapter to draw out a rather large scale chart of the biological oxidations taking place in intact mitochondria—in essence, the "wiring diagram" by which the Krebs citric acid cycle, the fatty acid oxidation cycle, and ketone body formation and utilization are enzymatically linked to the respiratory chains. The over-all patterns of the oxidative cycles have been known for some time, and no attempt will be made in this book to recapitulate the experimental development of current understanding.

It must be stressed, however, that the oxidative cycles are by no means devoid of experimental interest today simply because their flow sheet is understood. Actually, the component enzymes of these cycles require much further study and contemplation, since the molecular devices that enable the self-regulation and integration of the oxidative cycles with the respiratory chains are inherent in the catalytic and kinetic properties of the individual enzymes and the specificity of their active sites.

THE KREBS CITRIC ACID CYCLE

Isolated mitochondria from liver and kidney of higher animals, as well as many other tissues, contain the complete equipment for orderly oxidation of pyruvate and fatty acids via the Krebs cycle, including enzymes, coenzymes, and essential metals. The suspending medium requires, in addition to fatty acid or pyruvate as substrate, only Mg^{++}, P_i, and ADP, together with a small amount of a dicarboxylic acid such as malate or oxalacetate as "primer" for the Krebs cycle; but even the latter can be generated by mitochondria from simpler precursors. Often a phosphate-trapping system, such as hexokinase plus glucose, is employed to make ADP continuously available. Under these conditions the rate of oxidation of pyruvate by isolated mitochondria occurs with Q_{O_2} values (μl O_2 per mg dry weight per hr) in the range 40 to 80, in contrast with Q_{O_2} values for respiration in the intact tissues of between 7 and 22. Since the mitochondria make up some 20 per cent of the total dry weight of these tissues, the rate of oxidation by the isolated mitochondria easily accounts for the rate of respiration in the intact tissues. Mitochondria of the intensely active housefly flight muscle may have Q_{O_2} values as high as 400 to 600 with α-glycerophosphate as substrate.

The schematic diagram in Figure 3–1 shows the organization of the Krebs citric acid cycle, as it is understood today, together with its connections to the respiratory chain. Also shown are some points of entry and exit for various associated metabolites. Some comments on the individual enzyme steps and mechanisms follow.

The complex pyruvate dehydrogenase system of mitochondria, which is composed of three or more enzymes, has been under intensive investigation with respect to the mechanism of participation of α-lipoic acid and thiamine pyrophosphate, two of the specific coenzymes concerned in this reaction. The over-all reaction for pyruvate oxidation is

$$\text{pyruvate} + \text{NAD}^+ + \text{CoA} \rightarrow \text{acetyl-CoA} + \text{CO}_2 + \text{NADH} + \text{H}^+ \tag{3-1}$$

The NADH generated enters the respiratory chain, and the acetyl-CoA may enter the Krebs cycle following condensation with oxalacetate to form citrate. However, this reaction is far

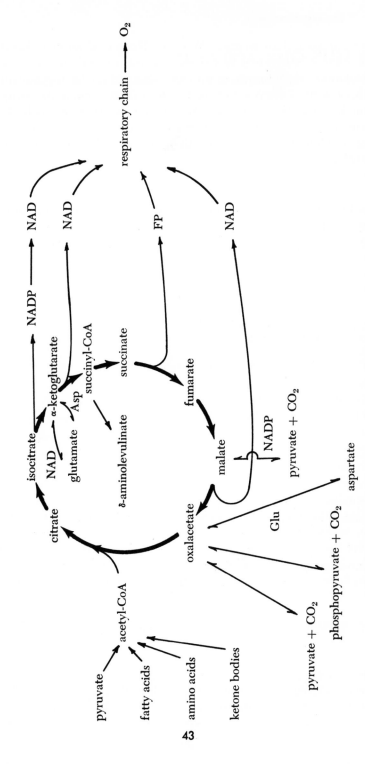

Figure 3–1 The Krebs citric acid cycle and associated reactions. Glu = glutamate; Asp = aspartate.

43

more complex than written. Work of Holzer, Krampitz, Reed, and other investigators has been devoted to defining the role of thiamine pyrophosphate and of α-lipoate in the mechanism of this energy-conserving oxidative decarboxylation of pyruvate.

In the first step, pyruvate is believed to combine with the thiamine pyrophosphate of the pyruvate carboxylase component to yield so-called active pyruvate or α-lactyl-2-thiamine pyrophosphate:

$$\text{pyruvate} + \text{thiamine-PP} \rightleftharpoons \alpha\text{-lactyl-2-thiamine-PP} \qquad (3\text{–}2)$$

This intermediate (attached to the enzyme) is unstable and loses CO_2 by decarboxylation to become so-called active acetaldehyde, or 2-hydroxyethylthiamine pyrophosphate:

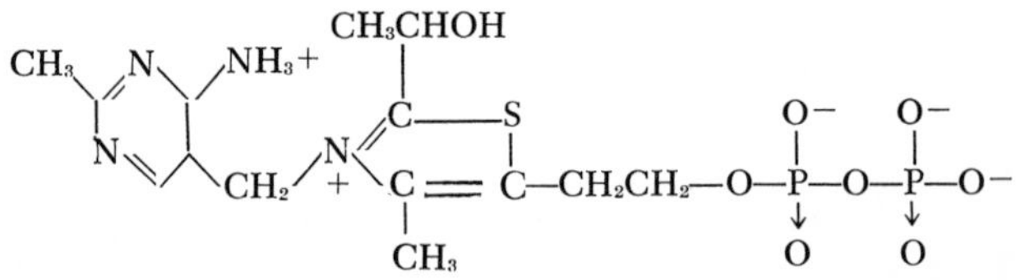

This derivative is believed to undergo oxidation of the hydroxyethyl group in situ to form an acetylated thiamine derivative, a reaction in which the cyclic disulfide of the α-lipoyl group of the enzyme is the electron acceptor:

$$\text{hydroxyethylthiamine-PP} + \text{R}\begin{matrix}\diagup\text{S}\\ \diagdown\text{S}\end{matrix}\Big| \rightarrow \text{2-acetylthiamine-PP} + \text{R}\begin{matrix}\diagup\text{SH}\\ \diagdown\text{SH}\end{matrix} \qquad (3\text{–}3)$$

The α-lipoyl group participating in this reaction is attached via an amide linkage to the ε-amino group of a lysine residue of the enzyme. Accompanying or following the above reaction, the acetyl group is transferred from the thiamine to the reduced α-lipoyl group to form a thioester, which then becomes the acetyl donor in a following reaction in which CoA is acceptor:

$$\text{2-acetylthiamine-PP} + \text{R}\begin{matrix}\diagup\text{SH}\\ \diagdown\text{SH}\end{matrix} \rightarrow \text{thiamine-PP} + \text{R}\begin{matrix}\diagup\text{SH}\\ \diagdown\text{SCOCH}_3\end{matrix} \qquad (3\text{–}4)$$

$$\text{R}\begin{matrix}\diagup\text{SH}\\ \diagdown\text{SCOCH}_3\end{matrix} + \text{CoA} \rightarrow \text{acetyl-CoA} + \text{R}\begin{matrix}\diagup\text{SH}\\ \diagdown\text{SH}\end{matrix} \qquad (3\text{–}5)$$

Finally, the electrons are delivered to NAD, and thus the respiratory chain, via the flavoprotein α-lipoyl dehydrogenase:

$$R\begin{matrix}\nearrow SH\\\searrow SH\end{matrix} + FAD \rightarrow R\begin{matrix}\nearrow S\\\searrow S\end{matrix}\Big| + FADH_2 \qquad (3\text{--}6)$$

$$FADH_2 + NAD^+ \rightarrow FAD + NADH + H^+ \qquad (3\text{--}7)$$

The enzymes catalyzing these complex reactions are organized into a large structured complex of molecular weight 4,000,000 that can be cleaved to produce two fragments: one catalyzes reactions (3–2) to (3–5) and the other catalyzes reactions 3–6 and 3–7. Reed has postulated that the interactions within this complex are brought about by a "swinging arm" mechanism in which the dithiol group at the end of the eight-carbon α-lipoyl group, which is in turn attached to the ϵ-amino group of a lysine residue of the enzyme complex, swings from one active site to another. As will be seen from Equations (3–3) to (3–6), the α-lipoyl group is involved in four separate steps: in oxidation, in two separate acyl transfers, and in reduction of the flavoprotein.

In the first step of the Krebs cycle proper, citrate is formed from acetyl-CoA and oxalacetate by citrate synthase, which has been obtained in crystalline form:

$$\text{acetyl-CoA} + \text{oxalacetate} + H_2O \rightleftharpoons \text{citrate} + \text{CoA} + H^+ \qquad (3\text{--}8)$$

This complex reaction involves both a condensation and a hydrolysis, but the steps have not been separated. The reaction goes essentially to completion as written, with a rather large decline in free energy. It is of some interest that another reaction that involves acetyl-CoA and oxalacetate and that has been found to occur in some mitochondria leads not to citrate but to malonyl-CoA, which is presumably a building block for lipid synthesis. This reaction, as well as certain others to be described, involves the citric acid cycle in certain biosynthetic activities.

Aconitase, an enzyme easily extracted from mitochondrial structure, catalyzes the reversible interconversion of citrate, *cis*-aconitate, and isocitrate. Isotopic experiments have indicated the occurrence of a common intermediate, probably a carbonium ion attached to the enzyme:

$$
\begin{array}{cc}
\text{citrate} & \text{isocitrate} \\
\end{array}
$$

$$
\left[\begin{array}{ccc}
COO^- & & COO^- \\
| & & | \\
CH_2 & & +CH \\
| & & | \\
+C-COO^- & \rightleftharpoons & HC-COO^- \\
| & & | \\
CH_2 & & CH_2 \\
| & & | \\
COO^- & & COO^- \\
\end{array}\right] \quad (3\text{-}9)
$$

$$
\text{intermediate carbonium ions}
$$

$$
\updownarrow
$$

$$
cis\text{-aconitate}
$$

Fe^{++} and a sulfhydryl group are required components, which are believed to engage in binding the substrates. At equilibrium, approximately 90 per cent citrate, 7 per cent isocitrate, and 3 per cent cis-aconitate are present; however, the kinetics of these reactions are anomalous and leave open the possibility of mutual interference among the tricarboxylic acids and thus a potential control system. Aconitase is also inhibited by certain dicarboxylic acids. In the aconitase reaction, the symmetrical molecule citric acid evidently binds to the enzyme at three specific points, making possible asymmetric conversion of citrate to isocitrate. This was first pointed out by Ogston to rationalize the finding that α-ketoglutarate formed from labeled acetate was asymmetrically labeled.

Isocitrate is oxidized to α-ketoglutarate and CO_2 in a reaction over which there has been some controversy, since two enzymes, one specific for NAD, the other for NADP, are known. The over-all reaction is identical for both enzymes, however:

$$
\text{isocitrate} + \text{NADP} \rightleftharpoons \alpha\text{-ketoglutarate} + CO_2 + \text{NADPH} + H^+ \quad (3\text{-}10)
$$

The NADP-linked enzyme is reversible and can fix CO_2; and although no intermediates can be found, the enzyme will decarboxylate or reduce *added* oxalosuccinate. On the other hand, the NAD-linked enzyme is not reversible, has no oxalosuccinate decarboxylase activity, and requires the presence of adenylic acid. It is generally believed that the NADP-linked enzyme is the major pathway in mitochondria. The NADPH formed in this reaction does not react directly with the respiratory chain; rather, it reacts with NAD^+ in a transhydrogenation reaction:

$$
\text{NADPH} + NAD^+ \rightleftharpoons NADP^+ + \text{NADH} \quad (3\text{-}11)
$$

As will be seen in a later chapter, the oxidation of isocitrate may in fact be more complex than indicated here. The NADPH formed by isocitrate dehydrogenase is in all probability an electron donor in the reductive biosynthesis of dicarboxylic acids, lipids, and other products in mitochondria.

The oxidation of α-ketoglutarate to succinyl-CoA is believed to follow the reaction pattern indicated for oxidation of pyruvate; it involves thiamine pyrophosphate, CoA, and the α-lipoyl group. NAD^+ is the ultimate electron acceptor. Succinyl α-lipoyl enzyme is formed, and in the presence of CoA as acceptor, succinyl-CoA is the end product. This undergoes deacylation in mitochondria by one of two routes. The usual route is by a phosphorolytic cleavage of exceedingly complex mechanism:

$$\text{succinyl-CoA} + P_i + GDP \rightleftharpoons \text{succinate} + GTP + CoA \quad (3\text{–}12)$$

This is a so-called substrate-level phosphorylation and is not inhibited by dinitrophenol; it is specific for GDP or IDP. ATP is finally formed by intervention of a nucleoside diphosphokinase:

$$GTP + ADP \rightleftharpoons GDP + ATP \quad (3\text{–}13)$$

Azzone and Ernster have recently pointed out that the specificity for GDP may be a device to compartment or sequester the phosphate bond energy arising from the substrate-level phosphorylation for some special function for which the main pool of ATP formed in respiratory chain phosphorylation is either unavailable or unreactive, just as NADPH is segregated from NADH. They have suggested GTP plays a special role in maintenance of mitochondrial structure.

Alternatively, the CoA group of succinyl-CoA may be transferred to acetoacetate in mitochondria, particularly in those of kidney or muscle:

$$\text{succinyl-CoA} + \text{acetoacetate} \rightleftharpoons \text{succinate} + \text{acetoacetyl-CoA} \quad (3\text{–}14)$$

This reaction is a point of interplay between the Krebs cycle and the mechanism of ketone body oxidation.

Succinate is oxidized to fumarate by a specific flavoprotein, succinate dehydrogenase, whose structure and properties will be considered in detail in the next chapter:

$$\text{succinate} + FP \rightleftharpoons \text{fumarate} + FP_{red} \quad (3\text{–}15)$$

It is of considerable significance, as will be seen later, that succinate dehydrogenase is competitively inhibited by oxalacetate, a later intermediate in the citric acid cycle. The significance of this fact for feedback control of the rate of the Krebs cycle oxidations is obvious.

In the next step, fumarase catalyzes reversible hydration of fumarate to form malate:

$$\text{fumarate} + H_2O \rightleftharpoons \text{L-malate} \tag{3-16}$$

This enzyme has been obtained in crystalline form, and the kinetics and mechanism of the reaction have been studied in great detail. It is again of some interest in connection with control mechanisms that fumarase may be either stimulated or inhibited by inorganic phosphate, depending on concentration of the latter. Furthermore, its optimum pH and substrate concentration differ in the forward and reverse directions and depend in a complex manner on the ionic components in the medium.

The terminal step of the cycle, which regenerates oxalacetate, is catalyzed by the NAD-linked malate dehydrogenase, which has also been isolated in crystalline form:

$$\text{L-malate} + NAD^+ \rightleftharpoons \text{oxalacetate} + NADH + H^+ \tag{3-17}$$

It is of some interest that the oxidation-reduction potential of the malate-oxalacetate couple, about -0.10 volt at pH 7.0, is much more positive than that of the $NADH\text{-}NAD^+$ couple, about -0.32 volt. The point of equilibrium of reaction (3-17) at pH 7.0 is far to the left. Oxalacetate is thus an avid acceptor of electrons from NADH and thus, in turn, from other NAD-linked substrates, which usually have a much more negative potential. This reaction equilibrium is one means by which the concentration of oxalacetate in mitochondria may be controlled. Furthermore, as we shall see in the case of isocitrate oxidation, the malate-oxalacetate couple may actually participate as an electron carrier system.

Mitochondria of higher animal tissues also possess the enzymatic apparatus to carry out a series of reactions by which the dicarboxylic acids necessary for operation of the Krebs cycle are formed or removed, thus providing an important element in control of the rate of the cycle. These enzymes include glutamate-oxalacetate and glutamate-pyruvate transaminases, glutamate dehydrogenase, and the enzymes responsible for reversible carboxylation of pyruvate or phosphopyruvate. These important reactions, and their metabolic relationship to the extra-mitochondrial systems, will be discussed later.

THE FATTY ACID OXIDATION CYCLE

Mitochondria of several tissues of higher animals have been found to be capable of oxidizing fatty acids to completion. As in the case of the Krebs citric acid cycle, the oxidation of fatty acids proceeds with a high degree of enzymatic autonomy, since only phosphate, ADP, Mg^{++}, and a dicarboxylic acid must be added to the medium to realize complete oxidation to CO_2 and H_2O. The rate of oxidation of higher fatty acids by liver and kidney mitochondria is very high, sometimes higher than the rate of pyruvate oxidation. The enzymatic reaction pattern of fatty acid oxidation is now fairly well known from work in the laboratories of Lynen, Green, Ochoa, Lardy, and Lehninger. The flow sheet for fatty acid oxidation, sometimes called a *spiral*, is shown in Figure 3–2.

Three different *activating enzymes* are known for formation of the fatty acid–CoA esters, which are specific in turn for short-, intermediate-, and long-chain fatty acids. They catalyze the general reaction:

$$RCOOH + ATP + CoA \rightleftharpoons RCOCoA + AMP + PP_i \quad (3–18)$$

The inorganic pyrophosphate formed is known to undergo hydrolytic removal by an inorganic pyrophosphatase in mitochondria, allowing the over-all reaction to proceed further to the right. Inorganic pyrophosphatase is inhibited by fluoride, and it is of some interest that fatty acid oxidation is also inhibited by this agent, which thus keeps reaction (3–18) from going far to the right.

The first dehydrogenation step is carried out by one of two or perhaps three flavoproteins called generically acyl-CoA dehydrogenases; these are specific for short-, intermediate-, and long-chain fatty acids. These enzymes contain FAD, which is bleached on reaction with the fatty acyl-CoA; they also contain Cu or Fe. The fatty acyl-CoA flavoproteins do not react directly with oxygen, or with cytochrome b or c; a second type of flavoprotein, the so-called electron-transferring flavoprotein of Bein-

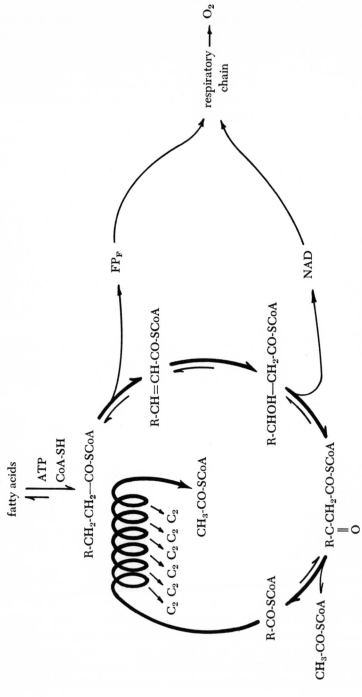

Figure 3–2 The fatty acid oxidation spiral.

ert, is required to reoxidize the reduced acyl-CoA dehydrogenase by a mechanism that is not yet entirely clear. The product of the first oxidative step is presumably α,β-unsaturated acyl-CoA.

The next step in the fatty acid oxidation cycle is the hydration of the α,β-unsaturated acyl-CoA ester by the enzyme crotonase or enoyl hydratase:

$$R\text{—}CH = CH\text{—}COCoA + H_2O \rightleftharpoons R\text{—}\overset{\displaystyle H}{\underset{\displaystyle OH}{C}}\text{—}CH_2\text{—}COCoA \qquad (3\text{–}19)$$

Crotonase causes the specific formation of L(+) β-hydroxyacyl-CoA esters in this reaction. This enzyme not only acts on either α,β- or β,γ-unsaturated acyl-CoA esters, in either *cis* or *trans* forms, but is also capable of catalyzing positional isomerization between the α,β- and β,γ-unsaturated compounds and, presumably, *cis-trans* isomerization. It has been suggested that two crotonases exist in mitochondria, one specific for *cis* and one for *trans* acids.

The second dehydrogenation enzyme is specific for the L-stereoisomer of β-hydroxyacyl-CoA, as first shown by Lehninger and Greville, and it is also specific for NAD$^+$; presumably, the reduced NADH so formed is then available for entry into the respiratory chain.

$$\text{L-}\beta\text{-hydroxyacyl-CoA} + \text{NAD}^+ \rightleftharpoons \beta\text{-ketoacyl-CoA} + \text{NADH} + \text{H}^+ \tag{3–20}$$

Curiously, there is also in mitochondria a racemase that interconverts D- and L-β-hydroxyacyl-CoA esters. While there are still some aspects of this situation that require further study, it now appears that fatty acid oxidation involves the L-β-hydroxyacyl-CoA as intermediate, whereas fatty acid synthesis by the fatty acid "synthetase" system involves a D-β-hydroxyacyl-ester as intermediate, according to recent work of Lynen.

Finally, the β-ketoacyl-CoA undergoes *thiolytic cleavage* to form acetyl-CoA and a fatty acyl-CoA having two fewer carbon atoms:

$$\beta\text{-ketoacyl-CoA} + \text{CoA} \rightleftharpoons \text{acyl-CoA} + \text{acetyl-CoA} \qquad (3\text{–}21)$$

The acetyl-CoA formed in this reaction may enter the Krebs cycle directly and become oxidized to CO_2. Alternatively, however, it may enter into acetoacetate formation in liver mitochondria, as is indicated in the following section. The other product is a fatty acyl-CoA ester now shorter by two carbon atoms than the starting substrate; it may now enter the cycle again for removal of the next acetyl unit. Successive cyclings of the gradually shortened fatty acyl-CoA esters produce the so-called spiral of fatty acid oxidation.

Oxidation of fatty acids by liver mitochondria may occur under two sets of conditions. In the absence of added Krebs cycle intermediates, some ATP is necessary to prime the oxidation, presumably for the first activation step. Under these conditions the fatty acid is oxidized exclusively to acetoacetate, no C_4-dicarboxylic acids being available to provide entry of acetyl-CoA into the Krebs cycle for oxidation of the acetyl-CoA units formed, which condense with each other to produce acetoacetyl-CoA. The latter then undergoes deacylation:

$$\text{acetyl-CoA} + \text{acetyl-CoA} \rightleftharpoons \text{acetoacetyl-CoA} + \text{CoA} \qquad (3\text{--}22)$$

$$\text{acetoacetyl-CoA} \rightarrow \text{acetoacetate} + \text{CoA} \qquad (3\text{--}23)$$

Once fatty acid oxidation is started in the presence of ATP, it becomes self-sustaining, since oxidative phosphorylation of ADP and AMP continues to provide more ATP to activate further molecules of fatty acid substrate.

On the other hand, when fatty acid oxidation occurs in the presence of Krebs cycle intermediates, less or even no acetoacetate is formed; the acetyl-CoA reacts with oxalacetate and is oxidized to completion by the Krebs cycle pathway. The latter is the usual pathway in mitochondria of kidney, muscle, and other extrahepatic tissues. Brain mitochondria are less active in fatty acid oxidation than in other tissues.

There are a number of unsolved problems. Most studies of fatty acid oxidation have been carried out with saturated intermediate or short-chain fatty acids. Little has been done on the mechanism and dynamics of oxidation by isolated mitochondria of the naturally occurring long-chain saturated and unsaturated fatty acids, particularly the polyunsaturated fatty acids, or on the competition among various fatty acids for entry into the oxidation cycle. Little is known of the specific forms of lipids in the cytoplasm and in the mitochondria that are direct donors of fatty acids for the oxidase system. Free fatty acids of blood plasma, carried by serum albumin, are known to be the immediately oxidized form of plasma fatty acids, but little is known of the mechanism of their entry into the cell and then into the mitochondrion. The growth factor *carnitine* has recently been implicated in fatty acid metabolism by Fritz and by Bremer. Carnitine esters of long-chain fatty acids are formed enzymatically from their CoA esters. These carnitine esters are more readily oxidized by isolated mitochondria than the free fatty acids, indicating that carnitine esters may be transport forms for entry of fatty acids into the mitochondrion.

KETONE BODY OXIDATION AND FORMATION

In extrahepatic tissues such as kidney and heart, isolated mitochondria readily oxidize D-β-hydroxybutyrate and acetoacetate to CO_2 and H_2O via the Krebs cycle through intervention of the following reactions:

$$\text{D-}\beta\text{-hydroxybutyrate} + \text{NAD}^+ \rightleftharpoons \text{acetoacetate} + \text{NADH} + \text{H}^+ \quad (3\text{--}24)$$

$$\text{acetoacetate} + \text{ATP} + \text{CoA} \rightleftharpoons \text{acetoacetyl-CoA} + \text{AMP} + \text{PP}_i \quad (3\text{--}25)$$

$$\text{acetoacetate} + \text{succinyl-CoA} \rightleftharpoons \text{acetoacetyl-CoA} + \text{succinate} \quad (3\text{--}26)$$

$$\text{acetoacetyl-CoA} + \text{CoA} \rightleftharpoons 2 \text{ acetyl-CoA} \quad (3\text{--}27)$$

Although all these reactions are reversible, it is interesting that oxidation of fatty acids by mitochondria of kidney or heart does not proceed with accumulation of ketone bodies, as it does in liver.

In liver mitochondria, on the other hand, D-β-hydroxybutyrate is readily and quantitatively oxidized to free acetoacetate according to reaction (3–24). The acetoacetate accumulates quantitatively, since liver mitochondria lack the enzymatic reactions to carry out its activation to acetoacetyl-CoA by reactions (3–25) and (3–26). Another difference in ketone body metabolism in liver mitochondria is that free acetoacetate accumulates during fatty acid oxidation; presumably, acetoacetyl-CoA is readily deacylated and thus escapes the thiolase reaction that normally leads to formation of two molecules of acetyl-CoA.

It was formerly believed that the deacylation of acetoacetyl-CoA in liver mitochondria occurred by a direct hydrolysis:

$$\text{acetoacetyl-CoA} + \text{H}_2\text{O} \rightleftharpoons \text{CoA} + \text{acetoacetate} \quad (3\text{--}28)$$

However, more recent work of Lynen and his colleagues indicates that a cyclic mechanism involving acetyl-CoA and hydroxymethylglutaryl-CoA occurs:

$$\text{acetoacetyl-CoA} + \text{acetyl-CoA} + H_2O \rightleftharpoons$$
$$\text{hydroxymethylglutaryl-CoA} + \text{CoA} \qquad (3\text{--}29)$$
$$\text{hydroxymethylglutaryl-CoA} \rightleftharpoons \text{acetoacetate} + \text{acetyl-CoA}$$
$$(3\text{--}30)$$

The acetyl-CoA that is regenerated then reacts with successive molecules of acetoacetyl-CoA.

Finally, some mention must be made of the finding of Lehninger and Greville that *both* the D and L isomers of free β-hydroxybutyrate may undergo oxidation in mitochondria, although it is the D isomer that accumulates in blood and urine during ketosis and has been presumed to be the "natural" form. It is curious that current knowledge provides no specific metabolic function for the existence in tissues and blood of free D-β-hydroxybutyrate; it seems to be a blind end. Later, the possible role of D-β-hydroxybutyrate in electron transport and in oxidation of extramitochondrial NADH will be described.

THE RESPIRATORY CHAIN

The respiratory chain is the "power train" of the mitochondrion, the site of conversion of respiratory energy into phosphate bond energy, into mechanochemical energy, and into osmotic energy. We shall here consider the general nature of the respiratory chain as a sequential multienzyme system that accepts electrons from the various NAD- and NADP-linked dehydrogenases and flavoprotein dehydrogenases of the Krebs cycle and the fatty acid oxidation cycle. Later, the electron carriers will be considered as individual molecules, as building blocks in experimental reconstructions of the respiration chain, and as elements in energy coupling.

The three major components of the respiratory chain, namely, the pyridine-linked dehydrogenases, the flavoproteins, and the cytochromes, have been studied for many years. In the 1930s the basic concept had emerged that the electron carriers are arranged in a chain of increasing oxidation-reduction potentials, with electrons flowing from the relatively electronegative substrates via the pyridine nucleotides and the flavoproteins to the increasingly electropositive cytochromes and, finally, to oxygen. However, it was not realized then that the respiratory chain contains energy-conserving devices leading to ATP formation, and there was no knowledge of the fact that some flavoproteins and cytochromes are extramitochondrial and play no primary part in the main stream of respiration.

It was the important work of Chance and his colleagues on the spectroscopy of the respiratory carriers in intact mitochondria beginning in 1953 that has given us a more detailed and precise picture of the composition, sequence, and dynamics of the respiratory chain. This has been supplemented by isolation and reconstruction efforts in the laboratories of Green, Okunuki, Singer, Slater, and many others.

Chance and Williams, by using an extremely sensitive double-beam spectrophotometer, were able to record difference spectra of the electron carriers in intact mitochondria. The turbidity and light scattering of the particles were canceled out by using a reference cell containing mitochondria with the carriers in the oxidized state as the reference blank, against which the spectrum of the fully anaerobic or reduced state could be identified. Figure 3–3 shows the major absorption peaks and troughs of the reduced pyridine nucleotides, flavoproteins, and cytochromes a, b, and c in such a spectrum. Difference spectra of the reduced state of the carriers in the presence of cyanide or carbon monoxide also made possible identification of peaks that Chance has concluded correspond to cytochromes a and a_3.

Another cytochrome of the respiratory chain, namely, cytochrome c_1, cannot normally be distinguished from cytochrome c in such spectra but can be visualized at very low temperatures, which produce sharpening of absorption peaks. A peak corresponding to ubiquinone, or coenzyme Q, has also been recognized in the difference spectrum of most mitochondria in the ultraviolet region at 275 $m\mu$. The place of coenzyme Q in the chain will be considered later.

When an excess of dithionite, a strong reducing agent, is added to intact, well-washed mitochondria in which the chain has already been enzymatically reduced in the presence of a respiratory substrate such as succinate or malate, there is usually no significant increase in the existing absorption peaks nor do new peaks appear. Therefore, all the electron carrier molecules present in intact mitochondria that are detectable in such spectra are reduced by the normal respiratory substrates; there

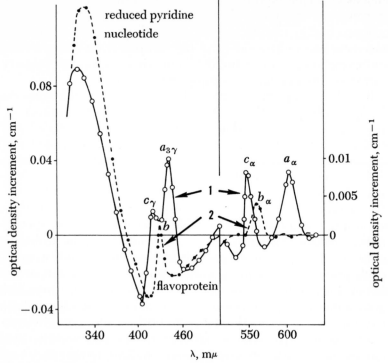

Figure 3–3 Difference spectra of the respiratory carriers in rat liver mitochondria. The solid line represents the absorbancy change produced by excess substrate under anaerobic conditions, and the
dashed line represents the change produced by excess substrate in the presence of antimycin A, measured against an
aerobic cuvette. The peaks are labeled. It is noted that cytochromes c and a are fully oxidized in the presence of antimycin
A, whereas the peak of reduced cytochrome b is clearly shown.
[From B. Chance and G. R. Williams, *Adv. Enzymol.*, **17**, 74
(1956).]

appear to be no "loose" electron carrier molecules that are not
in direct connection with the respiratory chain.

From such difference spectra, together with reasonable estimates of the molar absorbancy indices of the carriers, Chance
and Williams also calculated the absolute concentrations of
each of the carriers in intact mitochondria (see Table 3–1).
The flavoproteins and the cytochromes are present in concen-

Table 3–1 Respiratory carriers in rat liver mitochondria*

	NAD	Flavoprotein	cyt b	cyt $c + c_1$	cyt a	cyt a_3
Concentration, mμmoles per mg protein	3.8	0.72	0.18	0.34	0.20	0.22
Concentration ratio; cytochrome a = 1.0	19	3.6	0.9	1.7	1.0	1.1

* From Chance and Hess, 1962.

trations of the order of 0.2 mμmoles per mg protein. It is most striking that the cytochromes and flavoproteins appear to occur in simple molar ratios to each other. This finding is fundamental to the concept of the *respiratory assembly*, that is, an organized macromolecular assembly made up of one molecule of each component in a geometry favorable to their interaction.

Mitochondria of widely different tissues and species yield remarkably similar difference spectra, indicating that they contain the same basic set of carriers in the same simple molar ratios to each other. Unfortunately, the accuracy of such measurements may be compromised by some uncertainty about the molar absorbancy indices of the carriers in their native, bound form and by interference from light-scattering phenomena, which are perhaps incompletely corrected in the difference method.

Chance and Williams also deduced the functional sequence of the respiratory carriers in intact liver mitochondria from several considerations. The carriers in mitochondria respiring in the presence of excess substrate, ADP, and phosphate and oxygen are not all in the fully oxidized form but are instead in a dynamic steady state in which each carrier occurs in a characteristic ratio of reduced to oxidized form (see Chapter 7). The more electronegative components of the chain, the pyridine nucleotides, are relatively reduced, the flavoproteins are intermediate in oxidation-reduction state, and the cytochromes are more nearly completely oxidized, as shown in Table 3–2. This oxidation-reduction gradient in the aerobic steady state agrees

Table 3–2 The oxidation-reduction state of the respiratory carriers in the aerobic steady state (state 3*)

	NAD + NADP	Flavoprotein	cyt b	cyt c	cyt a
Per cent in reduced state	53	20	16	6	<4

* Chance and Williams, 1956.

with the gradient of the normal oxidation-reduction potentials of the carriers.

Chance and Williams also determined the time sequence in which the fully reduced carriers of anaerobic, intact mitochondria go into the oxidized state when oxygen is admitted. Cytochrome a was found to be oxidized first, followed by cytochrome c. Cytochrome b and flavoprotein did not become oxidized until all the cytochrome c had been oxidized; cytochrome b was oxidized before flavoprotein.

It was also demonstrated that cyanide, proposed by Warburg to block the action of the terminal enzyme of respiration, caused all the carriers observable by the difference method to go into the fully reduced form in the presence of excess substrate. However, when respiration was blocked by the antibiotic antimycin A, it was found that pyridine nucleotide, flavoprotein, and cytochrome b became fully reduced, whereas cytochrome c, a, and a_3 became fully oxidized, which provided evidence for the site of action of this agent as lying between cytochrome b and c. Similarly, application of the inhibitor Amytal (sodium amobarbital) caused only the pyridine nucleotides to remain fully reduced, thereby establishing the point of inhibition of this agent as lying between NADH and flavoprotein. These findings thus indicate the functional sequence of the carriers to be

$$\text{substrate} \rightarrow \text{NAD} \rightarrow \text{FP} \rightarrow \text{cyt } b \rightarrow \text{cyt } c(c_1) \rightarrow \text{cyt } a \rightarrow \text{cyt } a_3 \rightarrow O_2$$

Finally, a fundamental question regarding the enzymatic organization of electron transport must be considered, namely, whether one type of chain is required for oxidation of succinate, another for oxidation of NADH, and still another for fatty acid, for example, or whether a single type of chain serves as final

common pathway for electrons from all mitochondrial substrates. As indicated above, the earlier work of Chance showed
that NAD-linked substrates and succinate can reduce all the
respiratory chains of mitochondria essentially completely; these
results are consistent with either the occurrence of a single type
of respiratory chain that can accommodate electrons from all
substrates or with the occurrence of different types of respiratory chains each specific for an electron donor, provided there
are full interconnections between such chains. Kimura and
Singer have considered this question in some detail and have
obtained some supporting evidence from inhibitor studies for
a common span in the cytochrome region but with substrate-
specific bifurcations. More recent work of Chance and others
has strengthened the concept that succinate and NADH are
oxidized by the same terminal chain.

Figure 3–4 gives a schematic diagram of the respiratory
chain, showing entry of electrons from NADH, NADPH, succinate, fatty acids, α-glycerophosphate, and choline. This diagram serves to summarize much of the known information on
the sequence of the respiratory carriers and the points of entry
of electrons from various substrates. However, there is still significant uncertainty concerning the place of ubiquinone, or coenzyme Q, in the chain, as well as the sequence and identity of
the cytochromes. These points will be considered in Chapter 4.

Figure 3–4 does, however, serve to emphasize an important
aspect of the dynamics of electron transport. It may be noted
that in the final common pathway of the respiratory chain,
when equal amounts of fatty acid and Krebs cycle oxidations
are occurring, there must be the mixing and integration of five
pairs of electrons entering the cytochrome system from the
NAD-specific flavoproteins (that is, from pyruvate, isocitrate,
α-ketoglutarate, malate, and L-β-hydroxyacyl-CoA dehydrogenases), one pair from succinate dehydrogenase flavoprotein,
and one pair from fatty acyl-CoA dehydrogenase flavoprotein.
Normally, electrons entering from these basic sources, together
with others from such substrates as extramitochondrial NADH
and glutamate, must blend harmoniously. However, it is quite
evident that competition for entry into the chain could cause
disparities in the rate of oxidation of different intermediates of
the oxidative cycles; such competition has in fact been observed and may be one basis of integration and control of cycle
oxidations. For example, Krebs and his colleagues have shown

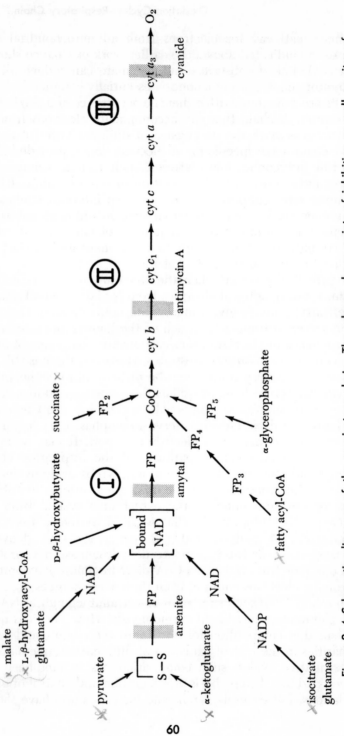

Figure 3-4 Schematic diagram of the respiratory chain. The scheme shows points of inhibition as well as sites of phosphorylation (Roman numerals).

that succinate oxidation may "monopolize" the respiratory chain and thus inhibit oxidation of NADH.

Finally, it may be pointed out that the NAD-linked D-β-hydroxybutyrate dehydrogenase, which is tightly bound to membrane structure, appears to have some special function in the respiratory chain other than as one of the several NAD-linked dehydrogenases channeling electrons into the chain. Lehninger and his colleagues have suggested that it may serve to "collect" reducing equivalents from other NAD-linked dehydrogenases and feed them to the NADH dehydrogenase. The properties of D-β-hydroxybutyrate dehydrogenase show a complexity reminiscent of that of the energy-conserving α-keto acid and D-glyceraldehyde phosphate dehydrogenase systems.

MITOCHONDRIAL PYRIDINE NUCLEOTIDES

Mitochondria from different tissues contain both NAD and NADP in the total amount of some 10 to 40 times the concentration of cytochrome a. The absolute amount of the total NAD is fairly constant, but the amount of NADP varies considerably from one type of mitochondria to another, as shown by the extensive analytical studies of Klingenberg and his colleagues (Table 3–3). Rat liver mitochondria contain approximately 6.5 moles total NAD and 11.5 moles NADP per mole of cytochrome c. In rat kidney mitochondria there is much less NADP,

Table 3–3 Pyridine nucleotide content of mitochondria in rat tissues and locust flight muscle, expressed in moles per mole of cytochrome c*

Characteristic	Liver	Heart	Kidney	Brain	Flight muscle
Total NAD	6.5	10	12	8.1	4
Total NADP	11.5	2.4	2.3	1.3	0
NADP/NAD	1.7	0.24	0.19	0.15	0
Fraction NAD reduced [†]	0.40	0.09	0.09	0	0.10
Fraction NADP reduced [†]	0.91	0.70	0.65	0.60	

* Data of Klingenberg, Slenczka, and Ritt, 1959.
[†] In controlled or ADP-less state. Substrate, pyruvate + malate.

whereas in locust flight muscle mitochondria there is no NADP.

The oxidation-reduction states of intramitochondrial NAD and NADP are usually not identical in freshly isolated mitochondria. In rat liver mitochondria in the controlled, or ADP-less, state, 90 per cent of the NADP is in the reduced state but only 40 per cent of the NAD is reduced. Thus, most of the reduced 340-mμ band corresponding to total pyridine nucleotides in the resting state in rat liver mitochondria is contributed by NADPH. In kidney or brain mitochondria, the NAD is only slightly reduced, whereas the NADP is quite substantially reduced. Clearly, the mitochondrial transhydrogenase activity does not bring about complete equilibration of the two pyridine nucleotides.

As will be discussed later, there is now significant evidence that mitochondrial NAD is compartmented. One type of NAD "pool" seems to be directly accessible to D-β-hydroxybutyrate dehydrogenase only and is not reduced directly by other NAD-linked dehydrogenases, as shown by Gamble and Lehninger, whereas another type of NAD pool is apparently readily reduced by succinate through energy-linked reversal of electron transport (see Chapter 7).

INTRAMITOCHONDRIAL LOCATION
OF RESPIRATORY ENZYMES

Early experiments of Schneider and Hogeboom revealed that sonication of rat liver mitochondria released some 55 per cent of the total mitochondrial protein in soluble form, which presumably derived from the matrix; the rest remained particulate and easily sedimented and represented membrane material. They found that over 90 per cent of the cytochrome oxidase activity of the original mitochondria was recovered in the particular fraction, presumably fragments of the mitochondrial membrane. Mitochondrial membrane fragments prepared in several laboratories by sonic or mechanical treatment, such as the thoroughly studied Keilin-Hartree heart particles and the so-called electron transport particles (abbreviated ETP) of Green, or by treatment with cholate or digitonin, show the presence of fairly complete respiratory chains with the same molar ratio of carriers as seen in intact mitochondria, although they usually lack cytochrome c, which is very easily extracted.

Membrane fragments also characteristically contain succinate,

D-β-hydroxybutyrate, and α-glycerophosphate dehydrogenases. When properly prepared under mild conditions, as in the case of digitonin fragments, they also show oxidative phosphorylation. On the other hand, membrane fragments do not catalyze organized Krebs cycle or fatty acid cycle oxidations; most of the enzymes catalyzing the substrate-level events of the Krebs and fatty acid cycles are easily extracted in soluble form and either occur in the matrix or are very loosely attached to the membranes.

Recent work in Bücher's laboratory has revealed the very significant fact that some of the Krebs cycle enzymes are found in such amounts as to give nearly constant ratios of activities with respect to each other in mitochondria from many different cell types, suggesting that these enzymes may be structurally and kinetically organized just as are the respiratory chain enzymes. These findings also imply that the enzymes of the cycle and the respiratory chain are synthesized in a quantitatively related pattern.

REFERENCES

Reviews

Alberty, R. A., "Fumarase," in P. D. Boyer, H. Lardy, and K. Myrbäck (eds.), *The Enzymes,* Academic, New York, 1962, 2d ed., Vol. 5, p. 495.

Beinert, H., "Acyl CoA dehydrogenase," in P. D. Boyer, H. Lardy, and K. Myrbäck (eds.), *The Enzymes,* Academic, New York, 1962, 2d ed., Vol. 7, p. 467.

Chance, B., and G. R. Williams, "The respiratory chain and oxidative phosphorylation," *Advan. Enzymol.,* **17,** 65 (1956).

Conn, E. E., "Comparative biochemistry of electron transport and oxidative phosphorylation," in M. Florkin and H. S. Mason (eds.), *Comparative Biochemistry,* Academic, New York, 1960, Vol. I, p. 44.

Dickman, S. R., "Aconitase," in P. D. Boyer, H. Lardy, and K. Myrbäck (eds.), *The Enzymes,* Academic, New York, 1962, 2d ed., Vol. 5, p. 495.

Holzer, H., "Wirkungsmechanismus von Thiaminpyrophosphat," *Angew. Chem.,* **73,** 721 (1961).

Krebs, H. A., and H. L. Kornberg, "Energy transformations in living matter," *Ergeb. Physiol.,* **49,** 212 (1957). Also published as a monograph, Springer, Berlin, 1957.

────── and J. M. Lowenstein, "The tricarboxylic acid cycle," in D. M. Greenberg (ed.), *Metabolic Pathways*, Academic, New York, 1960, 2d ed., Vol. 1, Chap. IV.

Lynen, F., "Lipide metabolism," *Ann. Rev. Biochem.*, **24**, 653 (1955).

Massey, V., "Lipoyl dehydrogenase," in P. D. Boyer, H. Lardy, and K. Myrbäck (eds.), *The Enzymes*, Academic, New York, 1962, 2d ed., Vol. 7, p. 275.

Mehler, A. H., *Introduction to Enzymology*, Academic, New York, 1957, p. 99.

Plaut, G. W. E., "Isocitrate dehydrogenase," in P. D. Boyer, H. Lardy, and K. Myrbäck (eds.), *The Enzymes*, Academic, New York, 1962, 2d ed., Vol. 7, p. 105.

Reed, L. J., "Lipoic acid," in P. D. Boyer, H. Lardy, K. Myrbäck (eds.), *The Enzymes*, Academic, New York, 1961, Vol. 3, p. 195.

Sanadi, D. R., "Pyruvate and α-ketoglutarate dehydrogenases," in P. D. Boyer, H. Lardy, and K. Myrbäck (eds.), *The Enzymes*, Academic, New York, 1962, 2d ed., Vol. 7, p. 307.

Stern, J. R., "Oxalacetate transacetase (condensing enzyme)," in P. D. Boyer, H. Lardy, and K. Myrbäck (eds.), *The Enzymes*, Academic, New York, 1962, 2d ed., Vol. 5, p. 367.

──────, "Crotonase," in P. D. Boyer, H. Lardy, and K. Myrbäck (eds.), *The Enzymes*, Academic, New York, 1962, 2d ed., Vol. 6, p. 511.

Wakil, S. J., "Hydroxyacyl CoA dehydrogenase," in P. D. Boyer, H. Lardy, and K. Myrbäck, (eds.), *The Enzymes*, Academic, New York, 1962, 2d ed., Vol. 7, p. 97.

Utter, M. F., "Non-oxidative carboxylation and decarboxylation," in P. D. Boyer, H. Lardy, and K. Myrbäck (eds.), *The Enzymes*, Academic, New York, 1962, 2d ed., Vol. 5, p. 319.

Research papers

Azzone, G. F., and L. Ernster, "Compartmentation of mitochondrial phosphorylations as disclosed by studies with arsenate," *J. Biol. Chem.*, **236**, 1510 (1961).

Bremer, J., "Carnitine in intermediary metabolism. The metabolism of fatty acid esters of carnitine by mitochondria," *J. Biol. Chem.*, **237**, 3628 (1963).

──────, "Carnitine in intermediary metabolism. Biosynthesis of palmitylcarnitine by cell subfractions," *J. Biol. Chem.*, **238**, 2774 (1963).

Chance, B., and B. Hess, "Metabolic control mechanisms. I. Electron transfer in the mammalian cell," *J. Biol. Chem.*, **234**, 2404 (1962).

Kimura, T., and T. P. Singer, "Functional organization of the respiratory chain in liver mitochondria," *Nature*, **184**, 791 (1959).

Klingenberg, M., W. Slenczka, and E. Ritt, "Vergleichende Biochemie der Pyridinnucleotide-Systeme in Mitochondrien verschiedener Organe," *Biochem. Z.*, **332**, 47 (1959).

Krebs, H. A., L. V. Eggleston, and A. d'Alessandro, "The effect of succinate and amytal on the reduction of acetoacetate in animal tissues," *Biochem. J.*, **79**, 536 (1961).

Lynen, F., U. Henning, C. Bublitz, B. Sörbo, and L. Kröplin-Rueff, "Der chemische Mechanismus der Acetessigsäurebildung in der Leber," *Biochem. Z.*, **330**, 269 (1958).

McCann, W. P., "The oxidation of ketone bodies by mitochondria from liver and peripheral tissues," *J. Biol. Chem.*, **226**, 15 (1957).

Pette, D., M. Klingenberg, and T. Bücher, "Comparable and specific proportions in the mitochondrial enzyme activity pattern," *Biochem. Biophys. Res. Commun.*, **7**, 425 (1962).

Schollmeyer, P., and M. Klingenberg, "Über den Cytochrom-gehalt tierischer Gewebe," *Biochem. Z.*, **335**, 426 (1962).

Ziegler, D. M., and A. W. Linnane, "Mitochondrial structure and dehydrogenase activity in isolated mitochondria," *Biochim. Biophys. Acta*, **30**, 53 (1958).

4

COMPONENTS OF
THE RESPIRATORY CHAIN
AND APPROACHES
TO ITS RECONSTRUCTION

The structure and mechanism of interaction of the electron carrier molecules of the respiratory chain constitute the central problems in the molecular biology of the mitochondrion. The carrier molecules are not only involved in electron transport and respiratory energy conversion but are also major building blocks in mitochondrial structure. We shall see later that the carriers make up some 25 per cent of the membrane protein. In this chapter we shall consider the molecular features of the isolated electron carrier proteins, the properties of "complexes" of these carriers, and finally, recent progress in reconstitution of the respiratory chain.

PROBLEMS IN ISOLATION AND IDENTIFICATION
OF THE ELECTRON CARRIERS

The electron carriers present a number of formidable problems. As a class, oxidation-reduction enzymes are the most complex and least understood of the different groups of enzymes, and the mechanisms of even simple, nonenzymatic, oxidation-

reduction reactions are less well known than those of hydrolytic or transfer reactions. Secondly, the enzymologist faces the
difficult experimental problem of solubilizing the flavoproteins
and the cytochromes from their firm and oriented attachment in
the mitochondrial membrane without damage to their structure
or activity. The basic chemical and physical forces that hold
together the components of the respiratory assemblies and the
membrane are not yet completely understood, and a fully rational technology for purification and handling of such proteins
has not yet emerged.

Finally, work on the electron carriers has been seriously
handicapped by their relative nonspecificity toward physiological or artificial electron donors and acceptors. Such nonspecificity has not only confounded efforts to resolve the properties of a given carrier when studied by two or more laboratories
employing different acceptors for assay, but it is also responsible
for faulty or irrelevant in vitro reconstructions of sequences of
the respiratory chain.

NADH DEHYDROGENASE

The difficulties just enumerated have been responsible for
the rampant confusion that has marked experimental work
on this central component of the respiratory chain. Work of
Warburg, Straub, Euler, Hogness, and others in the 1930s and
1940s showed that NADH or NADPH were readily oxidized by
methylene blue in the presence of widely distributed flavoproteins, such as *diaphorase,* and it was generally assumed that
specific flavoproteins served as the link between the pyridine
nucleotides and the cytochrome system. In 1952 Edelhoch and
Mahler and their colleagues in Green's laboratory isolated from
animal tissues a flavoprotein that catalyzed reduction not only
of methylene blue but also of cytochrome c in the presence of
NADH. It contained a flavin nucleotide similar to but not identical with FAD, as well as four atoms of iron. When the iron
was removed, the ability to reduce cytochrome c was lost, but
the enzyme could still react with methylene blue and other
dyes.

The work in Green's laboratory appeared, at the time, to solve
the problem of the enzymatic link between NAD and the cytochrome system, as well as the nature of the diaphorase reaction.
It was, however, almost immediately found incompatible with

other observations. Whereas electron transport in intact mitochondria is blocked by antimycin A and British antilewisite (BAL) at a point between flavoprotein and cytochrome c, the reduction of cytochrome c by the Mahler enzyme, which was named NADH–cytochrome c reductase, was completely insensitive to those agents. Furthermore Tsou and Wu found that the Mahler reductase could in fact be isolated from heart muscle particles in which the ability of NADH to reduce cytochrome c had been fully inactivated by treatment with BAL; they suggested that the Mahler enzyme had suffered degradation during the isolation procedure.

Other complications arose. Some NADH dehydrogenase preparations were found to contain FAD and some FMN, in contrast to Mahler's finding of a possibly new flavin mentioned above. These preparations also differed widely with respect to their sensitivity to Amytal and to antimycin A and their ability to reduce different acceptors, such as dyes, ferricyanide, cytochrome c, ubiquinone, and menadione (vitamin K_3). In fact, by 1960 the whole problem had become hopelessly tangled in a welter of conflicting data and claims. At that time King counted some 16 different enzymes or enzyme complexes that had been placed in nomination for the title of *the* flavoprotein of the NAD-linked chain. The original diaphorase flavoprotein of Straub was, however, clearly ruled out from further consideration; Massey had shown in 1958 that diaphorase is identical with α-lipoyl dehydrogenase, a component of the α-ketoacid dehydrogenase systems.

Work by Singer and by King is now beginning to establish some order. Singer and his colleagues have shown that the assay of NADH dehydrogenase with artificial acceptors can lead to faulty conclusions as to specificity and activity because the acceptor molecules themselves often inhibit at concentrations well below the true K_m for the acceptor; the true maximum velocity with a given acceptor must therefore be extrapolated. Using an appropriately designed assay with ferricyanide as acceptor, Singer and his colleagues have isolated a highly purified form of NADH dehydrogenase. It was rendered soluble by digestion of beef heart *electron transport particles* (ETP) with phospholipase A and then purified by standard methods that avoided organic solvents.

The essentially homogeneous Singer enzyme contains 1.0

mole of flavin and 16 gram-atoms of nonheme iron per 1,000,000 grams of protein, as well as 5 per cent lipid. The flavin is probably FAD but is apparently readily converted to FMN during extraction. The turnover number is about 4,000,000 per mole of flavin per min at 30°. The absorption spectrum of the reduced form is somewhat atypical, and Singer has suggested that the enzyme may normally cycle not between fully oxidized and fully reduced states, but rather through a semiquinone. The enzyme does not oxidize NADPH, but it does catalyze transhydrogenations between NADH and NAD^+ analogs. The purified enzyme reduces ferricyanide, phenazine methosulfate, 2,6-dichlorophenolindophenol, and methylene blue, but it reduces oxygen, cytochrome c, cytochrome b_5, lipoic acid, ubiquinone or its analogs, and vitamin K_3 only very slowly, if at all. Significantly, the purified enzyme is not inhibited by Amytal or antimycin, nor by Dicumarol, an antagonist of vitamin K having potent activity in uncoupling oxidative phosphorylation.

Singer and his colleagues have carried out a rather revealing experiment. They exposed their highly purified enzyme to the rather drastic acid-alcohol-heat treatments used earlier by Mahler to solubilize the enzyme. This treatment transformed the Singer enzyme into a form resembling the Mahler enzyme in many respects. Some 99 per cent of the activity with ferricyanide as electron acceptor was lost, but the enzyme actually gained considerable activity with cytochrome c as acceptor; similarly, its chromatographic behavior also underwent a profound change.

On the other hand, King and Howard, starting from similar snake venom digests, have isolated a highly purified NADH dehydrogenase from Keilin-Hartree particles differing from that of Singer's group in that its molecular weight is about 10^5 rather than 10^6, it contains FMN rather than FAD, and it reduces cytochrome c. From the work of Singer and King it now seems probable that the native NADH flavoprotein bound in the mitochondrial membrane structure readily undergoes alterations to its specificity, physical state, and particle weight during solubilization and purification. Slater has epitomized the moral of the story: "Degradation and purification often mean the same thing in biochemistry." Although the identity of NADH dehydrogenase is still not completely resolved, these developments have emphasized the necessity for a more rational understanding of the tertiary and quaternary structure of insoluble, struc-ture-bound enzymes, as well as more rational approaches to their isolation.

Singer and his colleagues have made the significant observa-tion that their highly purified NADH dehydrogenase reverts readily to polymerized and insoluble forms. As will be seen later, each of the cytochromes also shows a tendency to form polymers, which may be a fundamental characteristic of mito-chondrial membrane proteins.

SUCCINATE DEHYDROGENASE

The history of research on succinate dehydrogenase is also marked by problems; however, there is more substantial agree-ment regarding the dehydrogenase properties. The enzyme from beef heart mitochondria has been brought into soluble form by treatment with acetone and purified to near-homo-geneity by Singer and his colleagues. Its molecular weight is of the order of 200,000; it contains one molecule of FAD, which is tightly, perhaps covalently, bound to the protein, and four atoms of nonheme iron. It may also be obtained in a form hav-ing only two molecules of iron, depending on the isolation pro-cedure. The four-iron enzyme in turn exists in two forms differ-ing in specific catalytic activity; the less active form is activated by phosphate, succinate, or malonate. The stability of the enzyme is determined by its —SH groups, its nonheme iron content, and presence of the substrate. The highly purified enzyme reduces ferricyanide and phenazine methosulfate, but it does not react with methylene blue, cytochrome c, cyto-chrome b, or with ubiquinone.

Presumably, the ability of less purified preparations of suc-cinate dehydrogenase to reduce other acceptors is due to im-purities of other flavoproteins and cytochromes. There is now increasing evidence from electron spin resonance measurements that at least a part of the nonheme iron of succinate dehydro-genase may participate in electron transfer from substrate to acceptor through a cycle of valence changes.

NADH dehydrogenase and succinate dehydrogenase, which feed electrons into the respiratory chain at a common point, presumably ubiquinone or cytochrome b, appear to resemble each other in molecular architecture and mode of action. Both are proteins of considerable size, both contain flavin and nonheme iron atoms, and both occur in rather large amounts in mitochondria; it has been calculated that succinate dehydrogenase alone comprises about 4 per cent of the total protein of heart mitochondria.

FLAVOPROTEINS INVOLVED IN FATTY ACID OXIDATION

The two or more tightly bound flavoproteins known to participate in the first dehydrogenation step of fatty acid oxidation have been highly purified in Green's laboratory. These flavoproteins do not react directly with the cytochromes. Such a reaction is mediated by another flavoprotein, the so-called electron-transferring flavoprotein isolated by Beinert. The manner of its interaction with the respiratory chain is still not certain but is under detailed study.

UBIQUINONE (COENZYME Q)

Independent work by Morton and his colleagues in Liverpool and the groups of Green in Wisconsin and Folkers at the Merck laboratories led in 1957 and 1958 to the isolation and determination of the structure of the widely distributed ubiquinone (Figure 4–1). Because this quinone was found in relatively large quantities in heart mitochondria by Green and his colleagues, it was avidly pursued in that laboratory for evidence of a possible function as an electron carrier in the respiratory chain.

Ubiquinone is found in mitochondria in amounts that are usually manyfold higher than the molar amounts of the known respiratory carriers, such as the cytochromes. Early experiments in Green's laboratory showed that endogenous coenzyme Q became reduced to the quinol in anaerobic mitochondria, and the quinol was reoxidized to the quinone under aerobic conditions. These transitions could be observed by spectrophotometric measurements on lipid extracts. These encouraging findings led to other experiments in which it was demonstrated that added coenzyme Q_{10}, and particularly its lower homologs, is reduced by submitochondrial preparations in the presence of NADH or succinate and, conversely, that reduced Coenzyme Q is reoxidized by cytochrome oxidase preparations.

Another line of evidence supporting the view that ubiquinone is an intermediate carrier is the finding that extraction of co-

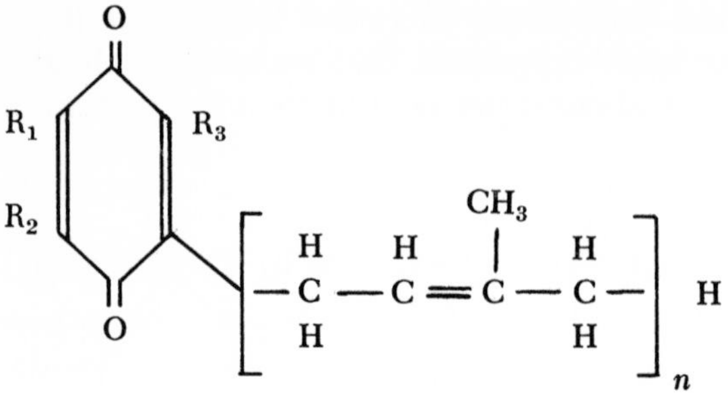

	n	R_1	R_2	R_3
coenzyme Q_{6-10}	6–10	$-OCH_3$	$-OCH_3$	$-CH_3$
plastoquinone	9	$-CH_3$	$-CH_3$	H
vitamin K_2	4–7	$\begin{array}{c} CH \\ \parallel \\ CH \\ \mid \end{array}$ ——	$\begin{array}{c} CH \\ \parallel \\ CH \\ \mid \end{array}$	CH_3

Figure 4–1 Structure of the coenzyme Q compounds, plastoquinone (chloroplasts), and vitamin K.

enzyme Q from mitochondria with isooctane or acetone causes impairment of electron transport that can be restored by adding coenzyme Q, usually in association with other lipids such as certain triglycerides and phospholipids. Also, as will be seen later, coenzyme Q can be used to bring together various complexes of the respiratory chain to reconstitute electron transport from NADH to oxygen. Finally, coenzyme Q appeared to offer an attractive molecule for rationalizing the mechanism of oxidative phosphorylation, since Todd and Wieland and their colleagues had shown that chemical oxidation of quinol monophosphate caused the formation of pyrophosphate from orthophosphate (see Chapter 6).

However, there is still considerable uncertainty about the role of coenzyme Q in electron transport. Actually, this class of compounds is found not only in mitochondria but also in cell

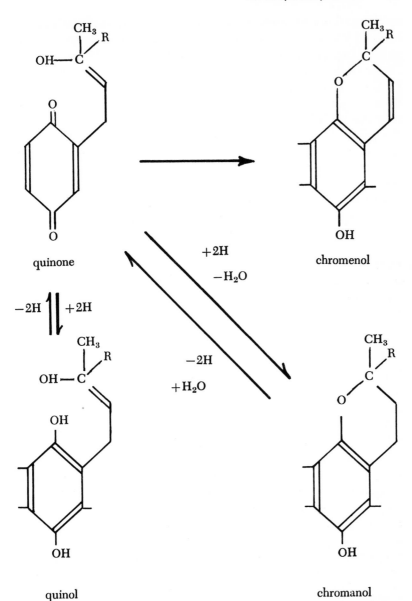

Figure 4–2 Reaction scheme showing capacity of coenzyme Q to undergo reversible reduction and conversion to chromenol, by cyclization with isoprene unit of side chain.

nuclei and microsomes; it appears to be associated with membranes. Work of Chance has indicated that endogenous coenzyme Q of mitochondria is not oxidized and reduced at rates compatible with the rates of known electron carriers. Also, it has been found, as will be seen below, that under some conditions only the lower homologs having a shorter side chain are reactive with enzymes of the respiratory chain. There is also the possibility that under some conditions coenzyme Q and its quinol are acting as an artificial or nonspecific electron acceptor or donor, despite the fact that coenzyme Q is of natural occurrence.

In spite of these uncertainties, coenzyme Q remains a compound of some interest, particularly since it shares some similarities with compounds of the vitamin K and vitamin E series. All three series of compounds have isoprenoid side chains and may exist in the form of quinone, quinol, and chromanol or chromenol derivates (see Figure 4–2). The capacity to undergo these transformations is very suggestive of their possible participation in oxidative phosphorylation, if not in electron transport per se.

THE CYTOCHROMES

Cytochrome b. Following earlier exploratory efforts in several laboratories, cytochrome b, which is firmly bound to the mitochondrial membrane, was successfully solubilized and purified, free from other cytochromes and from flavoproteins, by Sekuzu and Okunuki in 1956 and later by Goldberger and his colleagues, who extracted it with mixtures of deoxycholate and dodecyl sulfate. The purified protein in its monomeric form has a molecular weight of some 28,000; the molecule is highly asymmetrical, with an axial ratio of about 10. It contains no significant flavin, free porphyrins, nonheme iron, or other cytochromes, and less than 10 per cent lipid. The α, β, and γ bands of the reduced enzyme are at 562.5, 532.5, and 429 mμ. The heme is readily removed by acid acetone and has been identified as iron protoporphyrin IX.

Purified cytochrome b has a remarkable tendency to aggregate and polymerize, as shown in Green's laboratory. The monomeric form predominates in solutions of cationic detergents such as cetylmethylethylammonium ion, but in anionic or nonionic detergents it occurs as polymers with particle weights as high as 4,000,000. The oxidation-reduction potential of cytochrome b is reported to change greatly in the monomer-polymer transition; the monomeric form has a standard potential of about —0.340 volts and the polymeric or bound form about 0.0 volts.

The true physiological reductant and oxidant of cytochrome b are not known with complete certainty. There is considerable evidence that antimycin A, BAL, and hydroxyquinoline-N-oxide block the respiratory chain in intact mitochondria at the level of cytochrome b, but little work has been reported on the action of these agents on oxido-reduction catalyzed by the highly purified form of cytochrome b. There is some spectroscopic evidence that cytochrome b exists in two or more forms in mitochondria; the presence of antimycin A causes a significant alteration in the spectrum of cytochrome b. The properties of this portion of the chain are considered again below.

Cytochrome c_1. This cytochrome was first described by Yakushiji and Okunuki in 1940, but considerable controversy developed over its identity as a separate cytochrome. However, the controversy has been satisfactorily resolved by the spectroscopic identification of cytochrome c_1 in mitochondria by low-temperature methods in Chance's laboratory, as well as by its isolation in substantially pure form in the laboratories of Okunuki, Green, and Morrison. Cytochrome c_1 must be solubilized by deoxycholate and other detergents, whereas cytochrome c is easily extracted with salts. The molecular weight of the purified monomeric form of cytochrome c_1 is of the order of 40,000. Its structural similarity to cytochrome c is shown by the fact that its heme group is also covalently linked to the peptide chain via thioether linkages with cysteine residues. Cytochrome c_1 appears to undergo polymerization, but the conditions determining this process have not been studied in detail. Purified cytochrome c_1 is reduced by purified cytochrome b, as well as by cytochrome c, ascorbic acid, and quinols. Reduced cytochrome c_1 is reoxidized by cytochrome c.

Cytochrome c. This cytochrome differs from the rest in that it is easily extracted in soluble form from mitochondria by acids or neutral salt solutions. Following the early purification carried out by Keilin in 1930, cytochrome c was more highly purified and characterized by work of Theorell and Paul over a decade later. The groups of Bodo, Okunuki, and Theorell successfully crystallized cytochrome c from a variety of sources in 1956–

1957. The crystalline enzyme from beef heart has a molecular weight of 12,000 and a high isoelectric pH and contains a single iron porphyrin, the latter a derivative of protoporphyrin covalently bonded through two thioether linkages to two cysteine residues of the peptide chain.

Positions 5 and 6 of the iron are apparently coordinated to histidine residues at pH 7.0; cytochrome c has no tendency to react with oxygen or other ligands at neutral pH. The amino acid composition and sequence in cytochrome c from different species is under intensive investigation in a number of laboratories. The standard oxidation-reduction potential of cytochrome c is $+0.24$ volts. Okunuki and his colleagues have shown that the tertiary structure of cytochrome c changes markedly as a function of the oxidation-reduction state. Cytochrome c is reduced by thiols, ascorbate, quinols, and reduced cytochromes b and c_1, and it is reoxidized by ferricyanide, certain dyes, and cytochrome a.

A most significant property of cytochrome c, hitherto unsuspected despite the fact it has long been known as a relatively pure protein, has recently been revealed by Margoliash and Lustgarten, who found that cytochrome c undergoes polymerization in aqueous solution. They were able to crystallize its dimer, and they also purified its trimer and tetramer. The polymers do not react with cytochrome oxidase but do react with oxygen and CO. The secondary and tertiary structure of the cytochrome c molecule is now under intensive study with X-ray methods. Levin has recently found on electron microscopic study that cytochome c is a prism-shaped molecule of about 39×28.0 Å. The peptide chain appears to be a tightly folded α helix lying in three major segments in the direction of the long axis of the molecule.

Finally, Crane and his colleagues have shown that cytochrome c readily combines with lipids; with phosphatidylethanolamine cytochrome c forms a complex in which some 33 moles of the lipid are combined with 33 ϵ-amino groups of the lysine residues in this basic protein. The resulting complex, called lipocytochrome c, is soluble in lipid solvents.

Cytochrome a and a_3. There is now an increasing tempo of work on this terminal component of the respiratory chain, which is presumed to react in its reduced form with molecular oxygen. Following important early studies of Ball and Wainio on solubilized preparations of cytochrome oxidase, the enzyme has been purified by Okunuki's group, by Yonetani, and by Griffiths and Wharton; Yonetani has reported its crystallization starting from beef heart. Work in Okunuki's laboratory has also led to crystallization of cytochrome a of *Ps. aeruginosa*.

Like cytochromes b and c_1, cytochrome a is very tightly bound to mitochondrial structure. Indeed, Warburg remarked many years ago, after recognizing the firm binding of *Atmungsferment* to cell structure, that the *Atmungsferment* molecule was "as inaccessible as the stars." But the space age has since intervened; perhaps the structure of cytochrome a may become known sooner than Warburg may have expected. In its most highly purified form, which is not yet homogeneous, it apparently occurs as a pentamer or hexamer. It can be obtained as an inactive monomeric form that has a molecular weight of some 70,000 and is stable in sodium dodecylsulfate solutions. It is remarkable that Warburg's measurements of the action spectrum of the photodissociation of the CO-complex of the *Atmungsferment* made many years ago had indicated a minimum molecular weight of about this figure.

Keilin and Hartree showed some years ago that in the presence of CO or HCN the α band of about half of the cytochrome a of heart particles undergoes a shift. They designated the portion that was unreactive as cytochrome a and the component that reacted with cyanide as cytochrome a_3; the latter was postulated to be identical with Warburg's *Atmungsferment*. Chance has confirmed these spectroscopic findings and has supported Keilin's arguments for the sequence

$$\text{cytochrome } c \rightarrow \text{cytochrome } a \rightarrow \text{cytochrome } a_3 \rightarrow O_2$$

for the terminal end of the respiratory chain. However, only one cytochrome a protein has been isolated to date, and this accounts for essentially all of the cytochrome $a + a_3$ spectroscopically detected in the starting tissue.

Highly purified cytochrome a preparations contain one heme group per unit weight of 70,000. The heme differs significantly from the protoheme of cytochrome b and the derivatives of protoheme found in cytochromes c and c_1; heme a is a so-called "dichroic" or red-green heme. Porphyrin a possesses a formyl group, two ethylenic side chains, and a long saturated hydrocarbon side chain, but the exact location of these groups has not been established. Reagents combining with the formyl group cause loss of activity of cytochrome *a*. Caughey and York have obtained heme *a* in essentially pure form from beef heart and have crystallized porphyrin *a*. They are using nuclear magnetic resonance and infrared spectroscopy in its identification. No evidence was found in their study for two different *a* hemes that might correspond to the hemes of cytochromes *a* and a_3. More recently, Lynen and his colleagues have reported the results of an intensive series of chemical degradation studies on heme *a* that further narrow the possible assignments of structure.

One or two molecules of tightly bound copper per heme have been found in all highly purified cytochrome *a* preparations. Considerable controversy has raged regarding the function of Cu in the catalytic cycle. Beinert and his colleagues, on the basis of electron spin resonance measurements, have suggested that the two atoms of copper are in close juxtaposition in the enzyme, that one is Cu^+ and the other Cu^{++}, and that they undergo alternate oxidation-reduction cycles with a time constant compatible with the oxidation-reduction cycle of the heme. It has also been suggested that the copper atoms bind with oxygen, as they appear to do in all other copper-containing oxidases. Much further work remains to be done, however, before the role of copper in cytochrome *a* can be clarified.

Gibson and Greenwood have recently made a detailed study of the kinetics of the separate reaction steps involved in the action of cytochrome oxidase preparations. They find definite evidence for occurrence of kinetically distinct *a* and a_3 hemes, as proposed by Keilin and Hartree and by Chance. They suggest that the functional unit of cytochrome oxidase consists of four *a* heme units, two a_3 heme units, plus six atoms of Cu. They suggest that the monomeric cytochrome *a* isolated in Green's laboratory, which is itself inactive, is not the native form of cytochrome oxidase, but rather that the functional oxidase consists of perhaps six of such units, two of which are equivalent to a_3 and four to cytochrome *a*. Possibly this view can also accommodate the important finding of Okunuki and his colleagues that their cytochrome *a* preparation in the reduced state combines with oxygen but is not reoxidized until some cytochrome *c* is added. It is probable that cytochrome oxidase is actually a complex.

Finally, the activity of isolated cytochrome *a* preparations in

Table 4–1 Components of the respiratory chain

Component	Mol. wt	Prosthetic groups
NADH dehydrogenase	1,000,000	1 mole FAD 16 atoms nonheme Fe
Succinate dehydrogenase	200,000	1 mole FAD 2 or 4 atoms nonheme Fe
Coenzyme Q		3 to 15 moles per mole cytochrome b
Cytochrome b monomer	28,000	1 mole protoheme
Cytochrome c_1 monomer	40,000	1 mole heme c
Cytochrome c monomer	12,000	1 mole heme c
Cytochrome $a + a_3$ hexamer	$\sim$ 400,000	6 moles heme a 1 to 2 atoms Cu

vitro has been found to be greatly modified by the presence of cholate, detergents, lipids, and lipoproteins, as shown by work of Wainio, Okunuki, Green, and others. Presumably, a phospholipid is required to maintain the structure of cytochrome a in the active form. A tabulation of the basic molecular features of the respiratory carriers is given in Table 4–1.

COMPLEXES OF ELECTRON CARRIERS

A genuine reconstruction of electron transport employing only the highly purified carriers described above has not yet been reported; it is therefore evident that there are still many uncertainties in our understanding of the respiratory chain. For example, neither of the flavoproteins described above can react directly with cytochrome b, suggesting a need for additional carriers such as ubiquinone or for a specific structural organization. Furthermore, NADH dehydrogenase is not sensitive to Amytal, whereas the step it catalyzes is inhibited by Amytal in intact mitochondria. Although purified cytochromes b, c_1, and a do interact in the test tube, the physiological significance of these effects is still in doubt.

Actually, reconstructions involving pure cytochrome b have not been found to be sensitive to antimycin A, BAL, and other inhibitors specific for this site. Of paramount importance is the fact that interactions of highly purified carrier proteins have not yet been observed to occur with a coupled energy-conserving reaction, as is to be expected during oxidative phosphorylation. It is therefore probable that not all of the electron carriers have been identified to date and also that the physical state or manner of binding into the membrane assembly is crucial for function. Recognition of this state of affairs has prompted efforts to isolate *complexes* of two or more respiratory carriers representing limited segments of the respiratory chain.

Work in Green's laboratory has described a series of such complexes of carriers (Figure 4–3). The first is the *NADH–cytochrome c reductase complex*, which was separated from beef heart ETP in a form essentially free of cytochrome *a*. It was shown to contain NADH dehydrogenase, nonheme iron, coenzyme Q_{10}, cytochrome *b*, and cytochrome c_1, with the flavin and cytochromes present in nearly equimolar amounts. Significantly, its reduced spectrum suggested occurrence of reducible components other than those listed. This complex is inhibited by both Amytal and antimycin A.

The NADH–cytochrome *c* reductase complex can in turn be dissociated by treatment with cholate–sucrose–ammonium sulfate mixtures to yield two major components: the *NADH–coenzyme Q reductase complex*, which is relatively free of cytochromes, and the *reduced coenzyme Q–cytochrome c reductase complex*. The NADH–coenzyme Q reductase complex

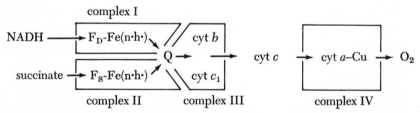

Figure 4–3 Schematic representation of the four functional primary complexes and their sequential arrangement in the electron-transfer system, in the reconstruction experiments of Hatefi and his colleagues. F_D = NADH dehydrogenase; F_S = succinate dehydrogenase; and Fe(n.h.) = nonheme iron. Complexes I + III = complex V (NADH–cytochrome c reductase system); complexes II + III = complex VI (succinate–cytochrome c reductase system); complexes V + IV + cytochrome c = NADH oxidase system; and complex VI + IV + cytochrome c = succinate oxidase system.

(complex I) contains one molecule of flavin, presumably that of NADH dehydrogenase, about 16 atoms of nonheme iron, about 3 molecules of coenzyme Q_{10}, less than 0.1 molecule of cytochrome $b + c_1$, and about 20 per cent lipid. Difference spectra indicate the presence of an unidentified component absorbing at 450 mμ that is reduced by NADH and oxidized by coenzyme Q. Electron spin resonance measurements suggest that the nonheme iron participates in the catalytic cycle. Reduction of added coenzyme Q analogs is sensitive to Amytal and to Dicumarol, whereas reduction of ferricyanide or menadione is not.

Complex I is inactivated by treatment with alcohols, detergents, or snake venom lipases. The complex I preparations can still reduce cytochrome c at a significantly high rate, and are thus not "pure." It is perhaps rather significant that although complex I can reduce coenzymes Q_1 and Q_2 at a significant rate, there is essentially no reduction of the natural homolog coenzyme Q_{10} when it is added to the system. Added and bound coenzyme Q_{10} apparently behave differently, possibly because of solubility and binding considerations.

A succinate–coenzyme Q reductase complex (complex II) has also been separated by similar procedures; it contains succinate dehydrogenase, nonheme iron, coenzyme Q, lipid, and relatively little cytochrome b or c_1. Its properties are similar to those of complex I; it is not inhibited by Amytal.

Complex III, namely, reduced coenzyme Q–cytochrome c reductase complex, has also been obtained from treatment of the NADH–cytochrome c reductase complex with cholate and ammonium sulfate. It contains cytochrome b, cytochrome c_1, nonheme iron, lipid, and relatively little flavin. It is completely inhibited by antimycin A. Work in Green's laboratory has shown that the presence of antimycin A inhibits the cleavage of complex III into its component cytochromes by bile salts; it is suggested that antimycin combines with a site involved as a normal structural link between cytochromes b and c.

Complex IV is the cytochrome oxidase system.

RECONSTITUTION OF ELECTRON TRANSPORT

Hatefi and his colleagues have demonstrated that complexes I to IV, each of which is greatly enriched in a given segment of the chain but not altogether pure, may now be used as building blocks to reconstitute part or all of the respiratory chain. For example, when complex I (NADH–coenzyme Q reductase) and complex III (reduced coenzyme Q–cytochrome c reductase) are mixed in a relatively high concentration, they associate in an approximately 1:1 ratio to form a sedimentable complex (complex V) containing both sets of activities. This complex, equivalent to the original NADH–cytochrome c reductase complex from which the components were derived, reduces cytochrome c at a high rate; the reduction is completely inhibited by antimycin A and Amytal.

Difference spectroscopy of the reconstituted complex V showed a content of carriers similar to that of the original NADH–cytochrome c reductase complex. In a similar way, Hatefi and his colleagues demonstrated recombination of complexes II and III to yield the succinate–cytochrome c reductase complex (complex VI). When complexes I to III are mixed in concentrated solution, another complex (complex VII) is formed; it is capable of causing reduction of cytochrome c by either NADH or succinate. Hatefi and his colleagues have presented some evidence that this is a true ternary complex and not a mixture of complexes V and VI.

Finally, combination of complexes IV and V and cytochrome c, or I, III, and IV, was found to yield complex VIII, namely, the NADH oxidase system; and combination of complexes II to IV and cytochrome c yielded the succinoxidase system. Complete reconstitution of the entire assembly (complex X, or the combined NADH oxidase + succinoxidase system) was achieved by mixing complexes I to IV and cytochrome c, as shown in Figure 4–3.

Insufficient analytical evidence has been presented to date to assess critically the stoichiometry, specificity, and physical chemical aspects of these reconstituted complexes. Also, it must be pointed out that the reconstituted complexes do not yield phosphorylation. Much is yet to be done also on the role of coenzyme Q in these complexes, as well as on the enzymatic distinction between bound and added coenzyme Q_{10}. The specter of a nonspecific carrier effect of added coenzyme Q has not been completely dispelled. Nevertheless, it is quite important that these reconstituted complexes show sensitivity to Amytal and antimycin A, whereas systems reconstructed from highly purified flavin and cytochrome components do not.

In 1962 Takemori and King, following earlier work of Sekuzu, described another complex of the chain, the cytochrome b–cytochrome c_1 complex, which is probably a subunit of the reduced coenzyme Q–cytochrome c reductase complex. By treatment of Keilin-Hartree particles with cholate–ammonium sulfate mixtures, they obtained a particle containing, per milligram of protein, 1.4 mμmoles cytochrome c_1, 2.4 mμmoles cytochrome b, 3.4 mμmoles nonheme iron, 0.8 mμmoles coenzyme Q_{10}, and about 19 per cent lipid. When this complex was mixed with soluble, highly purified succinate dehydrogenase, a firmly bound complex was formed and succinate–cytochrome c reductase activity sensitive to antimycin A was reconstituted.

RECONSTITUTION WITH PURIFIED
SUCCINATE DEHYDROGENASE

Reconstitution experiments with succinate dehydrogenase have special significance because they have revealed a new criterion of activity of enzymes of the respiratory assembly. The first reconstitution carried out with soluble succinate dehydrogenase was that reported by Keilin and King in 1958, who showed that addition of the soluble dehydrogenase to alkali-treated Keilin-Hartree particles having no succinoxidase activity restored antimycin-sensitive oxidation of succinate. The reconstitution was apparently stoichiometric when titrated in either direction, and the reconstituted oxidase could be sedimented many times without loss of the succinoxidase activity.

Other work by Singer and his colleagues, however, has shown that the alkali treatment of Keilin-Hartree particles does not really remove the succinate dehydrogenase flavin and that when soluble succinate dehydrogenase is "rebound," the resulting particles may contain much more flavin than the "native" Keilin-Hartree particles. Nevertheless, Keilin and King have introduced a new criterion of the native form of a purified enzyme of the respiratory chain, that is, that it be "reconstitutively active."

King has shown that the ability of succinate dehydrogenase to reconstitute with Keilin-Hartree particles is more labile than the enzymatic activity itself and that not all preparations of succinate or NADH dehydrogenase that have high catalytic activity are reconstitutively active. Furthermore, King has made the interesting observation that succinate itself is necessary for successful reconstitution of the dehydrogenase and particles, a fact that has led to the conclusion that the oxidation-reduction state of the particles and dehydrogenase is important in reconstitution.

It appears significant that reconstitution of antimycin- or Amytal-sensitive electron transport can be brought about only in complex systems still containing elements of the mitochondrial membrane, which may provide the oriented structural matrix for specific attachment of the carrier molecules. Since the membrane particles contain considerable lipid and structural protein, it appears possible that the latter are also essential elements in the three-dimensional molecular architecture of the respiratory assembly. Recent work in Green's laboratory has shown that purified cytochromes *c*, *b*, and *a* may form complexes with the monomeric form of structural protein and with lipids. Furthermore, extraction of respiratory particles with lipid solvents decreases their activity, which can be largely restored by addition of lipid factors. But even if electron transport can ultimately be reconstructed from the pure carriers, lipids, and structural proteins, it may not necessarily solve the entire problem, since a total reconstruction of the mitochondrial respiratory assembly must also restore oxidative phosphorylation, active ion transport, and the mechanochemical membrane changes to be described later.

REFERENCES

Reviews

Boyer, P. D., "Vitamin E," in P. D. Boyer, H. Lardy, and K. Myrbäck (eds.), *The Enzymes*, Academic, New York, 1960, 2d ed., Vol. 3, p. 353.

Lemberg, R., "Cytochromes of group A and their prosthetic groups," *Advan. Enzymol.*, **23**, 265 (1961).

Morton, R. K., "The cytochromes," *Rev. Pure Appl. Chem.*, **8**, 161 (1958).

Okunuki, K., "Cytochrome oxidase," in O. Hayaishi (ed.), *Oxygenases*, Academic, New York, 1962, p. 409.

Singer, T. P., "Flavoprotein dehydrogenases of the electron transport chain," in P. D. Boyer, H. Lardy, and K. Myrbäck (eds.), *The Enzymes*, Academic, New York, 1963, Vol. 7, p. 345.

——— and E. B. Kearney, "Succinate dehydrogenase," in P. D. Boyer, H. Lardy, and K. Myrbäck (eds.), *The Enzymes*, Academic, New York, 1963, Vol. 7, p. 383.

Warburg, O., *Schwermetalle als Wirkungsgruppen von Fermenten,* Verlag W. Saenger, Berlin, 1948, pp. 212 ff.

Papers in *Ciba Found. Symp., Quinones Electron Transport,* Little, Brown, Boston, 1961.

Research papers

Beinert, H., D. E. Griffiths, D. C. Wharton, and R. H. Sands, "Properties of the copper associated with cytochrome oxidase as studied by paramagnetic resonance spectroscopy," *J. Biol. Chem.,* **237,** 2337 (1962).

Caughey, W. S., and J. L. York, "Isolation of the green heme of cytochrome *a,*" *J. Biol. Chem.,* **237,** PC2414 (1962).

Crane, F. L., "Quinones in electron transport," *Biochemistry,* **1,** 510 (1962).

Criddle, R. S., R. M. Bock, D. E. Green, and H. Tisdale, "Physical characteristics of proteins of the electron transfer system and interpretations of the structure of the mitochondrion," *Biochemistry,* **1,** 827 (1962).

Gibson, Q. H., and C. Greenwood, "Reactions of cytochrome oxidase with oxygen and carbon monoxide," *Biochem. J.,* **86,** 541 (1963).

Goldberger, R., A. L. Smith, H. Tisdale, and R. Bomstein, "Studies of the electron transport system. XXXVII. Isolation and properties of cytochrome *b,*" *J. Biol. Chem.,* **236,** 2788 (1961).

Griffiths, D. E., and D. C. Wharton, "Purification and properties of cytochrome oxidase," *J. Biol. Chem.,* **236,** 1850 (1961).

―――― and D. C. Wharton, "Properties of copper in cytochrome oxidase," *J. Biol. Chem.,* **236,** 1857 (1961).

Hatefi, Y., A. G. Haavik, L. R. Fowler, and D. E. Griffiths, "Studies on the electron transfer system. XLII. Reconstitution of the electron transfer system," *J. Biol. Chem.,* **237,** 2661 (1962).

Keilin, D., and T. E. King, "Effect of inhibitors on the activity of soluble succinic dehydrogenase and on the reconstruction of the succinic dehydrogenase-cytochrome system from its components," *Proc. Roy. Soc. (London) Ser. B,* **152,** 163 (1960).

King, T. E., "Reconstitution of respiratory enzyme systems. VI," *Biochim. Biophys. Acta,* **59,** 492 (1962).

―――― and R. L. Howard, "The preparation and some properties of a reduced diphosphopyridine nucleotide dehydrogenase from the snake venom digest of a heart muscle preparation," *J. Biol. Chem.,* **237,** 1686 (1962).

Levin, O., "Electron microscopic observations of cytochrome *c,*" *Arch. Biochem. Biophys., Suppl.* **1,** 301 (1962).

Lynen, F., M. Grassl, U. Coy, and R. Seyffert, "Die chemische Konstitution des Cytohämins," *Biochem. Z.,* **338,** 771 (1963).

Margoliash, E., and J. Lustgarten, "Interconversion of horse heart cytochrome c monomer and polymers," *J. Biol. Chem.*, **237**, 3397 (1962).

Sekuzu, I., Y. Orii, and K. Okunuki, "Studies on cytochrome c_1. I," *J. Biochem. (Tokyo)*, **48**, 214 (1960).

Takemori, S., and T. E. King, "Reconstitution of respiratory chain systems. VII. Preparation of cytochrome b-c_1 complex from heart muscle," *Biochim. Biophys. Acta*, **64**, 192 (1962). "VIII. Reconstitution of succinate–cytochrome c reductase system," *Biochim. Biophys. Acta*, **64**, 194 (1962).

Yonetani, T., "Studies on cytochrome oxidase. I–IV," *J. Biol. Chem.*, **235**, 845, 3138 (1960); **236**, 1680 (1961); **237**, 550 (1962).

See also references to Chapter 3.

5

RESPIRATORY CHAIN
PHOSPHORYLATION:
EXPERIMENTAL OBSERVATIONS

The aerobic regeneration of ATP from ADP and phosphate by
energy coupling in the respiratory chain is the final step in cellular respiration, for which the Krebs citric acid cycle and the
fatty acid oxidation cycles are essentially preparatory processes.
Although we shall see later that the oxidation-reduction energy
of electron transport in mitochondria is also transformed into
osmotic energy and into mechanical energy, conversion into the
chemical energy of ATP is the major fate of respiratory energy
and may account for some 50 per cent or more of the total
energy set free.

With the advantage of hindsight, it is now possible to see
evidence for the occurrence of what we know today as oxidative
phosphorylation in many early studies of phosphate metabolism
in respiring cells and tissues, going back to Harden and Young's
studies on respiring yeast some 50 years ago. However, it was
not until the work of Kalckar and of Belitser between 1937 and
1941 that the true significance of oxidative phosphorylation was
grasped and that the outlines of present understanding took
shape. Kalckar clearly showed that aerobic phosphorylation was
specifically coupled to respiration and was independent of

glycolytic phosphorylation. Belitser first systematically compared the stoichiometry of coupled uptake of phosphate and oxygen and observed that the P:O ratio (i.e., the ratio of molecules of P_i esterified per atom of oxygen utilized) during respiration is at least 2.0. He recognized the thermodynamic significance of this finding and postulated that the energy of electron transport from substrate to oxygen was the probable source of the energy required to generate the two or more molecules of ATP observed to be formed per atom of oxygen consumed.

Study of oxidative phosphorylation was also taken up vigorously in the laboratories of Ochoa, Cori, Hunter, Lardy, Green, Lipmann, and Lehninger. By 1949 it was clear that respiration and phosphorylation take place in tissue granules, that capacity for oxidative phosphorylation is labile and inactivated by even rather mild treatments, and that phosphorylation can be uncoupled from respiration by dinitrophenol and other agents. The oxidations of the Krebs cycle yielded an average P:O ratio (molecules of P_i taken up per atom of oxygen taken up) of 3.0. NAD-linked oxidations gave a P:O ratio of 3.0; oxidation of succinate to fumarate, a ratio of 2.0; and α-ketoglutarate oxidation, a ratio of 4.0. One of the four phosphorylations in the latter case is dinitrophenol-insensitive and occurs at the substrate level, as shown in Chapter 3. However, no significant success attended efforts to confirm or deny Belitser's hypothesis that the phosphorylations were in fact occurring in the respiratory chain itself; the answer to this and some other important questions came only after the recognition in 1949 that oxidative phosphorylation takes place in the mitochondria.

PHOSPHORYLATION IN MITOCHONDRIA
AND SUBMITOCHONDRIAL SYSTEMS

Studies on mitochondria isolated by the sucrose method showed that oxidative phosphorylation is dependent on reasonably intact structure; actually, the ability to catalyze oxidative phosphorylation with a high P:O ratio was for a time considered a criterion for intactness of structure of isolated mitochondria. It was also soon recognized that the mitochondrial membrane is selectively permeable; Lehninger found in 1951 that intact mitochondria do not oxidize externally added NADH, although intramitochondrial NADH is, of course, rapidly oxidized. This finding raised the question of how extra-mitochondrial NADH of the cell formed during glycolysis can gain entry into the respiratory chain of mitochondria. "Compartmentation" of the reactions of respiration and phosphorylation by structural features of the mitochondria became an important consideration in experimental analysis of reaction patterns and mechanisms.

Electron-transport capability has long been known to survive a certain amount of degradation of mitochondrial structure, as in the case of the Keilin-Hartree particles of heart muscle, whereas the more labile process of oxidative phosphorylation usually was found not to survive significant damage to mitochondrial structure. However, in 1955 Cooper and Lehninger succeeded in showing that disruption of mitochondrial structure with digitonin yielded membrane fragments capable of both electron transport and oxidative phosphorylation, but at somewhat diminished P:O ratios. These preparations, whose average particle weight is about 1×10^9, or about 1/3000 of that of the intact rat liver mitochondrion, are less subject to compartmentation and permeability problems than intact mitochondria, and they have fewer extraneous enzymatic reactions. For example, it was found by Cooper and Lehninger that, in digitonin fragments, ADP is specific as phosphate acceptor in oxidative phosphorylation; on the other hand, it has been known that in intact mitochondria, which contain nucleoside diphosphokinase activity, other nucleoside 5'-diphosphates may also act as phosphate acceptors.

McMurray and Lardy, Kielley and Bronk, and Green and his colleagues were also successful in studying phosophorylation in submitochondrial particles obtained by mechanical or sonic disruption of mitochondria. Although oxidative phosphorylation has now been observed to occur in a wide variety of submitochondrial preparations, as well as in fragmented microorganisms, in all cases examined to date phosphorylation requires at least some semblance of membrane structure and has not been found in a truly soluble system.

OCCURRENCE OF PHOSPHORYLATIONS
IN THE RESPIRATORY CHAIN

We may now return to the problem of the site of the oxidative phosphorylations of ADP. Several early investigators of the problem had attempted to test Belitser's hypothesis—that phosphorylations take place in the respiratory chain itself when electrons pass from substrate to oxygen—by allowing tissue suspensions to oxidize NADH as sole electron donor. However, although vigorous oxidation of the NADH ensued, no phosphorylation was observed. This problem was clarified in 1951 when Lehninger demonstrated that added NADH is actually not oxidized at all by intact rat liver mitochondria and thus cannot give rise to oxidative phosphorylation.

When NADH is added to crude tissue suspensions, it is largely oxidized via nonphosphorylating microsomal flavoproteins and a nonphosphorylating cytochrome oxidase pathway in the mitochondria. However, if intact mitochondria are first briefly exposed to hypotonic conditions, their permeability increases and they become capable of oxidizing external NADH. Lehninger showed that under these conditions the oxidation was accompanied by at least two phosphorylations. Later experiments showed that P:O ratios approaching 3.0 could be observed with NADH as substrate. These experiments not only proved that Belitser's hypothesis was correct but also established the stoichiometry of respiratory chain phosphorylation in NAD-linked electron transport according to the following equation:

$$NADH + H^+ + 3P_i + 3ADP + \tfrac{1}{2}O_2 \rightarrow NAD^+ + 4H_2O + 3ATP \tag{5-1}$$

LOCATION OF PHOSPHORYLATION SITES

It became of interest to establish which carriers of the respiratory chain are specifically associated with energy-coupling mechanisms. In 1954, work in the laboratories of Lehninger and Lardy demonstrated that phosphorylation occurred when ascorbate, a nonenzymatic reductant of cytochrome c, was oxidized by mitochondria, with P:O ratios approaching 1.0. The implication that a phosphorylation was occurring on electron transport between cytochrome c and oxygen was shortly given more direct evidence when Nielsen and Lehninger showed that oxidation by rat liver mitochondria of pure reduced cytochrome c as a stoichiometric substrate, in the presence of antimycin A to block electron transport from endogenous substrates at the cytochrome b level, yielded net phosphorylation of ADP with maximum P:O ratios of 0.8. Since there is still some uncertainty regarding the specific role of cytochromes c and c_1 in the chain and their relationship to cytochrome a, it is not yet possible to specify the site of this phosphorylation more closely.

Since one of the three phosphorylations occurs between cytochrome c and oxygen, the other two evidently must lie between NAD^+ and cytochrome c. Lehninger and his colleagues observed P:$2e$ ratios approaching 2.0 for the span between D-β-hydroxybutyrate and added cytochrome c as oxidant in suspensions of rat liver mitochondria to which cyanide had been added to prevent reoxidation of cytochrome c. In efforts to obtain more detailed experimental information on the coupling sites in this span of the chain, artificial electron acceptors such as ferricyanide and quinones have been employed, but the results are complicated by the probability that the sites at which they tap into the chain may vary with conditions.

Some ingenious experiments on the so-called crossover points in the respiratory chain that independently identified the probable phosphorylation sites have been described by Chance and Williams. These experiments require some explanation. In the absence of ADP the rate of respiration of isolated intact mitochondria becomes very low and all the respiratory carriers are essentially completely in the reduced state (see Chapter 7). However, when ADP is now added to such a "controlled" system, the rate of respiration increases manyfold and the electron carriers go into a more oxidized steady state.

Chance and Williams studied the oxidation-reduction state of each carrier before and after addition of limiting amounts of ADP to mitochondria supplied with excess substrate. They were able to identify three crossover points along the respiratory chain where a deficiency in ADP caused the carrier at the substrate side of the crossover point to become more reduced and the carrier at the oxygen side to become more oxidized. One crossover point was found to lie between NAD and flavoprotein, one between cytochrome b and c, and one between cytochrome c and oxygen. These sites, hereafter called sites I, II, and III, are also consistent with the known oxidation-reduction potentials of the carrier pairs (Chapter 6).

SPECIFIC INHIBITORS

Specific inhibitors have become important tools in investigations of the patterns and mechanisms of respiratory chain phosphorylation. The widely different chemical structures of these agents, which may be classed in three major groups, give promise that they may also provide important leads in identifying the chemical structure of intermediates and active sites in the phosphorylating respiratory chain.

The first group includes *inhibitors of electron transport;* presumably these act by combining with one or another of the electron carriers per se, rather than with enzymes concerned in energy coupling. They include hydrogen cyanide, Amytal, antimycin A, BAL, 2-heptyl 4-hydroxyquinoline N-oxide, and rotenone, among others, as already described.

The second class of inhibitors is represented by the true *uncoupling agents,* which cause inhibition of the phosphorylation of ADP without greatly affecting the rate of electron transport; 2,4-dinitrophenol is the classical example of the uncoupling agents, as first shown by Loomis and Lipmann. Of greatest significance is the fact that the uncoupling agents stimulate the normally latent ATPase activity of intact mitochondria but inhibit the other *partial reactions* of oxidative phosphorylation that are described below.

The true uncoupling agents also include a number of other nitro- and halophenols, the anti-vitamin K agent dicumarol, the polypeptide antibiotics gramicidin D and tyrocidine, certain complex nitriles, long-chain fatty acids, and also arsenate. Most workers agree that the true uncoupling agents act by causing the discharge or breakdown of some high-energy intermediate, perhaps of the coupled carrier, to regenerate the free carrier and any other components required for continuous respiration. ATP is thus never formed in the presence of excess uncoupling agent. Inorganic phosphate is not required for the action of 2,4-dinitrophenol; the high-energy intermediate attacked by this agent is therefore one that is formed before phosphate is taken up.

The third group includes the *inhibitors* of phosphorylating oxidation. These compounds, of which the antibiotic oligomycin is the prototype, inhibit phosphorylating electron transport in intact mitochondria but do not inhibit nonphosphorylating electron transport, as in the Keilin-Hartree particles, for example. Lardy and his colleagues first described the properties of oligomycin and other agents of this group; they showed that when phosphorylating electron transport is blocked by oligomycin, the inhibition of respiration can be relieved by 2,4-dinitrophenol, an important finding that establishes the relative sites of attack of these two agents in the coupling mechanism.

Other inhibitors in the third group include the antibiotics aurovertin and valinomycin, guanidine and some of its derivatives, the glycoside potassium atractylate, the organometallic triethyltin, as well as sodium azide. Although these compounds are not precisely identical in their action, they appear to act by combining stoichimetrically with some intermediate in the coupling sequence to prevent its cycling through the full sequence of electron- and phosphate-transport reactions. This is in contrast to the action of the uncoupling agents, which discharge a high-energy intermediate to regenerate otherwise fully active components.

THE PARTIAL REACTIONS

The term "partial reactions" designates a series of dinitrophenol-sensitive reactions involving phosphate and/or ATP that can be observed to occur in the absence of net electron transport in mitochondria and submitochondrial preparations capable of oxidative phosphorylation; they are presumed to be reflections of the occurrence of reversible intermediate steps in the oxidative phosphorylation mechanism.

ATPase. The best-studied partial reaction is the ATPase activity, which is characteristically stimulated by dinitrophenol and the other uncoupling agents in both intact mitochondria and in phosphorylating submitochondrial fragments. The ATPase reaction is believed to be caused by reversal of the reactions involved in ATP formation, plus an abnormal or aberrant breakdown, perhaps hydrolytic, of some high-energy intermediate in the coupling mechanism.

It is highly significant that the true inhibitors of oxidative phosphorylation, oligomycin and atractylate, for example, inhibit dinitrophenol-stimulated ATPase activity. This fact, taken in conjunction with Lardy's finding that dinitrophenol relieves the inhibition of respiration by oligomycin, shows that dinitrophenol acts to discharge a high-energy intermediate at a point between the carrier and the point blocked by oligomycin. The ATPase activity of mitochondria is nearly completely inhibited when the chain is kept reduced by substrates in the presence of cyanide. Wadkins and Lehninger have pointed out that this fact may indicate that the dinitrophenol-sensitive high-energy complex is formed or occurs only when the carriers are in the oxidized state.

There is increasing evidence that the ATPase activity of mitochondria may involve the decomposition of more than one intermediate in the coupling sequence, depending on the agent. Thus dinitrophenol and arsenate may stimulate ATPase activity by discharge of different intermediates in the coupling sequence.

There is now some evidence from work in Slater's laboratory that two or even three different ATPase activities of mitochondria can be distinguished from tests of their pH dependence. These may correspond to the three coupling sites in the chain, which also differ in pH sensitivity. Whether there are three separate coupling systems, one for each site, or one enzyme system common to the three sites but differing in tightness of attachment as a function of pH is still not resolved.

The ATP-phosphate exchange reaction. In this mitochondrial reaction, first described by Cohn and by Boyer, inorganic phosphate labeled with P^{32} is rapidly incorporated into the terminal phosphate group of ATP in the absence of net electron transport. Since the reaction is inhibited by dinitrophenol and by oligomycin, it has been concluded that it reflects the reversibility of the steps of the coupling mechanisms between the point of phosphate uptake and the formation of ATP. The reaction has been studied in more detail in submitochondrial systems by Cooper and Lehninger, who showed that its rate is critically dependent on the concentration and molar ratios of ATP, ADP, and P_i. The exchange reaction is nearly completely inhibited when the respiratory chain is in the fully reduced state. The rate of this reaction, relative to the rate of electron transport and phosphorylation of ADP, is very high in intact mitochondria and relatively low in submitochondrial systems. It is possible it is associated with only one site in the chain; Ernster and his colleagues have postulated it occurs at the flavoprotein site.

The H_2O-P_i and H_2O-ATP oxygen exchange reactions. The oxygen atoms of the water of the medium rapidly exchange with those of inorganic phosphate and of the terminal phosphate of ATP when ATP + phosphate is incubated with mitochondrial preparations capable of oxidative phosphorylation; the reaction can be followed in either direction by use of O^{18} as tracer. The rate of these exchanges, which are inhibited by dinitrophenol and by oligomycin, may be 20 or 30 times greater than the over-all rate of net oxidative phosphorylation.

Although it has been tempting to consider the H_2O-P_i exchange as a first step in the over-all H₂O-ATP oxygen exchange, this may not be the case, since the latter proceeds at a much higher rate than the former. Work in Lehninger's laboratory has shown that electron transport alone can replace ATP as a requirement for the H_2O-P_i exchange; as many as 30 atoms of oxygen may exchange per pair of electrons flowing from substrate to oxygen. Myosin ATPase and inorganic pyrophosphatase are the only other phosphate-transferring enzymes known to catalyze H_2O-P_i oxygen exchange reactions.

The ATP-ADP exchange reaction. Wadkins and Lehninger have shown that intact mitochondria from all tissues examined catalyze a rapid reversible incorporation of labeled ADP into ATP. The exchange is inhibited by either oligomycin or dinitrophenol and occurs in the absence of net electron transport. Mitochondria also catalyze at least one other ATP-ADP exchange reaction, one that requires added Mg^{++} but is not sensitive to oligomycin or dinitrophenol and is thus not relevant to the mechanism of oxidative phosphorylation. The catalysis may be due to adenylate kinase, although other phosphate-transferring enzymes catalyze ATP-ADP exchanges.

The dinitrophenol-sensitive ATP-ADP exchange reaction of intact mitochondria is nearly completely inhibited when the respiratory carriers are kept reduced. From study of the properties and requirements of the ATP-ADP exchange reaction in digitonin fragments, Wadkins and Lehninger postulated that the reaction is catalyzed by the terminal enzyme of oxidative phosphorylation, which is responsible for bringing about transfer of ~P to added ADP at each of the three coupling sites. Their findings are compatible with the view that the uptake of P_i in covalent linkage precedes uptake of ADP. In a following reaction the phosphorylated intermediate is pictured as donating its phosphate group to the terminal enzyme, which then donates the phosphate group to ADP.

$$P \sim X + E \rightleftharpoons P \sim E + X \qquad (5\text{--}2)$$

$$P \sim E + ADP \rightleftharpoons ATP + E \qquad (5\text{--}3)$$

The terminal enzyme E is stable, and its action can be dissociated from earlier reactions by aging or by inhibitors. It is enzyme E that is presumed to catalyze the ATP-ADP exchange, which is represented by Equation (5–3). This sequence is consistent with the behavior of the ATP-P$_i$ and the ATP-ADP exchange reactions, with the O^{18} experiments of Boyer mentioned above, and with similar experiments on the terminal mechanism of photosynthetic phosphorylation. The enzyme catalyzing the ATP-ADP exchange has been isolated in soluble form and purified (see below).

There are some uncertainties regarding the partial reactions. It is not known, for example, whether all three phosphorylation sites contribute to each of the partial reactions and, if they do, in what proportion. In addition, some inhibitors affect these reactions in an anomalous manner. Furthermore, the kinetic complexities of isotopic exchanges in multienzyme systems at equilibrium may be too great to allow quantitative treatment of intermediate mechanisms. Nevertheless, the partial reactions remain as important diagnostic landmarks and as "indicators" in experimental efforts to reconstruct oxidative phosphorylation from component enzymes.

REVERSAL OF OXIDATIVE PHOSPHORYLATION AND ELECTRON TRANSPORT

Some years ago Chance and Williams observed that mitochondrial NAD becomes more reduced in intact mitochondria when succinate is added. The observation is rather unexpected, since reduction of NAD^+ ($E'_h = -0.32$ volt) by succinate ($E'_h = 0.00$ volt) is thermodynamically improbable without input of energy. Later investigations by Chance and Hollunger and by Klingenberg and his colleagues have indicated that this reduction may occur by reversal of the coupled respiratory chain at the expense of high-energy intermediates of electron transport that are normally precursors of ATP. They were led to this conclusion by the finding that the reduction of mitochondrial NAD by addition of succinate was prevented by antimycin A and by Amytal, which block electron transport at cytochrome b and flavoprotein, respectively. The blocking suggests that the electron flow from succinate to NAD occurred in the following segment of the bifurcated respiratory chain (see Figure 3–4):

$$\text{succinate} \rightarrow \text{FP}_2 \rightarrow \text{cyt } b \rightarrow \text{FP}_1 \rightarrow \text{NAD} \qquad (5\text{--}4)$$

Chance and Hollunger found that the reduction of NAD by succinate was also blocked by oligomycin and by 2,4-dinitrophenol. If the mitochondria are already "charged" with high-energy intermediates, they carry out reduction of NAD^+ without the necessity for adding ATP. However, addition of ATP can be shown to be required for the reduction, particularly in aged preparations. In fact, reduction of NAD^+ by succinate was shown by Klingenberg to be a function of the ratio [ATP] / [ADP] [P_i] (see Chapter 7). Chance and Hollunger, and also Klingenberg and his colleagues, concluded that the reduction of mitochondrial NAD took place via reversal of the electron-transport chain and was driven by either nonphosphorylated high-energy precursors of ATP or by ATP itself, as indicated in the two equations

$$\text{succinate} + NAD^+ + \sim I \rightarrow \text{fumarate} + NADH + H^+ + I \quad (5\text{--}5)$$

$$\text{succinate} + NAD^+ + ATP \rightarrow \text{fumarate} + NADH + H^+ + ADP + P_i \quad (5\text{--}6)$$

These formulations assume the pathway of electron transport given in (5–4). Thus this reversal of electron transport would also involve reversal of one of the phosphorylation sites. This interpretation of the data is consistent with known thermodynamic relationships.

Although most workers are agreed on the thermodynamic feasibility of the reaction and also the probability that reversed electron transfer can occur in tightly coupled mitochondria, the conclusions have been brought under criticism. The experiments described above have largely dealt with the measurement of dynamic steady states of mitochondrial NAD with fluorometric methods, rather than with net chemical transformations of some magnitude. Secondly, the experiments do not exclude the possibility that the NAD becomes reduced at the expense of reductants other than succinate; for example, malate formed from succinate has been suggested as the direct reductant of NAD.

Two more recent developments indicate that the respiratory chain can indeed be reversed. Work by Ernster and by Klingenberg has shown that a large net reduction of acetoacetate occurs in the presence of succinate. As discussed in Chapter 7, Klingenberg and Von Häfen have clearly demonstrated, by balance sheet experiments, that succinate is the direct source of electrons for reduction of acetoacetate. Secondly, the net reduction of *added* NAD^+ by submitochondrial preparations has been demonstrated by Löw, by Sanadi, and by Racker. In fact, Racker and Sanadi have utilized this reaction to study the activity of coupling factors.

As will be seen in Chapter 7, the reversal of energy-coupled electron transport takes place not only at site I but also at site II and possibly at site III.

COUPLING FACTORS AND THE RECONSTITUTION
OF OXIDATIVE PHOSPHORYLATION

A number of laboratories have recently reported some success in resolving particulate submitochondrial systems into two or more subfractions that are individually inactive in catalyzing oxidative phosphorylation but yield both respiration and phosphorylation when they are combined. Usually, such systems contain a particulate fraction bearing electron-transport activity but lacking capacity to phosphorylate ADP. The addition of the second fraction, usually a soluble, heat-labile component that itself has no electron-transport activity, restores coupled phosphorylation to the particles.

The implication of such experiments is that the soluble fraction may contain an enzyme or enzymes necessary to cause formation of ATP at the expense of a high-energy intermediate generated in the particle. Such coupling factors are not necessarily site-specific energy-converting enzymes; restoration of phosphorylation could also be achieved by enzymatic removal of an endogenous inhibitor, by prevention of an inhibitory enzymatic reaction, or by a structural "tightening" of the membrane fragment to bring together into juxtaposition preexisting but nonreactive electron-transport and phosphorylating enzymes in the membrane.

There are other problems associated with efforts to reconstitute oxidative phosphorylation. It is important to know which of the three phosphorylation sites of the NAD-linked chain is being restored to activity, since each site may have its own specific coupling enzyme(s). Furthermore, the number of coupling enzymes at each site is still unknown. If two were involved at each site, as many as six different coupling enzymes could be expected to exist. Finally, it is also a frustrating practical problem to damage mitochondrial preparations specifically and reproducibly in such a way as to obtain a useful assay system lacking only the one factor under assay.

Some of the known coupling factors may now be listed.

Soluble ATPase and other factors of Racker and Pullman. Pullman and Racker and their colleagues have described a purified soluble ATPase that is separated from beef heart mitochondria and is stimulated by dinitrophenol. This ATPase, which has the bizarre property of being labile at low temperatures but stable at room temperature, is capable of restoring phosphorylation of ADP coupled to the oxidation of succinate by pretreated beef heart particles that are unable to phosphorylate when tested alone. The phosphorylation that is restored is largely that occurring in site II. The soluble ATPase, which contains no respiratory carriers, shows neither the ATP-P_i nor the ATP-ADP exchange reactions, but it increases the activity of the former when added to the depleted respiratory particles. Pullman and Racker found that the ATPase activity paralleled ability to restore phosphorylation during purification.

It is very puzzling, however, that the soluble ATPase activity is not sensitive to oligomycin and shows no ATP-ADP exchange activity. It is conceivable that this ATPase may be identical with the "mitochondrial actomyosin" isolated recently by Ohnishi and Ohnishi, which also catalyzes a DNP-stimulated ATPase activity.

Racker and his colleagues have isolated three other factors required in restoration of oxidative phosphorylation; the ATPase is designated F_1 and the others F_2, F_3, and F_4. Factors $F_1 + F_4$ are required to restore the ATP-linked net reduction of NAD^+ by succinate in sonic submitochondrial particles prepared in the presence of soy bean phosphatides. The ATPase (factor 1) is thus required also at site I, together with F_4. Another factor (F_0) has been found to confer oligomycin sensitivity on the F_1 factor, namely, the soluble ATPase. Factor F_3 stimulates the ATP-P_i exchange reaction.

More recently, Sanadi and his colleagues have also described coupling factors for site I assayed for their capacity to support ATP-linked reduction of NAD^+ by succinate. Although they appear superficially to resemble those described by Racker, it is not certain they are identical.

The ATP-ADP exchange enzyme. The enzyme catalyzing the dinitrophenol-sensitive ATP-ADP exchange reaction of mitochondria has been rendered soluble and highly purified by Wadkins and his colleagues. It shows no sensitivity to dinitrophenol or oligomycin itself, but it was shown to recombine with mito-chondrial membrane fragments in a specific manner so that the sensitivity to dinitrophenol that is characteristic of this ex-change in intact mitochondria was restored. Wadkins and Lehninger have isolated a second heat-labile factor, the M fac-tor, that may also be considered as a coupling factor, since it increases the dinitrophenol sensitivity of the ATP-ADP ex-change reaction.

Wadkins has shown that highly purified preparations of the ATP-ADP exchange enzyme (300-fold purified) are able to re-store oxidative phosphorylation in rat liver mitochondria pre-viously extracted with 0.3 M ammonium sulfate, which removes the ATP-ADP exchange enzyme. The phosphorylation site re-stored is site III, the span between cytochrome c and oxygen. This enzyme may be identical with the site III factor described below. It has very recently been found to form a complex with reduced cytochrome c.

Site-specific coupling factors of Green and colleagues. Webster and Smith in Green's laboratory have briefly reported isolation of three protein fractions from beef heart mitochondria, each capable of restoring oxidative phosphorylation specifically at one of the three phosphorylation sites. Little detailed informa-tion concerning their action is available at the time of writing. However, it appears significant that the coupling factor for site III, that is, for the span cytochrome $c \longrightarrow$ oxygen, contains ATP-ADP exchange activity after substantial purification. This finding may equate the ATP-ADP exchange enzyme of Wadkins and Lehninger with the site III coupling factor of Webster. The latter factor also combines with cytochrome c (see below).

Formation of high-energy complexes of carriers and coupling factors. Pinchot and Hormanski have made what may be a significant discovery regarding the mechanism of reconstituted oxidative phosphorylation in fractions derived from Alcaligenes faecalis. Their system consisted of a particulate membrane fraction catalyzing electron transport, a soluble heat-labile fraction that restores phosphorylation, a polynucleotide that is apparently responsible for binding the two factors together, and NAD. Incubation of the particles, polynucleotide, the soluble fraction, and NADH in the absence of phosphate and ADP caused oxi-dation of NADH to NAD^+ and, with it, the apparently covalent binding of the NAD^+ to the soluble protein factor as electrons passed from substrate to oxygen. When the soluble protein factor was then separated from the particles by centrifugation, it was found to contain bound NAD^+. When this complex was incubated with P_i and ADP, ATP was formed and the NAD^+ dissociated from the soluble factor. These experiments indicated that electron transport in the particle caused the formation of a high-energy compound of NAD^+ with the specific coupling protein and that in the second incubation the compound underwent phosphorolysis to form a phosphorylated protein that then reacted to form ATP as follows:

$$NADH + E \stackrel{-2e}{\rightleftharpoons} NAD_{ox} \sim E$$
$$NAD_{ox} \sim E + P_i \rightleftharpoons P \sim E + NAD_{ox} \qquad (5\text{--}7)$$
$$P \sim E + ADP \rightleftharpoons E + ATP$$

Green and his colleagues have detected a similar reaction in beef heart mitochondrial systems involving site III factor and the cytochrome c–oxygen span. In the presence of cytochrome c and a purified coupling factor for this site (which contains ATP-ADP exchange activity), electron transport caused the formation of a coupling factor–cytochrome c complex, apparently of a high-energy nature. When this complex was incubated separately with P_i and ADP, ATP was formed, similarly to the reaction observed by Pinchot. In such experiments the rates of the separate reaction steps are very low.

Contraction factors. Lehninger and his colleagues have found that three different protein factors are required for contraction of swollen mitochondria by ATP, a process that is a reflection of the action of the coupling enzymes of oxidative phosphorylation, as will be described in a later chapter. These "contraction factors" also cause an increase in the P:O ratio of oxidative phosphorylation of digitonin fragments. These investigators have identified C factors I and II as glutathione peroxidase and catalase, respectively. Vignais and Vignais have identified phosphatidyl inositol as a contraction factor. This lipid specifically protects the dinitrophenol-stimulated ATPase activity of mitochondria against degradative conversion into a Mg^{++}-stimulated activity.

PHOSPHOPROTEINS

Some years ago it was observed by Friedkin and Lehninger that mitochondria contain a protein fraction that becomes phosphorylated during oxidative phosphorylation. Kennedy later found that such *phosphoproteins* contain phosphoserine residues, and he postulated that they might represent intermediate phosphorylated forms of coupling enzymes of oxidative phosphorylation. Recently, Boyer and his colleagues have isolated a very labile P^{32}-labeled peptide from respiring mitochondria incubated with P_i^{32}. The phosphorylated moiety was shown to be the imidazole ring of histidine that Boyer and colleagues suggested is present at the active site of an intermediate enzyme of oxidative phosphorylation. This phosphorylated peptide is also formed when P^{32}-labeled ATP is added to mitochondria. The formation of the labeled phosphopeptide is inhibited somewhat by uncoupling agents.

Wadkins has found that both acid-labile and acid-stable phosphoproteins are formed during oxidative phosphorylation, which correspond to occurrence of phosphohistidine and phosphoserine residues, respectively. The evidence indicates that these forms undergo enzymatic interconversion. Wadkins has shown that the acid-labile form can be converted to the acid-stable form, presumably through an $N \rightarrow O$ shift, in a reaction that requires some specificity of tertiary structure of the mitochondrial phosphoprotein. Since serine and histidine residues have been implicated in the mechanism of action of some of the hydrolytic enzymes, these recent findings are of some general interest.

OTHER INTERMEDIATES AND ENZYMES

The occurrence of three types of potential quinol-quinone-chromanol systems in mitochondria, namely, those of α-tocopherol, of ubiquinone (or coenzyme Q) and of vitamin K, must continue to be given serious consideration in relation to the mechanism of oxidative phosphorylation; they will be considered in the following chapter.

In 1962 Griffiths and Chaplain described a new phosphorylated derivative of NAD formed in mitochondria during oxidative phosphorylation; they suggest it is an intermediate. The chemical identity of this derivative is of considerable interest, since it appears possible it is a phosphate ester of a form of NAD in which the pyridine ring may have opened.

Mitochondria contain several enzymes that are capable of transforming ATP, ADP, or pyrophosphate groups. The role of these enzymes is now obscure, but it may ultimately be of crucial importance in the mechanism of oxidative phosphorylation. These enzymes include adenylate kinase, which catalyzes the reaction

$$ATP + AMP \rightleftharpoons ADP + ADP \tag{5-8}$$

This enzyme, which is attached to the mitochondrial membrane, has been postulated to be an instrument for transferring high-energy phosphate groups from within the mitochondrion to external ADP. Another phosphate-transferring enzyme, isolated by Chiga and Plaut, catalyzes a reversible exchange reaction among ATP, ADP, and P_i. Also to be mentioned is inorganic pyrophosphatase, which catalyzes a H_2O-P_i oxygen exchange reaction. Although these enzymes are not inhibited by oligomycin or dinitrophenol, they may yet prove to be components in respiratory energy coupling.

OUTLOOK

The search for intermediates in oxidative phosphorylation is now an intensive one, and considerable progress can be expected in the next few years. A major problem requiring resolution now is whether each phosphorylation site involves but a single coupling enzyme, as maintained by Green and his colleagues, or whether two or more specific proteins are required at each site, a view that is supported by Racker and Pullman and by Wadkins and Lehninger. However, some workers feel that the mechanism of oxidative phosphorylation may not ultimately be resolved in terms of the classical experimental approaches to analysis of multienzyme systems; that is, the isolation and purification of the separate enzymes, the reconstruction of the over-all system, and finally the analysis of the structure and action of the active sites of the enzymes involved.

Perhaps the mitochondrial membrane per se is an integral part of the system, required not simply as a piece of "floor space" but as a necessary element in transformation of respiratory energy into osmotic and mechanical energy as well, as postulated by Lehninger. In fact, Mitchell has gone so far as to suggest that oxidative phosphorylation is the consequence of vectorial transport mechanisms across the mitochondrial membrane, rather than the result of the action of a scalar multienzyme system having no structural or directional polarization.

His *chemiosmotic hypothesis* for the mechanism of oxidation and photosynthetic phosphorylation will be described later.

In this connection it must be pointed out that the lipid layer of the mitochondrial membrane may provide the medium in which some important step in oxidative phosphorylation occurs. For example, work in Slater's laboratory has revealed that the uncoupling action of dinitrophenol and its derivatives is directly related to their lipid solubility, a fact that implies that their uncoupling action takes place in a lipid rather than an aqueous phase. Cooper and Lehninger had earlier suggested that the great lability of the coupling mechanism and the release of ATPase activity is due to the instability of some crucial intermediate of the coupling mechanism in the presence of water and that the lipid-rich mitochondrial membrane provides a structural compartment in which the thermodynamic activity of water is very low, protecting or hiding the sensitive intermediate from an aberrant hydrolysis.

REFERENCES

Reviews

Boyer, P. D., "Phosphohistidine," *Science*, **141**, 1147 (1963).

Chance, B., and G. R. Williams, "The respiratory chain and oxidative phosphorylation," *Advan. Enzymol.*, **17**, 65 (1956).

Lehninger, A. L., "Oxidative phosphorylation," *Harvey Lectures, Ser.* 49, (**1953–1954**), 176 (1955).

―――― and C. L. Wadkins, "Oxidative phosphorylation," *Ann. Rev. Biochem.*, **31**, 47 (1962).

Racker, E., "Mechanisms of synthesis of adenosine triphosphate," *Advan. Enzymol.*, **23**, 323 (1961).

Slater, E. C., "Oxidative phosphorylation," *Rev. Pure Appl. Chem. (Aust.)*, **8**, 221 (1958).

Papers in B. Chance (ed.), *Energy-Linked Functions of Mitochondria*, Academic, New York, 1963.

Research papers

Conover, T. E., R. L. Prairie, and E. Racker, "A new coupling factor required by submitochondrial particles extracted with phosphatides," *J. Biol. Chem.*, **238**, 2831 (1963).

Griffiths, D. E., and R. A. Chaplain, "Some properties of a new phosphorylated derivative of NAD, an intermediate in oxidative phosphorylation," *Biochem. Biophys. Res. Commun.* 8, 497, 501 (1962).

Hemker, H. C., "Lipid solubility as a factor influencing the activity of uncoupling phenols," *Biochim. Biophys. Acta*, 63, 46 (1962).

——, "The contribution of the various phosphorylating steps in the respiratory chain to the dinitrophenol-induced ATPase of rat liver mitochondria," *Biochim. Biophys. Acta*, 73, 311 (1963).

Löw, H., and I. Vallin, "Succinate-linked diphosphopyridine nucleotide reduction in submitochondrial particles," *Biochim. Biophys. Acta*, 69, 361 (1963).

Peter, J. B., and P. D. Boyer, "The formation of bound phosphohistidine from adenosine triphosphate-P^{32} in mitochondria," *J. Biol. Chem.*, 238, PC1180 (1963).

——, D. E. Hultquist, M. DeLuca, G. Kreil, and P. D. Boyer, "Bound phosphohistidine as an intermediate in a phosphorylation reaction catalyzed by mitochondrial extracts," *J. Biol. Chem.*, 238, PC1182 (1963).

Pinchot, G. B., and M. Hormanski, "Characterization of a high energy intermediate of oxidative phosphorylation," *Proc. Natl. Acad. Sci. U.S.*, 48, 1970 (1962).

Prairie, R. L., T. E. Conover, and E. Racker, "Requirement of multiple factors for the ATP-linked reduction of DPN by succinate," *Biochem. Biophys. Res. Commun.*, 10, 422 (1963).

Racker, E., "Studies of factors involved in oxidative phosphorylation," *Proc. Natl. Acad. Sci. U.S.*, 48, 1659 (1962).

——, "A mitochondrial factor conferring oligomycin-sensitivity on soluble mitochondrial ATPase," *Biochem. Biophys. Res. Commun.*, 10, 435 (1963).

Sanadi, D. R., "Energy-requiring reduction of pyridine nucleotide by ascorbate in the presence of coenzyme Q or menadione," *J. Biol. Chem.*, 238, PC482 (1963).

Wadkins, C. L., and A. L. Lehninger, "Dissociation of the ATP-ADP exchange enzyme from mitochondrial structure and its relationship to oxidative phosphorylation," *J. Biol. Chem.*, submitted.

—— and ——, "Distribution of an oligomycin-sensitive adenosine triphosphate–adenosine diphosphate exchange reaction and its relationship to the respiratory chain," *J. Biol. Chem.*, 238, 2555 (1963).

Webster, G., "A protein factor required for the phosphorylation accompanying oxidation of reduced cytochrome *c*," *Biochem. Biophys. Res. Commun.* 7, 245 (1962).

6

ENERGETICS AND MECHANISMS
OF ELECTRON TRANSPORT
AND OXIDATIVE PHOSPHORYLATION

In this chapter we shall consider some of the thermodynamic relationships in electron transport and oxidative phosphorylation, as well as the chemical and physical reaction patterns involved in conversion of oxido-reduction energy into the so-called energy-rich bonds of ATP.

FREE ENERGY OF HYDROLYSIS OF ATP

In this discussion we shall use the rounded value of $\Delta G =$ —9.0 kcal per mole for the free energy of hydrolysis of ATP to ADP and P_i at pH 7.0 as being most appropriate for the relative concentrations of ATP, ADP, P_i, and Mg^{++} existing in the cell or in the usual in vitro conditions. There is now good evidence that the *standard* free-energy change (i.e., at 1 M reactants and products) for this process is nearer —7.0 kcal, but at an equimolar ratio of ATP to ADP the value becomes more negative as the concentration of P_i falls below 1 M.

YIELDS OF ATP DURING PYRUVATE OXIDATION

From the characteristic P:O ratios of NAD-linked and succinate-linked electron transport the total number of phosphorylations during pyruvate oxidation by isolated mitochondria may easily be summed up (Table 6–1). For each molecule of pyruvate oxidized completely to CO_2 and H_2O, 14 molecules of ATP are formed from ADP and P_i by the respiratory chain phosphorylations. These 14 are supplemented by the single substrate-level phosphorylation at the α-ketoglutarate step, making a total of 15.0. Since the free-energy change during combustion of 1 mole of pyruvate to CO_2 and H_2O is of the order of -280 kcal per mole, some 135 kcal, or 48 per cent of the total, is conserved as *phosphate bond energy.*

For the complete oxidation of one molecule of glucose to CO_2 and H_2O via the glycolytic cycle and the Krebs citric acid cycle, the total number of ATP molecules formed from ADP plus P_i is 36 (Table 6–2). Since the free-energy change for combustion of 1 mole of glucose is -680 kcal, the energy recovery of some 324 kcal represents 48 per cent efficiency. If we now contrast the molar yield of ATP derived from the purely extramito-

Table 6–1 Phosphorylations of ADP during oxidation of pyruvate via Krebs cycle

Steps	Carrier	Molecules ATP formed
1. Pyruvate $\rightarrow$ acetyl-CoA	Lipoyl $\rightarrow$ NAD	3
2. Isocitrate $\rightarrow$ α-ketoglutarate	NADP $\rightarrow$ NAD	3
3. α-Ketoglutarate $\rightarrow$ succinyl-CoA	Lipoyl $\rightarrow$ NAD	3
4. Succinyl-CoA $\xrightarrow{\text{GDP}}$ succinate		1
5. Succinate $\rightarrow$ fumarate	FAD	2
6. Malate $\rightarrow$ oxalacetate	NAD	3
	Total	15

Over-all equation
$$CH_3COCOOH + 2\tfrac{1}{2}O_2 + 15ADP + 15P_i \rightarrow 3CO_2 + 15ATP + 17H_2O$$

Partial reactions
$$CH_3COCOOH + 2\tfrac{1}{2}O_2 \rightarrow 3CO_2 + 2H_2O \qquad \triangle G = -280 \text{ kcal}$$
$$15ADP + 15P_i \rightarrow 15ATP + 15H_2O \qquad \triangle G = +135 \text{ kcal}$$

Table 6–2 Phosphorylations of ADP during oxidation of glucose via glycolytic and citric acid cycles

Step	Molecules of ATP formed or used
1. $ATP + glucose \rightarrow glucose\text{-}6\text{-}P + ADP$	-1
2. $ATP + fructose\text{-}6\text{-}P \rightarrow fructose\text{-}1,6\text{-}diP + ADP$	-1
3. $2\ glyceraldehyde\text{-}3\text{-}P + 2ADP + 2P_i \rightarrow 2\ P\text{-}glycerate$ $+\ 2ATP$	$+2$
4. $2\ phosphopyruvate + 2ADP \rightarrow 2\ pyruvate + 2ATP$	$+2$
Total	$+2$

Equation of glycolytic cycle
$$glucose + 2P_i + 2ADP + 2NAD^+ \rightarrow 2\ pyruvate + 2NADH$$
$$+\ 2H^+ + 2ATP + 2H_2O$$

Equation of Krebs cycle
$$2CH_3COCOOH + 5O_2 + 30ADP + 30P_i \rightarrow 6CO_2 + 30ATP$$
$$+\ 34H_2O$$

Equation of oxidation of glycolytic NADH
$$2NADH + 2H^+ + 4P_i + 4ADP + O_2 \xrightarrow[\text{cycle}]{\alpha\text{-glycero-P}} 2NAD^+ + 4ATP + 6H_2O$$

Over-all equation for glucose oxidation
$$glucose + 6O_2 + 36ADP + 36P_i \rightarrow 6CO_2 + 36ATP + 42H_2O$$

Partial reactions

$glucose + 6O_2 \rightarrow 6CO_2 + 6H_2O$	$\triangle G = -680\ kcal$
$36ADP + 36P_i \rightarrow 36ATP + 36H_2O$	$\triangle G = +324\ kcal$

chondrial glycolytic reactions, which is but 2 moles of ATP per
mole of glucose, with the yield in the mitochondrial phase,
namely, 34 moles of ATP per mole of glucose, it is evident that
the mitochondria are responsible for nearly 95 per cent of all
the ATP formed in glucose oxidation proceeding by this
pathway.

YIELDS OF ATP IN FATTY ACID AND LIPID OXIDATION

The first oxidative step in formation of an acetyl-CoA unit
from fatty acid, catalyzed by the flavoproteins described earlier,
presumably proceeds with a P:O ratio of 2.0, and the second
oxidative step, which is NAD-linked, has a P:O ratio of 3.0.
Thus, for each acetyl-CoA unit formed during oxidation of fatty

Table 6–3 Phosphorylations of ADP during complete oxidation of palmitate via Krebs cycle

Step	Molecules of ATP formed or used
1. Palmitate → palmityl-CoA	−1
2. Palmityl-CoA → 8 acetyl-CoA	
a. 7 flavoprotein (7 × 2 = 14)	
b. 7 NADH (7 × 3 = 21)	+35
3. 8 acetyl-CoA → $16CO_2$ + $8H_2O$ + 8CoA	
(8 × 4 × 3 = +96)	+96
Total	+130

Over-all equation

$$C_{15}H_{31}COOH + 23O_2 + 130ADP + 130P_i \rightarrow 16CO_2 + 130ATP + 148H_2O$$

Partial reactions

$$C_{15}H_{31}COOH + 23O_2 \rightarrow 16CO_2 + 16H_2O \qquad \Delta G = -2340 \text{ kcal}$$
$$130ADP + 130P_i \rightarrow 130ATP + 130H_2O \qquad \Delta G = +1170 \text{ kcal}$$

acids, 5 molecules of ATP are formed during electron transport (see Table 6–3). For formation of the 8 acetyl-CoA units that arise in oxidation of 1 molecule of palmitate, 35 molecules of ATP are generated. Since oxidation of each molecule of acetyl-CoA yields 12 molecules of ATP during the Krebs cycle, 1 molecule of palmitate leads to formation of a total of 131 molecules of ATP, minus 1 molecule of ATP for priming the cycle by forming palmityl-CoA in the activation reaction, for a net yield of 130 molecules of ATP per molecule of palmitate oxidized. Since the free-energy change in oxidation of 1 mole of palmitate is about −2340 kcal, some 1170 kcal, or 50 per cent of the total free-energy change, is conserved. The ATP yield in the case of the unsaturated fatty acids is, of course, smaller; it can be calculated by taking appropriate account of the operation of the fatty acid cycle.

ENERGY RECOVERY IN THE RESPIRATORY CHAIN

Enzymatic oxidation-reduction equilibria are usually expressed in terms of oxidation-reduction potentials. In biological systems it is conventional to use pH 7.0 as a standard condition and to use concentrations rather than thermodynamic activities. The standard relationship is

$$E = E_0' + \frac{0.06}{n} \log \frac{[A_{ox}]}{[A_{red}]} \qquad (6\text{--}1)$$

where E is the measured emf, in volts, E_0' is the oxidation-reduction potential adjusted for pH = 7 when the concentrations of A_{ox} and A_{red} are equal (i.e., the midpoint potential), and n = number of electrons participating in the formal equation of the reaction. Table 6–4 gives a list of E_0' values for

Table 6–4 Oxidation-reduction potentials of some mitochondrial systems; data* are for pH≅7.0 and for temperature zone 25 to 37°

System	E_0'
Isocitrate (→ α-ketoglutarate + CO_2)	−0.48
Hydrogen	−0.42
NAD	−0.32
NADP	−0.32
D-β-hydroxybutyrate (→ acetoacetate)	−0.29
α-lipoate	−0.29
Peroxidase	−0.25
L-β-hydroxybutyryl-CoA (→ acetoacetyl-CoA)	−0.24
Lactate (→ pyruvate)	−0.18
Glutamate (→ α-ketoglutarate + NH_3)	−0.15
Old yellow enzyme	−0.123
Malate (→ oxalacetate)	−0.10
Vitamin K_1	−0.06
NADH–cytochrome c reductase	0.0
Succinate	+0.03
Cytochrome b	+0.04
Ascorbate	+0.06
Butyryl-CoA dehydrogenase	+0.187
Cytochrome c	+0.26
Cytochrome a	+0.29
Coenzyme Q (in ethanol)	+0.542
Oxygen	+0.82

* The oxidized form of the couple is specified only in cases when more than one product is known.

various oxidation-reduction systems of mitochondria under conditions approximating pH 7.0 and 25°.

From the oxidation-reduction potential of the NAD system at pH 7.0 ($E_0' = -0.32$ volt) and that of the water-oxygen system ($+ 0.82$ volt), the free-energy change when one pair of electron equivalents passes from the NADH system to oxygen via the respiratory chain may be calculated from the relationship $\Delta G = nF \Delta E$, where $n =$ number of electrons (for this case 2.0), $F =$ the caloric equivalent of the faraday (23.062 kcal), and $\Delta E =$ the difference in midpoint potentials of the two reacting systems. The free-energy change for this process is thus 52.6 kcal per pair of electron equivalents. Since 3 moles of ATP are known to be generated in this process, the over-all efficiency of energy conservation is about $27/52.6 \times 100 = 51$ per cent.

Similar calculations for electron transport from succinate to oxygen show it to proceed with a free-energy change of -36.8 kcal per pair of electron equivalents; the P:O ratio of 2.0 observed for this span corresponds to an efficiency of $18/36.8 \times 100 = 49$ per cent. It is evident that the free-energy decrease when a pair of electrons is transferred from substrate to oxygen is much more than enough to cause the coupled formation of the known yields of ATP observed. In fact, there is a considerable amount of respiratory energy that is "left over," since the over-all ΔG for electron transport from NADH to oxygen, even after providing for the three phosphorylations, is still very large, approximately -25.6 kcal per pair of electron equivalents. Although this value indicates that phosphorylating respiration is essentially irreversible, we shall see that some of the remaining free-energy decrease may, in fact, be conserved in other ways.

In the oxidation of 1 mole of pyruvate to CO_2 and H_2O there are 5 oxidation steps proceeding with an average P:O ratio of 3. These steps are accompanied by a total free-energy decrease of $5 \times 52.6 = 263.0$ kcal. Since the oxidation of 1 mole of pyruvate to CO_2 and H_2O proceeds with a free-energy decrease of about 280 kcal, as mentioned above, it is evident that nearly all of the free-energy decrease in the over-all oxidation of pyruvate to CO_2 and H_2O occurs in the electron-transport steps, a consideration that originally led Belitser to postulate that oxidative phosphorylation must be associated with electron transport rather than with substrate-level reactions with intermediates of the Krebs cycle.

ENERGY RELATIONSHIPS
WITHIN THE RESPIRATORY CHAIN

The oxidation-reduction potentials of the various substrates and carriers of the respiratory chain are sufficiently well known to provide some information on the energy relationships in specific segments of the respiratory chain. Table 6–5 gives the midpoint potentials at pH 7.0 (in the zone 25 to 37°) of the carriers, as well as of various NAD-linked substrate systems. Also shown are the calculated values for the free-energy changes for passage of a pair of electron equivalents from one carrier to the next, on the basis that the caloric value of one high-energy bond of ATP, namely, 9.0 kcal, corresponds to the free-energy change when a pair of electrons traverses a span of potential equal to 0.20 volt.

The relationships in Table 6–5 permit some predictions concerning the ability of different segments of the chain to provide a sufficiently large free-energy decrease to allow coupled formation of 1 mole of ATP, for which the "quantum" of energy must be a potential span of 0.20 volt or a caloric value of 9 kcal per pair of electron equivalents. The segments of the chain that afford an energy change of sufficient magnitude to cause coupled synthesis of 1 mole of ATP are the spans NAD-flavoprotein, cytochrome b-cytochrome c, and cytochrome a-oxygen. Much less likely as sites of energy conservation by coupled ATP syn-

Table 6–5 Thermodynamic relationships in respiratory chain

Carrier	E_0' volts	$\triangle E_0'$ volts	$\triangle G$, kcal	Phosphorylation sites	
				From thermo-dynamic data	From cross-over points
NAD	−0.32				
		0.27	12.2	+	+
Flavoprotein	−0.05				
		0.09	4.05	0	0
Cytochrome b	+0.04				
		0.22	9.90	+	+
Cytochrome c	+0.26				
		0.03	1.35	0	0
Cytochrome a	+0.29				
		0.53	23.8	+	+
Oxygen	+0.82				

thesis are the spans flavoprotein-cytochrome b, cytochrome c_1-cytochrome c, and cytochrome c-cytochrome a. It also appears unlikely that the span substrate-NAD can be a site of one of the phosphorylations.

Tables 6–4 and 6–5 show the oxidation-reduction potentials of some of the substrate systems known to be direct reductants of NAD in mitochondria. The values for the malate, α-lipoyl, and β-hydroxybutyrate couples, for example, vary considerably and the value of the malate-oxalacetate is quite electropositive to that of the NAD couple, whereas the oxidation of all these substrates by oxygen yields the same P:O ratio of 3.0. In fact, experimental test has eliminated formation of ATP during direct reduction of mitochondrial NAD by substrates.

Although these relationships have predictive value that has been fully confirmed by actual tests of phosphorylation sites, either directly or by the crossover approach, as indicated in Chapter 5, there are some uncertainties. For one thing, the calculations are applicable to reversible systems at equilibrium, whereas the functioning respiratory chain is a dynamic "open system." They also assume that the carriers as they are bound in the respiratory assemblies in the intact mitochondrial membrane possess the same oxidation-reduction potentials as the isolated forms or as the forms existing in the nonphosphorylating, somewhat degraded preparations in which potentials have usually been measured. We have already seen, for example, that the potential of cytochrome b may vary considerably depending on its state of polymerization or association.

It is also obvious from contemplation of the energy relationships sketched out above that whenever an oxido-reduction is coupled energetically with the phosphorylation of ADP, the energy-coupling reaction has the end effect of either increasing the potential of the reducing system or lowering the potential of the oxidizing system by a factor of 0.20 volt. For example, if the reaction

$$\text{NADH} + \text{H}^+ + \text{FP} \rightleftharpoons \text{NAD}^+ + \text{FPH}_2 \qquad \begin{aligned} \triangle G &= -12.4\,\text{kcal} \\ \triangle E &= 0.27\,\text{volt} \end{aligned} \qquad (6\text{--}2)$$

is energetically coupled with the reaction

$$\text{ADP} + \text{P}_i \rightarrow \text{ATP} + \text{H}_2\text{O} \qquad (\triangle G = +9.0\,\text{kcal}) \qquad (6\text{--}3)$$

then the over-all $\triangle G$ for the coupled oxido-reduction must reduce from -12.4 to a net of -3.4 kcal and the over-all change in E_0' must reduce from 0.27 to about 0.07 volt to allow for the coupled formation of one molecule of ATP. This change can occur in one of two ways. Either the oxidation-reduction potential of the NAD system is in effect *increased* to about —0.12 volt, or conversely, the potential of the flavin system is *decreased* from —0.05 volt to about —0.25 volt. In the former case oxidation of NADH by flavoprotein yields an oxidized, energy-rich state of NAD that is the precursor of ATP; in the latter, reduction of flavoprotein by NADH yields a reduced, energy-rich state of flavoprotein. In most substrate-level phosphorylations, such as the glyceraldehyde phosphate oxidation, the coupling reaction has the effect of making the potential of the reductant more positive. Thus the actual potentials for the fully coupled NAD, cytochrome *b*, and cytochrome *a* systems, as they actually function in the phosphorylating chain, may be about —0.12, +0.20, and +0.49 volt, respectively, rather than the values shown in Tables 6–4 and 6–5, which are for noncoupled systems. These quantitative relationships must be considered in formulating feasible chemical mechanisms for oxidative phosphorylation.

The phosphorylation sites that have been predicted from such thermodynamic considerations and confirmed by experimental test are suggestive of a reaction pattern in the respiratory chain in which each of the three energy-conserving oxido-reduction steps is separated from the next by a noncoupled oxido-reduction step, essentially as postulated by Lehninger (Figure 6–1). This pattern rationalizes the occurrence of more than three carriers in the respiratory chain (which would be the irreducible minimum to account for the three phosphorylations of ADP), and also illustrates the point that the many-membered respiratory chain is a device to break up the very large free-energy decrease when oxygen oxidizes a substrate molecule into smaller units of a magnitude compatible with the dimensions of the standard energy-currency in the cell, namely, the ATP bond energy.

OTHER MEANS OF ENERGY CONSERVATION IN THE RESPIRATORY CHAIN

It has already been pointed out that even after the formation of three ATP molecules in the NAD-linked electron transport there is still a very large drop of free energy in coupled

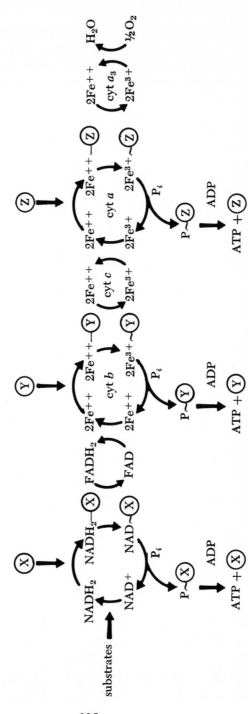

Figure 6–1 Schematic representation of possible reaction pattern of electron transport and the coupled phosphorylations. [From A. L. Lehninger, Science, **128**, 455 (1958).]

electron transport, almost 50 per cent of the total. Significantly, the largest part of this energy drop is in the span from cytochrome c to oxygen; the preceding portion of the chain is more closely coupled. These facts do not at first appear to be compatible with the recent demonstration that oxidative phosphorylation in intact mitochondria is reversible, that the oxidation-reduction state of the carriers of the chain is a reflection of the ratio [ATP] / [ADP] [P_i], and that ATP can inhibit respiration.

As we shall see in the following chapters, respiratory energy may be conserved not only to cause ATP formation but also to bring about the energy-requiring osmotic work of active transport and the mechanochemical work involved in contractile phenomena. It therefore seems possible that some of the remaining free-energy drop not required for coupled ATP synthesis is employed to "drive" ion-transport and mechanochemical events in such a way that the total amount of the oxido-reduction energy of electron transport conserved is the *sum* of those amounts used for ATP synthesis, for maintenance of ion gradients, and for bringing about conformational changes. The sum of these changes may be much higher than the 50 per cent recovered as ATP alone, but insufficient information is available to attempt a quantitative evaluation.

ONE-ELECTRON AND TWO-ELECTRON TRANSFERS

Before considering mechanisms of energy coupling, some attention must be paid to the fact that, although some of the electron carriers of the chain apparently transfer but one electron at a time, others may transfer two. In the reaction of substrate with NAD^+, two reducing equivalents are transferred to NAD^+, one as an electron and one as a hydrogen atom. When $NADH + H^+$ reacts with flavoprotein to produce $FADH_2$, again two reducing equivalents are transferred. However, when reduced flavin reacts with cytochrome b, there is a transition from the two-electron flavin system to the one-electron Fe(III)-Fe(II) transitions believed to be characteristic of the cytochromes. These statements are based on the formal stoichiometry of these reactions. Flavoproteins are known to be capable of reacting either as one-electron or two-electron systems, and this ability may be a molecular adaptation allowing flavoprotein to serve as the point of transition between the two-electron pyridine nucleotide systems and the one-electron transitions in the cytochrome system.

Although the respiratory chain has traditionally been written and thought of as a combined two-electron and one-electron system, as shown in Figure 6–2, there is in fact insufficient evidence to exclude two other alternatives. One is the possibility that the entire chain is a two-electron system, either by pairing of the one-electron cytochromes, as shown, or by intervention of two-electron steps in single cytochrome molecules, which is theoretically possible. The other alternative is that the entire chain is a one-electron system. On the other hand, since the work of Michaelis, it has been repeatedly postulated that formal two-electron oxido-reductions actually proceed through compulsory one-electron stages, which may differ only very slightly in their time constants.

Spectral and electron spin resonance measurements suggest that the succinate and NADH dehydrogenase flavoproteins do not necessarily become fully reduced during their normal activity but may oscillate between the oxidized and semiquinone forms. The solution to this problem obviously has a bearing on possible mechanisms involved in coupling ATP formation to transfer of electrons.

Actually, all biological energy-conserving oxido-reductions whose mechanisms are known are two-electron systems, at least in a formal sense, and such systems offer the simplest way of accounting for biological mechanisms of coupled synthesis of anhydride and other bonds. Secondly, the reduction of molecular oxygen to water is a process that requires uptake of four electrons per molecule of oxygen at the terminal carrier;

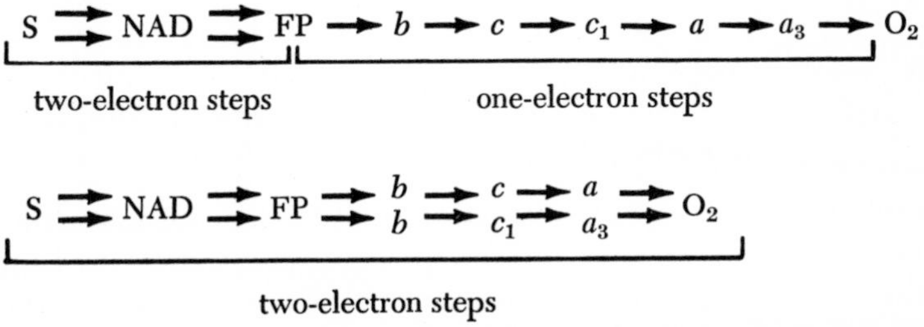

$$S \rightleftarrows NAD \rightleftarrows FP \rightarrow b \rightarrow c \rightarrow c_1 \rightarrow a \rightarrow a_3 \rightarrow O_2$$

two-electron steps   one-electron steps

$$S \rightleftarrows NAD \rightleftarrows FP \rightleftarrows {b \atop b} \rightleftarrows {c \atop c_1} \rightleftarrows {a \atop a_3} \rightleftarrows O_2$$

two-electron steps

Figure 6–2 Schematic representations of two possible electron-transfer patterns in the respiratory chain.

it is difficult to visualize reduction of oxygen occurring in four separate steps at the enzyme, as would be necessary in a one-electron system, particularly since the intermediates are likely to differ greatly in stability, reactivity, and energy content. Reduction of molecular oxygen in two two-electron steps, possibly via an intermediate stage of hydrogen peroxide bound to the enzyme, must still be given some consideration.

Actually, the possible formation of hydrogen peroxide in respiration, at least as an intermediate bound form, has not been given the attention it deserves in view of the fact that spectroscopic experiments of Chance and his colleagues have shown that hydrogen peroxide or a closely related compound is produced and used up in some respiring cells at a rate approximately equal to the rate of respiration. The recent finding in Lehninger's laboratory that catalase and glutathione peroxidase are mitochondrial contraction factors and can also increase the P:O ratio of mitochondrial systems may also be relevant to a role of peroxides in respiration and phosphorylation.

MECHANISMS OF ENERGY COUPLING
IN THE RESPIRATORY CHAIN

The enzymatic and chemical mechanisms of energy conservation in the respiratory chain culminating in formation of ATP are still unsolved and constitute perhaps the most important contemporary problem in the biochemistry of the mitochondrion. As has been pointed out earlier, it is possible that the solution of this problem will come only after the structure of the respiratory assembly is known, since oxidative phosphorylation has been observed to occur only in those systems in which some elements of membrane structure are still discernible.

In order to transfer chemical energy from one reaction to another, it is necessary that the energy-yielding reaction and the energy-accepting reaction have a common chemical intermediate. In the case of the energy-conserving glyceraldehyde 3-phosphate dehydrogenase reaction, the oxido-reduction step is

$$\text{glyceraldehyde 3-phosphate} + NAD^+ + P_i \rightleftharpoons \text{1,3-diphosphoglycerate}$$
$$+ NADH + H^+ \tag{6-4}$$

and the ATP-forming step is

$$\text{1,3-diphosphoglycerate} + ADP \rightleftharpoons \text{3-phosphoglycerate} + ATP \tag{6-5}$$

The intermediate that is common to the two reactions and that serves as the vehicle of energy transfer between the reactions is 1,3-diphosphoglycerate.

Most postulated mechanisms for oxidative phosphorylation are based on this principle of a common intermediate in electron transport and in ATP formation and follow the general pattern of the glyceraldehyde phosphate dehydrogenase system, as well as other known substrate-level, energy-conserving oxido-reductions. Slater has pointed out that most of the postulated reaction patterns for oxidative phosphorylation may be classified into two sorts, called type I and type II mechanisms. Type I mechanisms propose that some substance, not inorganic phosphate, that is variously designated by different workers as C, X, or I combines with the electron carrier during the coupled oxido-reduction to form a high-energy intermediate designated carrier $\sim C$, for example. This intermediate (which is common to the oxido-reduction and the ATP-forming reactions) is then postulated to react with P_i and ADP to form ATP, as follows:

$$AH_2 + B + C \rightleftharpoons A \sim C + BH_2 \tag{6-6}$$

$$A \sim C + P_i + ADP \rightleftharpoons A + C + ATP \tag{6-7}$$

$$\overline{AH_2 + B + P_i + ADP \rightleftharpoons A + BH_2 + ATP} \tag{6-8}$$

This mechanism was stated in more detail in 1954 by Lehninger, for the case of the NAD-linked phosphorylation, as follows:

$$NADH + HS\text{-}E \rightleftharpoons NADH\text{-}S\text{-}E \tag{6-9}$$

$$NADH\text{-}S\text{-}E + H^+ + FP_{ox} \rightleftharpoons NAD^+ \sim S\text{-}E + FPH_2 \tag{6-10}$$

$$NAD^+ \sim S\text{-}E + P_i \rightleftharpoons NAD^+ + P \sim S\text{-}E \tag{6-11}$$

$$P \sim S\text{-}E + ADP \rightleftharpoons HS\text{-}E + ATP \tag{6-12}$$

$$\overline{NADH + H^+ + FP_{ox} + P_i + ADP \rightleftharpoons NAD^+ + FPH_2 + ATP} \tag{6-13}$$

It is seen that in these type I reaction mechanisms inorganic phosphate does not react directly with the electron carrier molecules.

On the other hand, in type II mechanisms, inorganic phosphate is postulated as combining directly with the electron carrier molecule either before or during oxido-reduction, as follows:

$$AH_2 + B + P_i \rightleftharpoons A \sim P + BH_2 \tag{6-14}$$

$$A \sim P + ADP \rightleftharpoons A + ATP \tag{6-15}$$

$$\overline{AH_2 + B + P_i + ADP \rightleftharpoons A + BH_2 + ATP} \tag{6-16}$$

The over-all reactions [i.e., reactions (6–8) and (6–16)] are thus the same in type I and type II mechanisms.

Type I mechanisms are favored by most available evidence. Most, if not all, of the known substrate-level oxidative phosphorylations are of this type; in fact, the glyceraldehyde phosphate and the α-keto acid dehydrogenase systems utilize high-energy thioesters as the common intermediate. There is also the compelling experimental finding that when oxidative phosphorylation is uncoupled by dinitrophenol, inorganic phosphate is not required for electron transport. This finding implies that the carriers may interact with each other in the absence of inorganic phosphate.

Although there is substantial but not completely overriding support for type I mechanisms, there has been some disagreement as to whether the energized form of the electron carrier is in the oxidized or reduced state. Since the equations above are written for type I mechanisms, the energized form of the carrier (i.e., $A \sim C$ or $NAD^+ \sim S$-E) is in the oxidized state, as happens also to be the case in the mechanism of the glyceraldehyde phosphate and α-keto acid oxidations. However, an alternative formulation is thermodynamically possible, namely, that the energized carrier is in the reduced state, as proposed by Chance and Williams. For a prototype of their mechanism the following sequence of reactions may be written:

$$AH_2 + B + C \rightleftharpoons A + BH_2 \sim C \qquad (6\text{–}17)$$

$$\underline{BH_2 \sim C + P_i + ADP \rightleftharpoons BH_2 + ATP + C} \qquad (6\text{–}18)$$

$$AH_2 + B + P_i + ADP \rightleftharpoons A + BH_2 + ATP \qquad (6\text{–}19)$$

This sequence is directly comparable to reactions (6–6) to (6–8), in which the oxidized form is "energized."

A number of experimental approaches have been brought to bear on this question in the laboratories of Chance, Lehninger, Ernster, and others, but it is not yet possible to draw a firm conclusion, although biochemical precedent favors the oxidized state as the energized state. There is as yet no necessity to assume that all three phosphorylation sites of the NAD-linked chain are energized in the same oxidation state. The recent work of Pinchot and his colleagues, as well as similar work in the laboratories of Green on the formation of energized complexes of the respiratory carriers (Chapter 5), may lead to a direct answer to the problem of the oxidation state of the high-energy intermediate. Also relevant is the recent work (see below) on the role of quinones and quinols in oxidative phosphorylation.

DEDUCTIONS FROM THE PARTIAL REACTIONS AND THE ACTION OF INHIBITORS

Some internally consistent conclusions concerning the reaction pattern of the coupling mechanisms have come from many studies of different types of inhibitors or combinations of inhibitors applied to oxidative phosphorylation, to respiration and respiratory control, and to the so-called partial reactions of oxidative phosphorylation. These observations have had the effect of weaving a rather tight web of evidence, although taken singly they are perhaps not compelling. In interpreting these observations, it has been a tacit assumption that the mechanism of ATP formation is essentially identical at all three phosphorylation sites of the respiratory chain, since uncoupling agents in general inhibit all three sites, which are also approximately equal in stability and general properties. However, this is undoubtedly an oversimplification, since some significant differences among the sites have been observed on careful study, particularly with respect to susceptibility to uncoupling agents and to the participation in the so-called partial reactions of oxidative phosphorylation.

The most crucial experiments with inhibitors involve the contrasting effects of the true uncoupling agents such as dinitrophenol versus the true inhibitors of oxidative phosphorylation, such as oligomycin, as well as their action relative to each other. Three sets of observations are central to the problem and have been confirmed many times over. One set deals with the action of dinitrophenol, which (1) stimulates acceptor-less respiration, (2) does so without a requirement for inorganic phosphate in the medium, (3) uncouples without inhibition of respiration, (4) stimulates ATPase activity, (5) inhibits the ATP-P_i exchange, (6) inhibits the H_2O-P_i oxygen exchange, and (7) inhibits the ATP-ADP exchange in phosphorylating but not in nonphosphorylating mitochondrial preparations.

The second set of observations involves the action of oligomycin, first described by Lardy and his colleagues. This agent (1) inhibits phosphorylating respiration, (2) has no effect on nonphosphorylating respiration, (3) inhibits ATPase activity,

(4) inhibits the ATP-P_i exchange and the H_2O-P_i oxygen exchange, and (5) inhibits the ATP-ADP exchange in phosphorylating but not in nonphosphorylating or loosely coupled systems. Atractylate, azide, and triethyltin give essentially similar effects.

The third set of observations involves the relationship between the points of action of oligomycin and dinitrophenol. Specifically, Lardy has found that when phosphorylating respiration is inhibited by oligomycin, the inhibition may be completely relieved by addition of uncoupling concentrations of dinitrophenol. Secondly, oligomycin blocks the stimulation of ATPase activity ordinarily given by dinitrophenol.

This information may be combined with the available observations on the properties and requirements of the partial reactions of oxidative phosphorylation. One crucial set of observations on the partial reactions, those of Wadkins and Lehninger, is that ATP, ADP, and P_i are required for the ATP-P_i exchange but that the ATP-ADP exchange can be observed to occur in the absence of P_i. They have found that the ATP-ADP exchange is a separable step in the over-all ATP-P_i exchange. Phosphate is taken up first in a step labile to aging and then ADP in a relatively stable step. The second set of observations came from use of O^{18} as tracer; these indicated that the O^{18} exchange occurs at the point of uptake of P_i and that the bridge oxygen of the terminal phosphate group of ATP is furnished by the ADP added and not by P_i, an observation that excludes a high-energy ADP~enzyme precursor of ATP.

These crucial observations are accounted for by the reaction pattern shown in Figure 6–3, which indicates the general nature of the partial reactions and their interrelationships as well as the characteristic site of action of the inhibitors. The formulation shown involves the oxidized form of the carrier as the energized form, which is believed to best accommodate all known facts and particularly the fact that the reduced state of the carriers causes substantial inhibition of all the partial reactions. However, in order to show the essential agreement regarding the general reaction pattern, the scheme of Chance and Williams is also shown; it proposes the reduced form as the energized form of the carrier. In most other respects it is essentially similar in design. In general, it is a current working philosophy to test these hypotheses by application of new diagnostic inhibitors and by direct attempts to isolate components

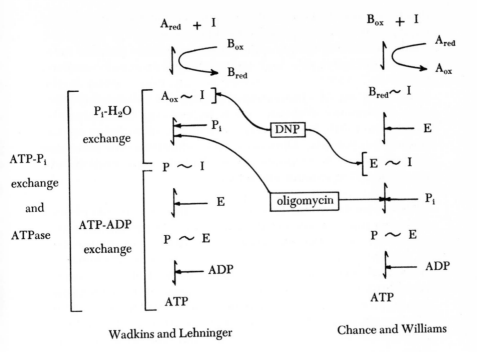

Figure 6–3 Reaction schemes for oxidative phosphorylation, showing sites of action of dinitrophenol and oligomycin, as well as probable form of partial reactions. Dinitrophenol is thought to cause breakdown of $A_{ox} \sim I$ to $A_{ox} + I$ (or of $E \sim I$ to $E + I$).

predicted by these schemes and to reconstruct phosphorylation and its partial reactions. The recent work of Wadkins and Lehninger, described in Chapter 5, on the enzyme catalyzing the terminal reaction of ADP formation illustrates one of the current approaches.

FUNCTIONAL GROUPS IN OXIDATIVE PHOSPHORYLATION

Carbonyl groups. From time to time speculations have been made as to the role of certain functional groups in one or another of the respiratory carriers in phosphorylation mechanisms. For example, Ball has called attention to the carbonyl groups of the isoalloxazine ring system of flavin nucleotides as possible vehicles for formation of a high-energy phosphate bond. Similarly, Glahn and Nielsen have pointed to the formyl group in the porphyrin ring of cytochrome *a,* which also can be visualized as a nucleus for formation of a high-energy grouping. The latter possibility has recently been given more force by the finding in Okunuki's laboratory that cytochrome *a* is inhibited by hydroxylamine in amounts known to cause the formation of an oxime of the cytochrome *a* heme.

Sulfhydryl groups. In Lehninger's mechanism for the NAD-linked phosphorylation given above, a specific —SH group of the coupling enzyme E was postulated, comparable to the central role of the —SH group in the substrate-level oxidative phosphorylations. Early experiments by Lehninger showed that some agents capable of attacking —SH groups uncoupled oxidative phosphorylation. That —SH groups may be involved in electron transport was first shown by Slater, who demonstrated that a step between cytochrome *b* and *c* is sensitive to BAL (British antilewisite). More recently, Sanadi and Fluharty have provided evidence from inhibitor studies with arsenite and other divalent reagents that vicinal dithiol groups are involved in the coupling mechanisms of oxidative phosphorylation. From recent work on the role of —SH groups of lipoic acid in the α-keto acid dehydrogenations a new understanding of the role of —SH groups in oxidative phosphorylation may emerge.

Serine and histidine residues. The phosphorylation of these amino acids in mitochondrial proteins has already been described in Chapter 5; these residues have been postulated to be part of the active sites of phosphorylating enzymes.

Quinones as intermediates. In Chapter 4 the structures and some properties of coenzyme Q, vitamin K, and α-tocopherol were outlined with emphasis on the considerable similarity in their isoprenoid side chains and the potentiality of each group of compounds to occur as a quinone or quinol and, by a cyclization reaction involving a single isoprenoid group of the side chain, as chromanols or chromenols. The evidence for the participation of these compounds as true electron carriers in the respiratory chain, although strong, is certainly not conclusive.

These compounds do, however, possess interesting chemical potentialities as intermediates in oxidative phosphorylation, which derives in the first instance from the chemical studies of Wieland and Patterman and of Todd and his colleagues, who showed that chemical oxidation of quinol phosphates proceeded with transfer of the phosphate group with formation of a pyrophosphate:

$$HO\!\!-\!\!\langle\;\rangle\!\!-\!\!O\!\!-\!\!PO_3H_2 + H_3PO_4 \xrightarrow{-2e} O\!\!=\!\!\langle\;\rangle\!\!=\!\!O + H_4P_2O_7$$

More recently, Wieland and his colleagues have synthesized the quinol monophosphate derivatives of vitamin K, vitamin K_3 (menadiol), and coenzyme Q and tested their oxidation in mitochondria and submitochondrial particles, as well as their capacity to support ATP formation. Neither of the vitamin K derivatives were active, but the P^{32}-labeled monophosphate of the quinol form of coenzyme Q was very slowly oxidized by digitonin particles with simultaneous formation of labeled ATP. The P:O ratio of the process was between 1.0 and 2.0; the formation of ATP was blocked by either cyanide or 2,4-dinitrophenol. This demonstration seems very convincing, but it does not yet suffice to prove that this compound is an intermediate. Unexplained as yet is how the covalent quinol monophosphate intermediate is formed in the first place. It has been suggested that it might arise by reaction of inorganic phosphate with the 6-chromenol derivations of coenzyme Q (i.e., ubichromenol) or corresponding derivatives of vitamin K_1 or α-tocopherol.

Brodie and his colleagues earlier carried out some interesting work on the role of vitamin K derivations in oxidative phosphorylation in *Mycobacterium phlei*. Ultraviolet irradiation, which destroys vitamin K, inactivates electron transport and phosphorylation in *M. phlei* extracts. Vitamin K_3 (menadione), which has no isoprenoid side chain and thus cannot cyclize to form a naphthochromanol, restores electron transport but not oxidative phosphorylation. However, vitamin K_1, which can form the naphthochromanol, restores both. Brodie has isolated a phosphorylated derivative of vitamin K that was enzymatically formed in the extracts. This derivative also causes formation of ATP when incubated with the extracts, but the reaction is slow and in this case there is some question whether the phosphorylated vitamin K_1 derivative, presumably of the naphthochromanol, is the immediate precursor of ATP. Nevertheless, the work of Brodie and of Wieland seems highly significant and may lead to decisive chemical identification of at least one intermediate.

In animal tissues the role of vitamin K in oxidative phosphorylation seems very uncertain, but coenzyme Q is a much more likely candidate. Folkers and his colleagues, who have carried out very detailed chemical studies of coenzyme Q and its derivatives, have recently stressed the possible role of other features of the molecule in oxidative phosphorylation.

H^+ AND OH^- EXCHANGES

In phosphorylating electron transport it is highly significant that H^+ and OH^- ions are formed or absorbed at several different points. We have seen that when NAD^+ is reduced by substrate, NADH and H^+ are formed; however, when NADH reduces flavoprotein, H^+ must be absorbed from the medium again to form $FADH_2$. When reduced flavoprotein now reacts with cytochrome b, two H^+ from $FADH_2$ are delivered to the medium again. On the other hand, when cytochrome $a + a_3$ reacts with oxygen, $-OH$ ions are formed. In the over-all equation of electron transport, however, there is no *net* formation of excess H^+ or OH^- ions; but we shall see that the sites of formation of these ions may be geometrically separated, a fact that may have important consequences in active ion-transport mechanisms.

On the other hand, if we consider the coupled formation of ATP from ADP and P_i that occurs at three sites in the respiratory chain, we can see that there are large net changes in the balance of H^+ and OH^- ions during ATP formation. In fact, during oxidative phosphorylation at pH 7.4, H^+ ions must be absorbed from the medium in the ratio of nearly one per molecule of ATP formed, according to the equation

$$ADP^{3-} + HPO_4^{=} + H^+ \rightleftharpoons ATP^{4-} + H_2O \qquad (6\text{--}20)$$

It can be calculated from the known acid dissociation constants of the components that at pH 7.4 about 0.9 mole of H^+ is absorbed per mole of ATP formed. Phosphorylating respiration is thus accompanied by a massive uptake of H^+ ions, and it should result in making phosphorylating mitochondrial suspensions more alkaline:

$$NADH + H^+ + 3HPO_4^= + 3ADP^{3-} + 3H^+ + \tfrac{1}{2}O_2 \rightarrow$$
$$NAD^+ + 3ATP + 4H_2O \qquad (6\text{--}21)$$

In the intact cell the absorption of H^+ by oxidative phosphorylation is, of course, counterbalanced by the reformation of H^+ as the ATP formed by oxidative phosphorylation undergoes net hydrolysis in extramitochondrial sites. However, it is evident that in the microscopic organization of the mitochondrion, formation and disposal of H^+ and OH^- may become crucial elements in determining rates of phosphorylation and respiration, and, as we shall now see, they may be elements in active ion-transport processes.

CHEMIOSMOTIC COUPLING

Recently Mitchell, following an earlier suggestion by Davies and Ogston, has proposed a chemiosmotic mechanism for oxidative and photosynthetic phosphorylation. It is proposed that electron transport along the respiratory chains in the mitochondrial membrane brings about separation of H^+ and OH^- ions across the mitochondrial membrane. The H^+ ions arise on one side of the membrane because of specific orientation of the active sites of enzymes that cause discharge of H^+ during dehydrogenation of the respiratory substrate (succinate, for example and the reduced form of coenzyme Q). The OH^- ions in turn arise on the other side of the membrane by appropriate orientation of cytochrome oxidase.

Mitchell proposes that the mitochondrial membrane is impermeable to H^+ and OH^-, for which he has presented evidence; it is thus seen that electron transport "drives" a pH gradient across the membrane. Mitchell now proposes that the "sinks" of H^+ and OH^- so formed in the two aqueous phases separated by the membrane are used to "pull" the formation of ATP from ADP and phosphate by the reverse action of an anisotropic ATPase in the mitochondrial membrane. In this reaction, which is formally a condensation involving removal of H_2O from ADP + phosphate, it is proposed that the H^+ and OH^- ions formed in the reverse reaction are discharged on opposite sides of the membrane into the sinks of OH^- and H^+, respectively, formed during electron transport. There are therefore no real chemical intermediates common to the oxido-reduction reactions and those leading to ATP formation; the coupling is not a chemical one but a physical one made possible by specific orientation of enzyme molecules in a membrane impermeable to H^+ and OH^- (Figure 6–4).

This conception has a number of interesting features. Uncoupling agents such as dinitrophenol are visualized as increasing the permeability of the membrane to H^+ and OH^-, by

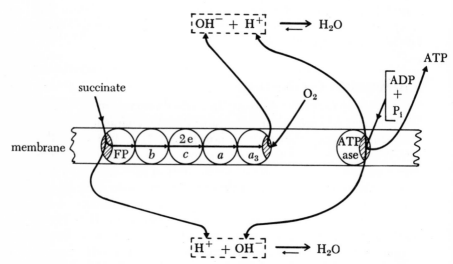

Figure 6–4 Principle of Mitchell's hypothesis of chemiosmotic energy coupling. In this hypothesis the dehydrogenation of succinate causes the delivery of protons on the lower side of the membrane, whereas the reduction of oxygen causes delivery of OH^- ions to the upper side of the membrane, through asymmetric orientation of the active sites of succinate dehydrogenase and cytochrome oxidase, respectively. The accumulation of OH^- and H^+ on opposite sides of the membrane can then "pull" reverse action of asymmetric ATPase, by causing asymmetric extraction of H^+ and OH^- from ADP and P_i, in the opposite sense. Since the ion product $[H^+]$ $[OH^-]$ is very low (1×10^{-14}), the formation of ATP from ADP and P_i may be driven by electron transport, providing the membrane is impermeable to H^+ and OH^-.

acting as lipid-soluble proton conductors, and thus destroying the ion gradient across the membrane and with it the driving force for synthesis of ATP without interrupting electron transport. Mitchell has demonstrated that DNP, arsenate, and Dicumarol stimulate H^+ uptake by intact mitochondria, as his theory demands. The chemiosmotic hypothesis can also explain the occurrence of selective ion accumulations in the mitochondria, as well as conformational changes in the membranes; the latter are suggested to result from electrical stresses induced by the unequal ion distribution and large membrane potential. On the other hand, there are many objections. Mitchell's theory fails to account satisfactorily for the more or less exact maximum stoichiometry of phosphorylation, particularly for specific segments of the chain such as the NAD $\rightarrow$ cytochrome c and cytochrome $\rightarrow$ oxygen spans, or for the occurrence of oxidative phosphorylation in submitochondrial systems with badly damaged membranes.

Nevertheless, Mitchell's hypothesis stresses the importance of vectorial, or directional, processes in biology, versus scalar, or nondirectional, processes. Above all, his idea provides some rationale for the fact that the respiratory and phosphorylating enzymes are located in the membrane, rather than in granules or in solution within the matrix.

REFERENCES

Reviews

In addition to references on oxidative phosphorylation cited in Chapter 5, the following are important:

Burton, K., and H. A. Krebs, "The free energy changes associated with the individual steps of the tricarboxylic acid cycle, glycolysis, and alcoholic fermentation, and with the hydrolysis of the pyrophosphate groups of adenosine triphosphate," *Biochem. J.*, **54**, 94 (1953).

Clark, W. M., *Oxidation-Reduction Potentials of Organic Systems*, Williams & Wilkins, Baltimore, 1960.

George, P., and R. J. Rutman, "The high-energy phosphate bond concept," *Progr. Biophys. Biophys. Chem.*, **10**, 1 (1960).

Huennekens, F. M., and H. R. Whiteley, "Phosphoric acid anhydrides and other energy-rich compounds," in M. Florkin and H. S. Mason (eds.), *Comparative Biochemistry,* Academic, New York, 1960, Vol. I, p. 107.

Lehninger, A. L., C. L. Wadkins, and L. F. Remmert, "Control points in phosphorylating respiration and the action of a mitochondrial respiration-releasing factor," *Ciba Found. Symp., Regulation Cell Metab.,* Little, Brown, Boston, 1959, p. 130.

——, ——, C. Cooper, T. M. Devlin, and J. L. Gamble, Jr., "Oxidative phosphorylation," *Science,* **128,** 450 (1958).

Slater, E. C., "Oxidation-reduction potentials and their significance in hydrogen transfer," in W. Ruhland (ed.), *Encyclopedia of Plant Physiology,* Springer, Berlin, 1960, Vol. XII, p. 114.

Papers in *Ciba Found. Symp., Quinones Electron Transport,* Little, Brown, Boston, 1961.

Research papers

Crane, F. L., "Quinones in lipoprotein electron transport systems," *Biochemistry,* **1,** 510 (1962).

Davies, R. E., and A. G. Ogston, "On the mechanism of secretion of ions by gastric mucosa and other tissues," *Biochem. J.,* **46,** 324 (1950).

Dervartanian, D. V., C. Veeger, and J. D. W. van Woorst, "Studies by electron spin resonance of the nature of succinate dehydrogenase," *Biochim. Biophys. Acta,* **73,** 660 (1963).

Erickson, R. E., A. F. Wagner, and K. Folkers, "Coenzyme Q. XLVIII. Data on quinone methines as reaction intermediates and their possible role in oxidative phosphorylation," *J. Am. Chem. Soc.,* **85,** 1535 (1963).

Fluharty, A., and D. R. Sanadi, "On the mechanism of oxidative phosphorylation. IV," *Biochemistry,* **1,** 276 (1962).

—— and ——, "On the mechanism of oxidative phosphorylation. VI. Localization of the dithiol in oxidative phosphorylation with respect to the oligomycin inhibition site," *Biochemistry,* **2,** 519 (1963).

Gibson, Q. H., and C. Greenwood, "Reaction of cytochrome oxidase with oxygen and carbon monoxide," *Biochem. J.,* **86,** 541 (1963).

Gruber, W., R. Höhl, and T. Wieland, "Hydroquinone monophosphates and oxidative phosphorylation," *Biochem. Biophys. Res. Commun.,* **12,** 242 (1963).

Heytler, P. G., "Uncoupling of oxidative phosphorylation by carbonyl cyanide phenylhydrazones," *Biochemistry,* **2,** 357 (1963).

Huijing, F., and E. C. Slater, "The use of oligomycin as an inhibitor of oxidative phosphorylation," *J. Biochem. (Tokyo),* **49,** 493 (1961).

Lardy, H. A., D. Johnson, and W. C. McMurray, "A survey of toxic antibiotics in respiratory, phosphorylative, and glycolytic systems," *Arch. Biochem. Biophys.,* **78,** 587 (1958).

Mitchell, P., "A chemiosmotic hypothesis for the mechanism of oxidative and photosynthetic phosphorylation," *Nature*, **191**, 144 (1961).

Russell, P. J., Jr., and A. F. Brodie, "Enzymic formation of reduced intermediates from vitamin K," *Biochim. Biophys. Acta*, **50**, 76 (1961).

Vignais, P. V., P. M. Vignais, and E. Stanislas, "Action of potassium atractylate on oxidative phosphorylation in mitochondria and in submitochondrial particles," *Biochim. Biophys. Acta*, **60**, 284 (1962).

Wagner, A. F., and K. Folkers, et al., "Coenzyme Q. XLVII. New 5-phosphomethyl-6-chromanyl derivatives from a novel reaction of interest in oxidative phosphorylation," *J. Am. Chem. Soc.*, **85**, 1534 (1963).

7

CONTROL, COMPARTMENTATION, AND INTEGRATION

Too often, metabolic cycles are regarded as mere wiring diagrams or flow sheets to describe metabolic precursors, intermediates, and products. However, multienzyme systems are now being found to have self-regulating and self-adjusting properties that are the consequence of their sequential organization, the specific properties of the individual component enzymes, and of feedback and other types of inhibition.

In this chapter we shall consider first the dynamics of electron transport in mitochondria and its control by ADP, P_i, and ATP. Then we shall examine some elements of the complex network of interrelationships by which the individual reactions of the Krebs citric acid cycle are brought into self-regulation and integration. Finally, we shall analyze the dynamic interplay of energy-linked reactions between the intra- and extramitochondrial compartments of the cell.

THE RESPIRATORY STATES;
CONTROL OF RESPIRATION BY ADP

That the rate of respiration must depend on the supply and concentration of respiratory substrates and oxygen is, of course, self-evident. However, it is now clear that the rate of respiration of mitochondria also depends on the concentration of the reactants ADP and P_i and the product ATP of the coupled oxidative phosphorylations occurring in the respiratory chain. The requirement of ADP for maximum rates of respiration in intact phosphorylating mitochondria was first studied systematically by Lardy and his colleagues, who made the important suggestion that the concentration of ADP may control the rate of respiration within the cell. This basic thesis has since been elaborated in great detail by Chance and his colleagues and has been more recently expanded to include control by ATP and P_i.

Chance and Williams have systematized the general conditions affecting the respiratory rate of intact mitochondria and the oxidation-reduction state of the components of the respiratory chain (Table 7–1). State 1 is the condition in which both ADP and respiratory substrate are lacking, and state 2 is the condition in which respiratory substrate only is lacking. State 3 is the condition in which all required components are present and the respiratory chain itself is the rate-limiting factor; that is, it is the state of "active" respiration. State 4 is the condition in which only ADP is lacking; this is the so-called controlled or resting or ADP-less state. State 5 is the condition in which only oxygen is lacking.

Table 7–1 also gives an indication of the oxidation-reduction state of the respiratory carriers in each respiratory state. The carriers are in their most oxidized state when the substrate is limiting and all other components are present in excess. In the aerobic steady state (i.e., state 3) there is an intermediate degree of reduction with a gradient of increasing degree of oxidation between pyridine nucleotides and oxygen. A still higher degree of reduction of carriers is observed in the controlled state (state 4), and the most completely reduced state is given in the absence of oxygen. The rate of respiration and the steady-state equilibrium of the electron carriers are thus exquisitely poised and are a function of concentration of respiratory substrate, ADP, and oxygen. However, as we shall see later, ATP and P_i also play a role.

Chance and his colleagues have placed great emphasis on the concentration of ADP as the most critical element in the determination of respiratory rate in either isolated mitochondria or in the intact cell. In Figure 7–1 is shown a typical experiment

Table 7-1 The metabolic states of mitochondria according to Chance and Williams, 1956

	Characteristics					Steady-state percentage reduction of components				
State	[O₂]	ADP level	Substrate level	Respiration rate	Rate-limiting substance	a	c	b	Flavo-protein *	DPNH
1	>0	low	low	slow	ADP	0	7	17	21	~90
2	>0	high	~0	slow	substrate	0	0	0	0	0
3	>0	high	high	fast	respiratory chain	<4	6	16	20	53
4	>0	low	high	slow	ADP	0	14	35	40	>99
5	0	high	high	0	oxygen	100	100	100	150	100

* These values are based upon the amount of flavoprotein that is reduced upon addition of antimycin A to the mitochondria in state 2, that is, two-thirds the state 5 value.

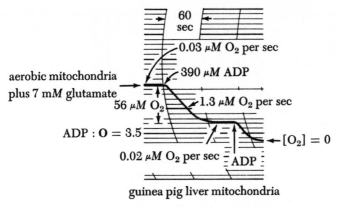

60
sec

0.03 μM O_2 per sec

aerobic mitochondria
plus 7 mM glutamate →

390 μM ADP

56 μM O_2

1.3 μM O_2 per sec

ADP : O = 3.5

← [O_2] = 0

0.02 μM O_2 per sec

ADP

guinea pig liver mitochondria

Figure 7–1 Control of respiration by level of ADP and the determination of the ADP:O ratio. [From B. Chance and G. R. Williams, *Adv. Enzymol.*, **17**, 92 (1956).] The experiment is described in the text.

reported by Chance and Williams that demonstrates the response to ADP. The rate of oxygen uptake of isolated guinea pig liver mitochondria in the presence of substrate and oxygen, but in the absence of ADP, is shown to be very low, i.e., 0.03 μM O_2 per sec. On addition of 390 μM ADP the rate immediately increased some 43-fold to 1.3 μM O_2 per sec and remained essentially constant until the ADP was completely phosphorylated to ATP, at which point the rate of respiration sharply decreased to 0.02 μM O_2 per sec. The rate of respiration in the presence of ADP (i.e., 1.3 μM O_2 per sec) divided by the rate in its absence (0.03 μM O_2 per sec) is defined as the *respiratory control index*, or, better, the *acceptor control ratio*; in this case the ratio is about 43. "Tightly coupled" intact mitochondria are those having very high acceptor control ratios, as in the above experiment. On the other hand, "loosely coupled" mitochondria have little or no dependence of respiratory rate on ADP; in this case the acceptor control ratio is much lower and may approach 1.0.

Tightly coupled mitochondria always have high P:O ratios. Although mitochondria showing loose coupling often have low P:O ratios, this is not always the case; sometimes the P:O ratio may approach 3.0. In effect, there is no simple quantitative relationship between the acceptor control ratio and the P:O ratio.

It is of some interest that a high acceptor control ratio is a more rigorous criterion of intactness of mitochondrial structure than a high P:O ratio.

A second point may be made from the experiment in Figure 7–1. In the period of rapid state 3 respiration, there was a decrease of 56 μM in the concentration of oxygen during the removal of 390 μM ADP; the ADP:O ratio was therefore 3.5. Since the ADP:O ratio in the tightly coupled mitochondria is numerically equivalent to the P:O ratio, the oxygen electrode is very convenient for determination of the P:O ratio in intact mitochondria. However, the P:O ratio of loosely coupled mitochondria, as well as of most submitochondrial systems, cannot be evaluated from the response of respiration to ADP.

Chance and Williams have examined the sensitivity of the respiratory response of isolated mitochondria to the concentration of ADP. Half-maximal responses were given by concentrations as low as 8 μM, indicating that respiration may occur at near-maximum rates at ADP concentrations normally occurring in intact liver or kidney, but may be limited by the low concentration of ADP found in resting muscle.

The stimulation of the rate of respiration of isolated mitochondria by ADP, over a range of 40-fold or more, is consistent with the sometimes very wide range of respiratory rates in intact tissues, depending on activity. In support of their thesis that the ADP supply is the most important element in intracellular control of respiration, Chance and his colleagues have carried out experiments on the relationships between oxygen uptake and ADP supply in intact cells or organs. They have found that starved baker's yeast cells have a low rate of respiration that can be increased substantially by adding measured small amounts of ethanol. However, the increased respiration quickly falls off even when ample ethanol is left to support further respiration at a high level. They have concluded from spectroscopic examination of the respiratory chain that the respiration ceases in this case because the ADP is used up during oxidation of ethanol, i.e., the respiratory chain goes from state 3 to state 4. From such experiments Chance was able to identify in the respiratory chain of the yeast cells three crossover points that are controlled by endogenous ADP in a manner similar to the behavior of isolated mitochondria, and he inferred that the P:O ratio in the intact yeast cell is about 3.0.

Chance also found that the respiration of a suspension of starved yeast cells abruptly increased on addition of small measured amounts of glucose to the medium. After exhaustion of the glucose, the rate of respiration returned to the previous endogenous level. He has concluded that the addition of glucose causes the equimolar formation of ADP by the hexokinase reaction in the yeast cell:

$$\text{glucose} + \text{ATP} \rightarrow \text{glucose-6-phosphate} + \text{ADP} \qquad (7\text{--}1)$$

The limited amount of ADP so formed makes possible an increased rate of respiration, but this increase persists only until the ADP so formed is used up by oxidative phosphorylation. Analytical data showed that for each molecule of glucose added, a specific increment of oxygen uptake occurred; the ADP:O ratio in the intact cell was deduced to be in the range 2.0 to 3.0. Other interpretations of these findings may be made, but such experiments on yeast cells, as well as on Ehrlich ascites tumor cells, are consistent with the view that the ADP concentration in the cell may determine the rate of respiration and, furthermore, that the P:O ratio of oxidative phosphorylation in these cells is high and near that seen in vitro, that is, $\sim$3.0. Presumably, mitochondria in the intact cell can respond only to ADP that is available to them, but not to bound or "compartmented" ADP.

Chance and his colleagues have also carried out experiments on the role of ADP concentration in controlling the respiratory rate of resting and stimulated intact muscles. It is well known that the respiration of skeletal muscle in mammals may increase 100-fold and that of the flight muscles of insects perhaps 1000-fold in the transition from rest to full activity. Although some of the findings on muscle are still difficult to interpret, they are consistent with the view that the large increase in respiration of certain types of muscle following stimulation appears to be due to the ADP made available after ATP breakdown; this effect may be masked in some types of muscle because of the rapid regeneration of ATP by phosphocreatine rather than by oxidative phosphorylation.

The respiratory rate of intact cells may also be controlled by the rate of secretory activity, again through the ADP concentration. Whittam has shown, for example, that the respiration of kidney, which normally engages in vigorous active transport processes that are presumably dependent on ATP, can be inhibited by ouabain, a specific inhibitor of active transport of Na^+ and K^+ and of the Na^+- and K^+-requiring ATPase activity in this tissue that is responsible for translocating these ions.

It is a reasonable inference that when ATP utilization for active transport is inhibited by ouabain, the decrease in ADP production causes a decrease in respiratory rate. These findings on control of respiration by ADP levels thus support Mitchell's concept that respiration and ATP-requiring functions are closely geared together in a continuous process; he has proposed that the endergonic ADP-producing processes of contraction, active transport, and biosynthesis actually pull respiration by the ADP they form, in contrast with the more traditional view that respiration drives the endergonic functions.

REVERSAL OF PHOSPHORYLATING RESPIRATION; CONTROL OF RESPIRATION BY ATP

Work in the laboratories of Klingenberg and Chance indicates that the rate of respiration in tightly coupled mitochondria may also be controlled by the concentration of ATP. In Chapter 5 we saw that mitochondrial NAD^+ may undergo reduction at the expense of succinate, an energy-requiring reaction that under some circumstances may be driven by ATP. This reaction is believed to represent the reversal of phosphorylating electron transport in the span NAD–cytochrome b.

More recently, both Chance and Klingenberg have shown that reduction of mitochondrial NAD can be brought about not only by succinate but also by reducing equivalents arising from reduced cytochrome c. In fact, Klingenberg and Schollmeyer have found that the oxidation-reduction state of the entire respiratory chain of intact mitochondria becomes more reduced when ATP is added in the absence of ADP and P_i, an effect that is in turn enhanced by addition of oxalacetate, a relatively electropositive acceptor of electrons from mitochondrial NADH. They have shown that the oxidation-reduction state of mitochondrial cytochrome c is a predictable function of the ratio $[ATP] / [ADP] [P_i]$; from this finding Klingenberg and Schollmeyer were able to calculate the ΔG of hydrolysis of the high-energy precursor of ATP as being about 12 kcal per mole.

These important findings, which indicate that the oxidation-reduction state of the respiratory chain is a sensitively poised function of the [ATP] / [ADP] [P$_i$] ratio, that is, the so-called phosphate potential, led to the demonstration by Klingenberg and Schollmeyer of the inhibition of respiration in tightly coupled mitochondria by ATP (Figure 7–2). This inhibition is maximum at a high ratio of [ATP] / [ADP] [P$_i$]. Half-maximal respiratory inhibition is given by ATP concentrations in the range 50 to 100 μM, which are below those normally occurring in the intact cell.

From these findings it may be concluded that the respiratory rate of mitochondria is controlled not just by ADP alone, as Chance and Williams had originally postulated, but also by ATP and by P$_i$. The concentrations of ATP, ADP, and P$_i$ in intact cells are compatible with the view that all three are elements in controlling the rate of respiration in intact cells. Finally, it is of interest that inhibition of respiration by ATP is perhaps the most sensitive criterion known for intactness of mitochondrial structure.

THE REDUCTION OF ACETOACETATE BY SUCCINATE

Work in the laboratories of Krebs, Ernster, and Klingenberg has shown that acetoacetate added to tissue homogenates or mitochondria is very rapidly reduced to D-β-hydroxybutyrate when succinate is present in the medium. Two interpretations have been placed on this finding. Following the work of Chance and Klingenberg on reversal of electron transport, the interpretation has been made that the reduction of acetoacetate occurs by transfer of hydrogen (or electrons) from succinate to acetoacetate via the respiratory chain through reversal of the action of the first phosphorylation site of the chain.

Simple transfer of hydrogen from succinate to acetoacetate without input of energy is, of course, not possible, since the standard oxidation-reduction potential of the β-hydroxybutyrate-acetoacetate couple (−0.28 volt) is much more negative than that of the succinate-fumarate couple (0.0 volt). Electron transport in reverse, driven by ATP or an energetically equivalent mitochondrial high-energy intermediate, would appear to be a feasible means of driving the reduction.

On the other hand, Krebs and his colleagues have concluded that the reduction of acetoacetate that occurs in the presence of succinate is not caused by a direct hydrogen or electron transfer via the chain but rather is a reflection of the inhibition

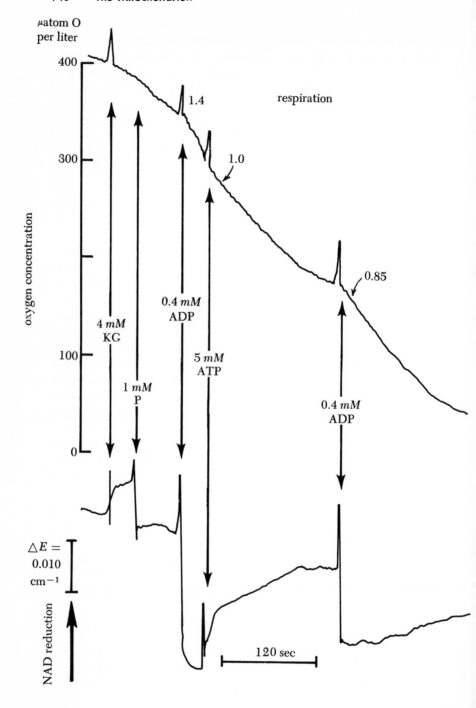

of the oxidation of NADH by the respiratory chain by succinate, which monopolizes the respiratory chain. Under these circumstances acetoacetate becomes reduced by direct electron and hydrogen transfer from the accumulated NADH, which arises not at the expense of succinate, but from other NAD-linked substrates, in particular, malate. Krebs and his colleagues do not deny that reversal of electron transport may occur in the fashion pictured by Ernster, Chance, and others; rather, they feel that it is unnecessary to postulate such a complex mechanism when a simpler one will suffice.

This matter has been a subject of some controversy, since both explanations are quite feasible and all parties agree both types of effects can occur in specific circumstances. More recently, in a careful analytical and kinetic study of acetoacetate reduction in intact mitochondria, Klingenberg and Von Häfen have been able to resolve the controversy and have also proposed a physiological function for the phenomenon they studied. The authors carried out balance sheet experiments in which acetoacetate disappearance, β-hydroxybutyrate formation, succinate disappearance, and formation of fumarate $+$ malate were measured quantitatively and related to oxygen consumption. They found that in respiring liver mitochondria supplemented with succinate and acetoacetate, more succinate disappeared than could be accounted for by the oxygen uptake; the extra succinate consumption was equal to the amount of acetoacetate reduced to β-hydroxybutyrate.

The amount of malate $+$ fumarate that was recovered equaled the amount of succinate that disappeared. When oxygen was omitted from the system, the succinate-linked reduction of acetoacetate occurred only in the presence of added ATP, clearly demonstrating the dependence of the reduction

Figure 7–2 Inhibition of respiration by ATP and stimulation by ADP and P_i. The rate of oxidation of succinate is decreased by addition of ATP. Addition of P_i and ADP accelerates respiration again. The numbers indicate the rate of respiration in μatoms oxygen per liter per sec. [M. Klingenberg and P. Schollmeyer, *Biochem. Z.*, **333**, 338 (1961).]

on energy. The reduction of acetoacetate by succinate under respiring conditions was inhibited by Amytal and dinitrophenol, demonstrating that the reduction occurred via intermediate steps normally involved in oxidative phosphorylation.

Oligomycin also inhibited the ATP-dependent reduction. Apparently one high-energy bond of ATP or of a preceding high-energy intermediate is required, in addition to a pair of electrons, to reduce each molecule of acetoacetate. Finally, Klingenberg and Von Häfen showed that the rate of the reduction of acetoacetate may be almost as high as the rate of "forward" respiration.

Thus the rates of reverse and forward electron transport are of the same order of magnitude, as could be predicted from earlier work of Klingenberg and of Chance on the rate of reduction of mitochondrial NAD by added succinate. These experiments, which involved relatively large net changes in the balance sheet of the added substrates, rather than measurement of relatively small amounts of intramitochondrial NADH, provide a convincing demonstration of the reversibility of electron transport in tightly coupled mitochondria.

The question that now arises is the function of this reversibility, particularly since it leads to reduction of acetoacetate to β-hydroxybutyrate. Klingenberg and Von Häfen present a rather interesting explanation. They point out that there is no known metabolic function for the D-β-hydroxybutyrate-acetoacetate system, as has been mentioned earlier. The NAD-linked D-β-hydroxybutyrate dehydrogenase is found in the mitochondria of all higher animal tissues examined to date, and it is present only in the mitochondria, as shown by Lehninger and his colleagues. Klingenberg and Von Häfen showed that the ratio [β-hydroxybutyrate] / [acetoacetate] is a mirror of the ratio of mitochondrial [NADH] / [NAD$^+$], which in turn is a measure of the so-called phosphate potential, namely, the quotient [ATP] / [ADP] [P$_i$].

Since both β-hydroxybutyrate and acetoacetate are present in the blood stream, Klingenberg and Von Häfen suggest that this oxidation-reduction couple serves as a "chemical messenger" from the mitochondria of the liver, which produces the ketone bodies, to the mitochondria of peripheral tissues. The diffusion of these compounds in a characteristic ratio reflecting the "phosphate potential" of the liver mitochondria into the blood stream makes possible the "poising" of the oxidation-reduction state and/or phosphate potential of the mitochondria in the peripheral organs, since these substrates are known to penetrate into the latter.

The chemical messenger suggestion provides a possible rationalization for the occurrence of ketone bodies in the blood and their elevation in diabetes and fasting, as well as the well-known changes in ratio of β-hydroxybutyrate and acetoacetate in the blood in different physiological and pathological states. Klingenberg and Von Häfen point out that this messenger function is similar to that of the lactate-pyruvate couple, which performs a similar function in the poising of the phosphate potential of glycolysis; the ratio of lactate and pyruvate in the blood is a measure of the oxidation-reduction state of the glycolytic NAD. Further work on this idea should be most interesting.

CONTROL AND INTEGRATION
OF THE KREBS CITRIC ACID CYCLE

The rate of oxidation of pyruvate or fatty acids via the Krebs cycle is determined not only by the supply of these fuels in the cytoplasm, by the availability and concentration of ADP, P_i, and ATP, as we have seen above, and by the enzymatic capacity of the cycle and of the respiratory chain, but also by the concentration and proportions of the tricarboxylic and dicarboxylic acids that comprise the intermediates of the cycle. The rate of each step of the Krebs cycle depends not only on the concentration of its substrate but also on the relative concentrations of other intermediates, since some of the intermediates are capable of specific inhibition of other steps.

The concentrations and ratios of tri- and dicarboxylic acids in mitochondria are controlled in several ways. First we may consider the enzymatic reactions by which the cycle intermediates are formed from other, noncycle precursors and by which they are transformed into metabolites that are not members of the cycle. For example, α-ketoglutarate may be formed from L-glutamate by deamination via two essentially different pathways. One is by oxidative deamination:

$$\text{glutamate} + \text{NAD}^+ (\text{NADP}^+) \rightleftharpoons \alpha\text{-ketoglutarate} + \text{NH}_3$$
$$+ \text{NADH(NADPH)} + \text{H}^+ \qquad (7\text{--}2)$$

The second is by transamination:

$$\text{glutamate} + \text{oxalacetate} \rightleftharpoons \text{aspartate} + \alpha\text{-ketoglutarate} \qquad (7\text{-}3a)$$

$$\text{glutamate} + \text{pyruvate} \rightleftharpoons \text{alanine} + \alpha\text{-ketoglutarate} \qquad (7\text{-}3b)$$

Although glutamate dehydrogenase is present in most mitochondria, recent work indicates that the major pathway for oxidation of glutamate by mitochondria involves transamination with oxalacetate followed by oxidation of the resulting α-ketoglutarate.

Since the dehydrogenase and transaminase pathways are both reversible, they can account for removal as well as formation of cycle intermediates. For example, it has long been known that NH_4^+ is highly inhibitory to the Krebs citric acid cycle; this inhibition is caused by reversal of reaction (7-2) so that α-ketoglutarate is "trapped" out of the cycle as glutamate.

Another prominent mechanism for formation of new cycle intermediates is the enzymatic synthesis of malate or oxalacetate from monocarboxylic acids by carboxylation reactions. For example, the malic enzyme of Ochoa causes the reductive synthesis of malate from pyruvate at the expense of NADPH:

$$\text{pyruvate} + CO_2 + \text{NADPH} + H^+ \rightleftharpoons \text{malate} + \text{NADP}^+ \qquad (7\text{-}4)$$

Oxalacetate may also be formed in mitochondria (or removed) by the following reactions:

$$\text{oxalacetate} \rightarrow \text{pyruvate} + CO_2 \qquad (7\text{-}5)$$

$$\text{GTP} + \text{oxalacetate} \rightleftharpoons \text{GDP} + CO_2 + \text{phosphopyruvate} \qquad (7\text{-}6)$$

$$\text{oxalacetate} + P_i + \text{ADP} \rightleftharpoons \text{pyruvate} + CO_2 + \text{ATP} \qquad (7\text{-}7)$$

Reaction (7-6) has two metabolic functions. It causes formation of new oxalacetate for the Krebs cycle from phosphopyruvate, and it also leads to formation of extramitochondrial phosphopyruvate, which is required for reversal of glycolysis, by a route that is kinetically if not thermodynamically more favorable than the direct formation from pyruvate and ATP in the hyaloplasm.

There are additional reactions by which cycle intermediates are lost. These include the utilization of succinyl-CoA for synthesis of δ-aminolevulinic acid, and thus porphyrins via the "succinate-glycine" pathway, and the utilization of oxalacetate in a transcarboxylation reaction leading to formation of malonyl-CoA, and thus ultimately to synthesis of fatty acids:

$$\text{oxalacetate} + \text{acetyl-CoA} \rightleftharpoons \text{malonyl-CoA} + \text{pyruvate} \qquad (7\text{--}8)$$

The latter reactions are again instances of the role of the Krebs cycle in biosynthetic reactions.

Some intermediates of the Krebs cycle exert important internal integrative functions by means of feedback relationships. The classical example is the competitive inhibition of succinate dehydrogenase by oxalacetate. By this reaction, oxalacetate, an important intermediate for the condensation reaction of the Krebs cycle, can in effect control its own formation by adjusting the rate of oxidation of its precursor.

It is remarkable that the inhibition of succinate oxidation by oxalacetate is in turn controlled by ATP, the presence of which can relieve the inhibition, as first shown by Pardee and Potter. Although it had long appeared that this effect of ATP was brought about by the enzymatic conversion of oxalacetate to enol-phosphopyruvate [by reaction (7–6)], Tyler has shown that the addition of ATP to oxalacetate-inhibited systems does not cause actual destruction of oxalacetate, but instead prevents its inhibitory action on the succinate oxidation. ATP thus appears to "shield" succinate dehydrogenase from oxalacetate. It is most probable that this shielding is caused by tightening of the mitochondrial membrane through the contracting action of ATP, leading to a decreased permeability to external oxalacetate.

Oxalacetate is an avid acceptor for electrons from other NAD-linked reactions because of its relatively high oxidation-reduction potential. It is evident that its concentration in mitochondria can be lowered by such reductions; a decrease in oxalacetate concentration would be followed by an increase in rate of oxidation of succinate. Actually, Chappell has provided evidence that the oxidation of isocitrate in intact mitochondria has the following pattern:

$$\text{isocitrate} \rightarrow \text{NADP} \rightarrow \text{NAD}_1 \rightarrow \text{oxalacetate} \rightarrow \text{NAD}_2 \rightarrow$$
$$\text{FP} \rightarrow \text{cytochromes} \rightarrow \text{O}_2 \qquad (7\text{--}9)$$

In this scheme, which is based on the finding that the presence of oxalacetate greatly accelerates oxidation of isocitrate, reduced NADP formed from isocitrate is oxidized by one compartment of mitochondrial NAD^+ (i.e., NAD_1) through mitochondrial transhydrogenase, which recent work suggests is "activated" by ATP. The NADH so formed is then reoxidized by oxalacetate, which in turn is reduced to malate. The malate then reduces a second compartment of mitochondrial NAD^+ (i.e., NAD_2) that is directly reactive with the respiratory chain.

Figure 7–3 shows that the level of oxalacetate in mitochondria is the product of a dynamic balance among a number

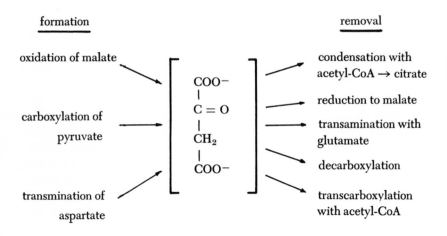

formation		removal
oxidation of malate		condensation with acetyl-CoA → citrate
	COO^-	reduction to malate
carboxylation of pyruvate	$C = O$	transamination with glutamate
	CH_2	decarboxylation
	COO^-	
transmination of aspartate		transcarboxylation with acetyl-CoA

functions of oxalacetate

1. catalyst for oxidation of acetyl-CoA

2. catalyst for oxidation of glutamate

3. catalyst for oxidation of isocitrate

4. catalyst for biosynthesis of fatty acids

5. precursor of phosphopyruvate for glycogen synthesis

6. inhibitor of malate oxidation

7. inhibitor of succinate oxidation

Figure 7–3 Functions of oxalacetate and enzymatic reactions controlling its concentration in mitochondria.

of reactions capable of increasing its concentration and a number capable of lowering its concentration; it is the net of these manifold reactions, as well as the level of ATP, that controls the rate of succinate oxidation and the rate of citrate formation in mitochondria.

There are other instances, less well studied, of internal adjustment mechanisms in the Krebs cycle. Among these are the remarkable effects of inorganic phosphate on the fumarase and succinate dehydrogenase reactions (see Chapters 3 and 4) and the effects of dicarboxylic acids on the aconitase reactions. Much work remains to be carried out on the complex network of control mechanisms inherent in the flow pattern of the Krebs cycle and in the molecular design of its component enzyme molecules, which were presumably selected during the course of evolution for their cybernetic potentialities as well as their catalytic activity.

CRYPTICITY AND COMPARTMENTATION

Mitochondria are now known to show rather striking impermeability toward specific substrates, intermediates, and electron donors and acceptors. On the one hand, these barriers may thus separate certain extramitochondrial substrates from the mitochondrial enzymes capable of oxidizing or reducing them; on the other hand, they may prevent escape of essential cofactors and intermediates from the intramitochondrial compartment.

The most conspicuous example of a specific impermeability barrier is that toward pyridine nucleotides. Lehninger found in 1951 that isolated rat liver mitochondria do not oxidize external, or added, NADH, although they readily oxidize the internal NADH generated by reduction of intramitochondrial NAD by the mitochondrial β-hydroxybutyrate or malate dehydrogenases. It is now generally accepted that the impermeability to extramitochondrial NADH is a characteristic of virtually all mitochondria, whether in vitro or in vivo; in fact, as will be seen below, it is the basis of important mechanisms of control and integration between the mitochondria and the extramitochondrial cytoplasm. Isolated rat liver mitochondria will, however, readily oxidize external NADH if they are first exposed to conditions, such as a hypotonic medium, that can increase the permeability of the mitochondrial membrane.

Intact mitochondria are impermeable not only to NADH and NADPH but also to their oxidized forms, at least under certain conditions. This conclusion is supported not only by direct tests with isotopically labeled nucleotides but also by the finding that certain pyridine-linked dehydrogenases of the mitochondria are cryptic to external nucleotides. For example, the reduction of external NAD^+ by external substrates in the presence of intact mitochondria containing large amounts of the substrate-specific dehydrogenase (such as β-hydroxybutyrate, malate, or glutamate dehydrogenases) may be very slow compared to the rate of oxidation of the substrate by the respiratory chain via internal NAD. However, if the mitochondria are first exposed to hypotonic conditions, the rate of reduction of external NAD^+ is greatly increased.

Some NAD-linked dehydrogenases exist in rather soluble form in the mitochondrial matrix, as in the case of glutamate dehydrogenase, and their activity is completely unmasked by mild hypotonic treatment. On the other hand, D-β-hydroxybutyrate dehydrogenase is rather hidden in its location, since much more vigorous treatment is required to expose its full activity to external NAD^+.

Mitochondrial swelling agents, such as phosphate, thyroxine, and Ca^{++}, increase the permeability of the mitochondrial membrane and cause "leakage" of the intramitochondrial pyridine nucleotides into the suspending medium. Kaufman and Kaplan have shown that it is only the oxidized form of NAD that leaks readily; the reduced form remains fixed in the structure. Mitochondria that have lost pyridine nucleotides by leakage will rebind them again in the presence of ATP by a process that is still obscure.

The mitochondrial membrane is also relatively impermeable to substrates of the Krebs citric acid cycle. For example, Peters and his colleagues observed that citrate generated from its normal precursors during Krebs cycle oxidations in isolated kidney mitochondria was oxidized much more rapidly than added external citrate. Actually, isolated mitochondria have been found to contain very high concentrations of citrate.

Perhaps the most striking evidence for the relative impermeability of the mitochondrial membrane to substrates of the Krebs cycle has come from recent studies of the mitochondria of the intensely respiring flight muscle of the housefly by Van den Bergh and Slater. Such mitochondria oxidize the combination of pyruvate + malate, presumably via the Krebs cycle, at a relatively enormous rate and with efficient phosphorylation and a high degree of respiratory control (Table 7–2). However, intermediates of the Krebs cycle such as succinate, α-ketoglutarate, and isocitrate are only feebly oxidized by intact housefly mitochondria when they are added to the test medium in place of pyruvate + malate. Sonic treatment of the flight muscle mitochondria evokes oxidation of these substrates at very high rates, presumably by increasing the permeability. Since flight muscle mitochondria have perhaps the highest rate of oxygen uptake of any yet studied, it is evident that maintenance of a high intramitochondrial concentration of intermediates of the Krebs cycle by the impermeable membrane is an adaptation that is especially well suited for their function.

Mitochondria are also relatively impermeable to adenine nucleotides and to phosphate. The terminal P of internal ATP is known to "turn over" at a rate quite different from that of external ATP. It has been suggested by Siekevitz and Potter that the internal ATP does not physically escape from the mitochondria but rather transfers its terminal $\sim$P group to external ADP via membrane-bound carriers of $\sim$P, possibly by phospho-transferases such as adenylate kinase. Such "compartmentation" of ATP within mitochondria has been invoked by

Table 7–2 Effect of sonic vibration on respiratory rate of housefly mitochondria; impermeability of NADH and Krebs cycle intermediates*

Substrate	Q_{O_2}	
	Intact mitochondria	Sonic-treated mitochondria
α-Glycerophosphate	721	520
Pyruvate + malate	228	208
NADH	36	347
Cycle intermediates:		
Isocitrate	20	257
α-Ketoglutarate	31	163
Succinate	40	288
Malate	25	80

* Data of Van den Bergh and Slater, 1962.

Chance and Hess to explain some aspects of the integration of glycolysis and respiration.

There is increasing evidence that some intramitochondrial substances (the intramitochondrial NAD, for example) are in turn subcompartmented into two or more pools. Chappell's suggestion of such pools has been noted above. It confirms earlier evidence for separate pools of NAD that are available for reduction by succinate or by D-β-hydroxybutyrate, as has already been mentioned in Chapter 3. Mitochondrial substrates or NAD may be structurally compartmented not only by the impermeable membrane, in a macroscopic sense, but may also be microscopically compartmented on the active sites of specific enzymes, such as the mitochondrial D-β-hydroxybutyrate dehydrogenase.

SHUTTLES FOR OXIDATION
OF EXTRAMITOCHONDRIAL NADH

NAD^+ in the extramitochondrial cytoplasm is continuously reduced by extramitochondrial dehydrogenases such as the glyceraldehyde 3-phosphate dehydrogenase of the glycolytic cycle. Despite the inability of NADH itself to penetrate the membrane, electrons of external NADH are in fact capable of reacting with the respiratory chain of mitochondria through so-called shuttle systems. The best understood shuttle is the α-glycerophosphate-dihydroxyacetone phosphate system, which was first observed in the laboratories of Bücher and Sacktor. The extramitochondrial cytoplasm of many cells, such as the flight muscle of insects, contains large amounts of soluble NAD-linked α-glycerophosphate dehydrogenase. In the presence of dihydroxyacetone phosphate, this enzyme catalyzes reoxidation of NADH produced in the oxidation step of the glycolytic cycle:

$$\text{glyceraldehyde 3-phosphate} + P_i + NAD^+ \rightleftharpoons \text{1,3-diphosphoglycerate} + NADH + H^+ \qquad (7\text{--}10)$$

$$NADH + H^+ + \text{dihydroxyacetone phosphate} \rightleftharpoons NAD^+ + \text{α-glycerophosphate} \qquad (7\text{--}11)$$

The second reaction proceeds far to the right because of the relatively positive oxidation-reduction potential of the α-glycerophosphate-dihydroxyacetone phosphate system. The reducing equivalents of the external NADH are thus transformed into those of the reduced product α-glycerophosphate. As it happens, mitochondria also contain an α-glycerophosphate dehydrogenase that is not NAD-linked, as is the extramitochondrial enzyme, but is probably flavin-linked and reacts with cytochrome b of the respiratory chain.

External α-glycerophosphate readily penetrates the mitochondria, in contrast to NADH, and is rapidly oxidized; the dihydroxyacetone phosphate so formed leaves the mitochondria again. It may then accept electrons from another molecule of external NADH. On passage of electrons from the intramitochondrial α-glycerophosphate dehydrogenase to oxygen, two phosphorylations occur. In this manner the α-glycerophosphate-dihydroxyacetone phosphate system may serve as a catalytic shuttle for the energy-conserving oxidation of external NADH by the respiratory chain of mitochondria. Sacktor has shown that in blowfly muscle the glycerophosphate shuttle operates as the sole mechanism for the oxidation of extramitochondrial NADH. Other investigations indicate this shuttle to be operating in many cells; as will be seen later, however, it may be inoperative in tumor cells.

Similar shuttles for oxidizing extramitochondrial NADH that employ external malate or lactate dehydrogenases have been proposed, but the evidence is not convincing. Devlin and Bedell have found that extramitochondrial NADH is readily oxidized by rat liver mitochondria if catalytic amounts of either β-hydroxybutyrate or its NAD-linked oxidation product acetoacetate are added to the medium. Presumably, external NADH causes reduction of acetoacetate to D-β-hydroxybutyrate by action of one type of tightly bound D-β-hydroxybutyrate dehydrogenase of the mitochondrion. The β-hydroxybutyrate so formed is readily oxidized by mitochondria via the internal intramitochondrial NAD and the respiratory chain, and a molecule of acetoacetate is regenerated. Acetoacetate is inert in liver mitochondria and presumably diffuses out. It can then reoxidize additional molecules of external NADH.

The shuttle of Devlin and Bedell provides another possible function for D-β-hydroxybutyrate dehydrogenase, which is exclusively a mitochondrial enzyme of very wide distribution, as well as a function for the two metabolites it interconverts. However, the physiological significance of this type of shuttle remains unproved.

INTEGRATION OF MITOCHONDRIAL RESPIRATION
AND EXTRAMITOCHONDRIAL GLYCOLYSIS

The mechanism of the inhibition of fermentation or of lactate formation by respiration, termed the Pasteur effect, and its converse, the inhibition of respiration by glucose, namely, the Crabtree effect, has long challenged students of metabolic control mechanisms. Many theories for the Pasteur effect have been postulated, and no attempt can be made to review them here. However, one of the most influential was that of Johnson and of Lynen, who independently proposed that the concentration of inorganic phosphate in the cell determined the relative rates of glycolysis and of respiration.

Since maximal rates of glycolysis are achieved only in the presence of relatively high concentrations of phosphate, whereas oxidative phosphorylation may proceed at maximal rates in the presence of rather low concentrations, it was suggested that the "braking" or inhibition of glycolysis that is exerted by respiration is caused by maintenance of relatively low levels of intracellular P_i by oxidative phosphorylation. This mechanism also explained inhibition of the Pasteur effect and thus the stimulation of glycolysis by uncoupling agents such as dinitrophenol. This theory has more recently received further experimental support from work of Lynen and of Racker.

Chance and his colleagues have postulated an alternative hypothesis, namely, that availability of ADP is the crucial factor that integrates glycolysis and respiration. In principle, Chance has suggested that intracellular ADP and ATP are each in turn segregated into compartments or pools, the components of which are not equally accessible to the glycolytic and mitochondrial systems. Competition between the glycolytic and mitochondrial systems for the nonhomogeneous ADP supply is pictured as being the main controlling mechanism in the Pasteur and Crabtree effects. Since the K_m for ADP of the respiratory chain is very low, of the order of 10 μM, and that of the glycolytic cycle much higher, glycolysis is normally kept in a controlled or ADP-less state. Lynen and Racker have, however, summarized some important evidence against the position taken by Chance.

Recently Boxer and Devlin have made an important and well-documented contribution to the understanding of the integration of glycolysis and respiration; it supplements and may clarify the effects of P_i and of ADP. They have pointed out that extramitochondrial NADH formed by the oxidative step of glycolysis has two major routes of reoxidation: either by pyruvate to form lactate, by action of extramitochondrial lactate dehydrogenase, or by the respiratory chain of mitochondria, via a shuttle.

Lactate arises when the cell is anaerobic because extramitochondrial NADH cannot be reoxidized by the respiratory chain and must be reoxidized by pyruvate. When oxygen is present, on the other hand, most cells must reoxidize extramitochondrial NADH via the respiratory chain, since lactate normally does not accumulate in aerobic cells. Lactate could, however, arise in aerobic cells by reoxidation of NADH by pyruvate if the shuttle systems for entry of the extramitochondrial NADH into mitochondria fail to operate.

The α-glycerophosphate shuttle requires extramitochondrial NAD-linked α-glycerophosphate dehydrogenase as an essential link in its operation. This enzyme has been found in liberal amounts in the soluble hyaloplasm of most normal tissues such as liver, brain, and muscle. However, Boxer and Devlin have found by direct analysis that this enzyme is very low or lacking altogether in most malignant tumor cells, in which there is uniformly a high aerobic formation of lactate, as Warburg originally showed. Because of the essentially complete lack of this enzyme in tumor cells, which may in fact be determined by a genetic deletion, much of the extramitochondrial NADH produced by tumor cells fails to be oxidized by the respiratory chain of mitochondria and must be reoxidized by pyruvate, with formation of lactate.

The reoxidation of extramitochondrial NADH by pyruvate is actually a metabolic necessity in the tumor cell; only by reoxidation of NADH can glycolysis and thus ATP formation proceed. Boxer and Devlin also point out that the failure of extramitochondrial NADH to be oxidized by tumor mitochondria is a fact that poises this type of cell in favor of reductive biosynthesis.

It is of some interest and significance that each of the major theories for the mechanism of the Pasteur effect is based on the principle of competition between the extramitochondrial glycolytic system and the mitochondrial respiratory chain for a component required by both: phosphate in the theories of Lynen, Johnson, and Racker; ADP in the theory of Chance; and NADH in the theory of Boxer and Devlin.

Perhaps there is no single unitary explanation of the Pasteur effect applicable to all observations. Rather, it appears more likely that the Pasteur effect is the result of the interplay of a network of factors, all based ultimately on the fact that the glycolytic cycle and the respiratory chain are essentially reversible systems in which the oxidation-reduction state of the components is poised by and poises the ratio [ATP] / [ADP] [P$_i$]. At least five factors, namely, NAD, NADH, ATP, ADP, and P$_i$, can control the rates of glycolysis and of respiration, and each may be critical for integration of glycolysis and respiration depending on the conditions existing.

Chance and his colleagues have approached the problem of analyzing the interaction between glycolysis and respiration by computer representation. This approach appears to be quite feasible, but perhaps additional information is required on the occurrence of "allosteric" devices for the control of enzymatic reactions in these systems before a complete picture can be obtained.

REFERENCES

Reviews

Boxer, G. E., and T. M. Devlin, "Pathways of intracellular hydrogen transport," *Science,* 134, 1495 (1961).

Chance, B., and B. Hess, "Spectroscopic evidence of metabolic control," *Science,* 129, 700 (1959).

―――― and G. R. Williams, "The respiratory chain and oxidative phosphorylation," *Advan. Enzymol.,* 17, 65 (1956).

Chappell, J. B., "Integrated oxidations in isolated mitochondria," in T. W. Goodwin and O. Lindberg (eds.). *Biological Structure and Function,* Academic, New York, 1961, Vol. 2, p. 71.

Lehninger, A. L., and C. L. Wadkins, "Oxidative phosphorylation," *Ann. Rev. Biochem.,* 31, 47 (1962).

Lynen, F., "Phosphatkreislauf und Pasteur-effekt," *Proc. Intern. Symp. Enzyme Chem., Tokyo, Kyoto,* 1957 (1958), p. 25.

Mitchell, P., "Metabolism, transport and morphogenesis: Which drives which?" *J. Gen. Microbiol.,* 29, 25 (1962).

Slater, E. C., "The role of oxaloacetate in the control of the metabolism of carbohydrate, fat, and protein in mitochondria," *Chem. Weekblad,* 52, 1 (1962). In English.

Utter, M. F., "Non-oxidative carboxylation and decarboxylation," in P. D. Boyer, H. A. Lardy, and K. Myrbäck (eds.), *The Enzymes*, Academic, New York, 1961, Vol. V.

Papers in *Ciba Found. Symp., Regulation Cell Metab.*, Little, Brown, Boston, 1961. The papers on respiratory control and the Pasteur and Crabtree effects are especially interesting.

Research papers

Chance, B., and G. Hollunger, "The interaction of energy and electron transfer reactions in mitochondria. I–VI," *J. Biol. Chem.*, **236**, 1545, 1549, 1555, 1562, 1569, 1577 (1961).

———, D. Garfinkel, J. Higgins, and B. Hess, "Metabolic control mechanisms. V. A solution for the equations representing interaction between glycolysis and respiration in ascites tumor cells," *J. Biol. Chem.*, **235**, 2426 (1960).

Devlin, T. M., and B. M. Bedell, "Effect of acetoacetate on the oxidation of reduced diphosphopyridine nucleotide by intact rat liver mitochondria," *J. Biol. Chem.*, **235**, 2134 (1960).

Ernster, L., "Reaction pathways of succinate-linked acetoacetate reduction in tissue homogenates and isolated mitochondria," *Nature*, **193**, 1050 (1962).

Estabrook, R. W., and B. Sacktor, "α-Glycerophosphate oxidase of flight muscle mitochondria," *J. Biol. Chem.*, **233**, 1014 (1958).

Gatt, S., and E. Racker, "Regulatory mechanisms in carbohydrate metabolism. I. Crabtree effect. II. Pasteur effect," *J. Biol. Chem.*, **234**, 1015, 1024 (1959).

Kaufman, B. T., and N. O. Kaplan, "Mechanism of depletion of mitochondrial pyridine nucleotides," *Biochim. Biophys. Acta*, **39**, 332 (1960).

Kimura, T., and T. P. Singer, "Functional organization of the respiratory chain in mitochondria," *Nature*, **184**, 791 (1959).

Klingenberg, M., and H. von Häfen, "Wege des Wasserstoffs in Mitochondrien. I. Die Wasserstoffübertragung von Succinat zu Acetoacetat," *Biochem. Z.*, **337**, 120 (1963).

——— and P. Schollmeyer, "Zur Reversibilität der oxydativen Phosphorylierung," *Biochem. Z.*, **333**, 335 (1960); **335**, 231, 243 (1961).

Krebs, H. A., "The physiological role of the ketone bodies," *Biochem. J.*, **80**, 225 (1961).

———, L. V. Eggleston, and A. d'Alessandro, "The effect of succinate and amytal on the reduction of acetoacetate in animal tissues," *Biochem. J.*, **79**, 537 (1961).

Kulka, R. G., H. A. Krebs, and L. V. Eggleston, "The reduction of acetoacetate to β-hydroxybutyrate in animal tissues," *Biochem. J.*, **78**, 105 (1961).

Lehninger, A. L., "Phosphorylation coupled to oxidation of dihydrodiphosphopyridine nucleotide," *J. Biol. Chem.*, **190**, 345 (1951).

——, H. C. Sudduth, and J. B. Wise, "The D-β-hydroxybutyric dehydrogenase of mitochondria," *J. Biol. Chem.*, **235**, 2450 (1960).

Monod, J., J. P. Changeux, and F. Jacob, "Allosteric proteins and cellular control systems," *J. Mol. Biol.*, **6**, 306 (1963).

Siekevitz, P., and V. R. Potter, "Biochemical structure of mitochondria. I, II," *J. Biol. Chem.*, **215**, 221, 237 (1955).

Van den Bergh, S. G., and E. C. Slater, "The respiratory activity and permeability of housefly sarcosomes," *Biochem. J.*, **82**, 362 (1962).

Wise, J. B., and A. L. Lehninger, "The stability of D-β-hydroxybutyric dehydrogenase and its relationship to the respiratory chain," *J. Biol. Chem.*, **237**, 1363 (1962).

Wu, R., and E. Racker, "Regulatory mechanisms in carbohydrate metabolism. I. Limiting factors in glycolysis of tumor cells," *J. Biol. Chem.*, **234**, 1029 (1959).

Zebe, E., A. Delbrück, and T. Bücher, "Über den Glycerin-1-P-cyclus im Flügmuskel von *Locusta migratoria*," *Biochim. Z.*, **331**, 254 (1959).

8

ACTIVE ION TRANSLOCATION
IN MITOCHONDRIA

Respiration ultimately furnishes most of the energy for active
ion transport in aerobic cells and tissues by causing the regeneration of ATP, which brings about the active translocation of
specific molecules or ions between cytoplasm and the cell ex-
terior by means of ATP-splitting enzyme systems that are
located in the plasma membrane. This is a major mechanism,
but an indirect one, by which mitochondria participate in active
ion transport. Actually, mitochondria participate in active ion
transport in another manner; they can actively accumulate certain ions from the surrounding medium in a process that is
apparently integral with respiratory chain phosphorylation.
This activity of mitochondria is receiving much attention currently and will now be considered in some detail.

PHYSICAL AND BIOLOGICAL CRITERIA
OF ACTIVE TRANSPORT

The movement of a specific substance into a zone where it
has a higher chemical potential does not proceed spontaneously,
since that would increase the free energy of the system. Such

an endergonic movement can occur only if it is energetically coupled to a second process that proceeds spontaneously with a decline in free energy, i.e., an energy-yielding or exergonic reaction. Furthermore, for *net* active transport of a substance into an area of higher potential to occur, it is essential that there is a *net* decline in free energy of the sum of the two coupled processes, so that the decrease in free energy in the driving reaction is greater than the increase in free energy in the driven reaction.

It is very rare that these thermodynamic criteria for active transport can be satisfied experimentally in biological systems because of the difficulty of estimating the true thermodynamic activities or potentials of the substance undergoing transport, the usually inadequate knowledge of the molecular or ionic species in the initial and final states, and the fact that biological transport systems are dynamic open systems that are not properly analyzed by classical equilibrium, or closed-system, thermodynamics. However, a useful biological definition ot active transport has evolved; it is based on increasing knowledge of the energy relationships in metabolism. Active transport is a movement of specific ions or molecules against a real or at least an *apparent* gradient of concentration that is directly dependent on some biological source of energy, such as respiration, glycolysis, an ATP supply, or any other source of "metabolic energy." Thus simple cations such as Na^+ and K^+, as well as neutral molecules such as glucose, are often found to undergo such biologically defined active transport; the dependence of these movements on energy-yielding processes can often be shown by use of inhibitors of phosphorylating respiration, such as dinitrophenol or cyanide.

Active transport is most conspicuous in specialized organs or tissues such as the kidney and the gastric mucosa, the secretions of which are derived from the blood through the action of an intervening barrier of epithelial cells. This active transport may be called *transcellular*. The transport gradients may be quite high; the H^+ concentration of gastric juice is over 10^{-2} M, whereas that of the blood plasma is less than 10^{-7} M, a concentration ratio of over 10^5. Actually, active transport is not limited to transcellular processes; it is a property of all cells by which they maintain their intracellular solute composition constant and metabolically favorable with respect to a fluctuating or unfavorable external environment. This preservation of internal solute homeostasis may be called *homocellular active transport;* an example is the maintenance of a constant concentration of K^+ as the major intracellular cation in muscle cells or erythrocytes in the face of the fact that Na^+ is the major extracellular cation. Mitochondria very likely participate in both transcellular and homocellular forms of active transport, depending on the type of cell, in two different ways: as an ATP-generating system and as a respiration-dependent ion-sequestering system.

CATION AND ANION MAINTENANCE
IN ISOLATED MITOCHONDRIA

Between 1952 and 1954, Bartley and Davies in Sheffield, Mac-Farlane and Spencer, as well as Spector, in London, and Stanbury and Mudge in New York independently reported that isolated kidney or liver mitochondria respiring in vitro under conditions in which oxidative phosphorylation was taking place were able to maintain preexisting levels of cations such as K^+, Na^+, Ca^{++}, and Mg^{++} or even to accumulate them from the medium. Evidence has also been adduced by work in the laboratories of Green, Potter, and Davies that certain anions, in particular, inorganic phosphate and sulfate, can be accumulated by isolated mitochondria.

Table 8–1 shows the average metal-ion content of normal rat liver mitochondria freshly isolated from sucrose homogenates

Table 8–1 Metal-ion content of freshly isolated rat liver mitochondria*

Ion	$m\mu$moles per mg protein
K^+	130
Na^+	6.3
Mg^{++}	42.0
Ca^{++}	5.6
Zn^{++}	1.9
FE^{++} (Fe^{+++})	7.5
Mn^{++}	0.4

* Data recalculated from Thiers, Reynolds, and Vallee, 1960.

and washed in metal-free 0.25 M sucrose prior to analysis. It is seen that K^+ and Mg^{++} are most abundant, but there are also significant amounts of Na^+, Ca^+, and $Fe^{2+(3+)}$. Acid-soluble phosphates comprise the major counterions for these metals; they include ATP, ADP, AMP, and the pyridine nucleotides, as well as inorganic phosphate. A certain fraction of each cation, with the possible exception of $Fe^{2+(3+)}$, is relatively labile and requires respiration to be maintained, whereas the remainder is tightly and presumably passively bound.

For example, Spector and others have shown that if normal mitochondria are exposed to hypotonic solutions, to detergents, or to swelling agents such as phosphate, or if they are incubated at 37° in the absence of respiratory substrates, essentially all the K^+ and Na^+ and a large part of the Mg^{++} and Ca^{++} leaks into the medium; about half of the Mg^{++} and Ca^{++} remains firmly bound to the mitochondrial structure. However, in the presence of respiratory substrate, adenine nucleotide, Mg^{++}, and oxygen, that is, conditions in which phosphorylating respiration can take place, the level of K^+ or Na^+ of intact mitochondria can be maintained constant or increased somewhat, even if the concentration in the ambient medium is considerably lower.

The K^+ content of nonrespiring fresh mitochondria can be significantly increased simply by exposure of the mitochondria to high concentrations of KCl; however, such an increase in K content is passive and simply reflects the ambient concentration of K^+ in the medium. A single washing with 0.25 M sucrose removes the excess K^+ but leaves the normal, actively maintained K^+.

Bartley and Davies have shown that the levels of K^+, Na^+, Mg^{++}, Ca^{++}, H^+, and $HPO_4^=$ of kidney mitochondria may be maintained by respiration, as are the Krebs cycle intermediates fumarate, α-ketoglutarate, and citrate. On the other hand, oxalacetate was found to be excluded. The apparent concentration gradients of these ions, between the wet mitochondrial pellet and the medium from which they were recovered, varied from a maximum of 23 for sodium (however, 3 to 5 was a more usual observation) to only fractional gradients for the other components. For example, the gradient of K^+ achieved in such experiments is of the order of 1.5. In general, the accumulation ratios in such experiments on isolated mitochondria are rather low compared with the accumulation ratio of some 25:1 for intracellular K^+ in intact erythrocytes or the extraordinary ratio of 10^5 or higher in the case of gastric H^+ secretion. However, more recent work to be described below has revealed extremely high concentration ratios in the mitochondrial uptake of Ca^{++}.

Mitochondrial ion accumulation appears to be relatively specific. For example, Gamble has shown that actively accumulated K^+ is not replaced by Na^+ from the medium; in fact, the rates of uptake and exchange and the amounts of K^+ and Na^+ actively taken up by mitochondria are relatively independent of each other. Similarly, as will be shown below, the uptake of Ca^{++} is specific and opposed to that of K^+.

K^+ UPTAKE BY MITOCHONDRIA

Gamble has demonstrated that the mechanisms that bring about K^+ uptake by rat liver mitochondria are relatively stable at $0°$ but rapidly lose activity if the mitochondria are incubated alone in buffered sucrose solution at $23°$. The rate of decline of K^+ uptake activity is greatly accelerated by 2,4-dinitrophenol. Especially destructive to the system are mitochondrial swelling agents, particularly inorganic phosphate, exposure to which causes leakage of NAD and other components from the mitochondria. The K^+ uptake system is maintained best when the suspending medium contains D-β-hydroxybutyrate as a respiratory substrate, phosphate, and ADP; but addition of dinitrophenol or cyanide to this system abolishes K^+ maintenance as well as oxidative phosphorylation.

On the other hand, the glycoside *ouabain*, which in low concentrations is known to inhibit Na^+ and K^+ transport across the plasma membrane, presumably by inhibiting the specific Na^+ and K^+-requiring ATPase activity of the membrane, does not prevent the active maintenance or uptake of K^+ by isolated mitochondria. In fact, in no case of mitochondrial ion accumulation so far reported has ouabain shown inhibitory activity. This finding clearly differentiates mitochondrial K^+ and Na^+ accumulation mechanisms from those located in the cell membrane.

Hg^{++} and certain organic mercurials were found by Gamble to cause a decline in the amount of K^+ bound by isolated mitochondria as well as a decline in rate of oxidation phosphorylation. However, as will be seen below, they greatly stimulate the K^+ exchange reaction.

RESPIRATION-DEPENDENT K$^+$ EXCHANGE

Stanbury and Mudge in 1953 showed with use of radioactive K$^+$ that a rapid exchange reaction may occur between the extra- and intramitochondrial K$^+$ pools. Although other workers also observed such an exchange, its properties and kinetics appeared to differ widely with experimental conditions and the technique of analysis.

More recently, Gamble has found that the actively maintained K$^+$ in freshly isolated mitochondria, which is stable to washing with sucrose, exchanges with radioactive K$^+$ added to the medium under conditions in which there is essentially no net uptake or loss of the bound K$^+$. The rate of this exchange is relatively low in relation to respiration. On the other hand, the adventitious K$^+$, the type that is easily washed out, exchanges with K$^+$ of the medium extremely rapidly. The K$^+$ exchange rate of the actively maintained K$^+$ was found to be dependent on external K$^+$ concentration; it was nearly maximum at about 0.1 M KCl. Na$^+$ added to the medium depresses the K$^+$ exchange, but Na$^+$ does not replace the specifically bound K$^+$. The K$^+$ exchange rate is greatly inhibited by cyanide and by dinitrophenol.

Of special interest is the action of Hg^{++} and organic mercurials on the K$^+$ exchange reaction. These agents depress the ability to maintain bound K$^+$ in mitochondria, as do dinitrophenol and cyanide. However, the mercurials greatly increase the rate of the K$^+$ exchange reaction, whereas dinitrophenol inhibits the exchange reaction. This effect of Hg^{++} could be prevented by —SH compounds and by other metal-binding agents. Hg^{++} apparently causes discharge of actively accumulated K$^+$ without causing proportional inactivation of the K$^+$ uptake mechanisms or of oxidative phosphorylation. As a consequence, external radioactive K$^+$ rapidly replaces the discharged "cold" K$^+$. Gamble found rather selective effects of different mercurials, suggesting a basis for the selective action of mercurial diuretics in vivo.

ACTIVE Ca^{++} UPTAKE BY MITOCHONDRIA

From investigations of the type described to this point it has not been possible to determine whether mitochondrial ion uptake is a relatively insignificant or a relatively massive process, or whether it has a stoichiometric relationship to electron transport. In the few instances in which significant *net* accumulation of K^+ has been observed, insufficient data were obtained to assess the stoichiometry between ion transport and electron transport.

There have been a number of experimental difficulties in analyzing these factors quantitatively in mitochondrial ion transport. The time required for centrifugal recovery of the mitochondria from the reaction medium is rather long compared with the time constant of respiration. The experimental procedures for assessing the volume and ion content of the intramitochondrial and extramitochondrial water spaces of such pellets are cumbersome and inadequate, and the net accumulations of K^+ are low and unpredictable. However, experiments on Ca^{++} uptake by Vasington, extended by Lehninger and Green and their colleagues, have provided conclusive evidence regarding the magnitude of mitochondrial ion accumulation as well as its stoichiometric relationship to electron transport and ATP hydrolysis.

Vasington and Murphy were able to show that there may be a 50-fold or larger increase in the Ca^{++} content of rat kidney mitochondria during respiration in vitro in a medium containing Ca^{++}. The Ca^{++} uptake by kidney mitochondria is so dramatic that it can proceed to essentially complete exhaustion of the Ca^{++} in the suspending medium. Net Ca^{++} uptake by kidney mitochondria was found to require a respiratory substrate such as β-hydroxybutyrate, malate, succinate, or α-ketoglutarate. It does not occur when respiration is blocked by cyanide, antimycin A, or Amytal.

In addition to respiration, active Ca^{++} uptake required the presence of both inorganic phosphate and ATP in the medium. AMP, ADP, or the 5'-triphosphates of other nucleosides were inactive in replacing ATP, even when full respiration was occurring. Mg^{++} ions were also absolutely necessary to observe net Ca^{++} uptake by the intact mitochondria, which was further stimulated by the presence of either Na^+ or K^+. In the presence of such a maximally active system, Ca^{++} was taken up by the mitochondria at a linear rate until either the Ca^{++} in the medium was essentially exhausted or a saturating level of about 2.5 μmoles Ca^{++} per mg mitochondrial protein was reached. The amounts of Ca^{++} that are taken up when the mitochondria are fully "loaded" are startlingly high.

Ca^{++} uptake in such systems is prevented by the uncoupling agents dinitrophenol, Dicumarol, or gramicidin, but not by oligomycin. It is significant that Ca^{++} is accumulated by respiring mitochondria even when there is no net formation of ATP; Ca^{++} is itself a strong uncoupling agent in the concentrations added to such systems. Nevertheless, although phosphorylation is already "uncoupled" by the Ca^{++} added to the system, the addition of dinitrophenol inhibits Ca^{++} uptake by the mitochondria. It is therefore clear that some early, dinitrophenol-sensitive intermediate in respiratory energy coupling is required to bring about active accumulation of Ca^{++} and that ATP formation per se is not required.

The Ca^{++} taken up from the medium by kidney mitochondria is stable to careful washing of the mitochondria with cold sucrose or KCl solutions, but it is completely discharged on exposure to dinitrophenol, gramicidin, or Dicumarol or on incubation of the mitochondria in dilute KCl at $20°$. Ca^{++} uptake by mitochondria does not occur at $0°$, at which temperature the rate of electron transport is nearly nil. Isolated liver microsomes or nuclei were found to lack the ability to bind Ca^{++} under these conditions.

UPTAKE OF PHOSPHATE
ACCOMPANYING ACCUMULATION OF Ca^{++}

Vasington and Murphy pointed out that there are insufficient phospholipid molecules in intact kidney mitochondria to bind all the Ca^{++} taken up at saturation levels, which may attain the value of 2.5 μmoles per mg protein, whereas the mitochondria contain only some 0.3 to 0.5 μmole of phospholipid per mg protein. Furthermore, it is unlikely that the total mitochondrial protein itself can bind this amount of Ca^{++}, since at Ca^{++} saturation, approximately 130 millimoles of Ca^{++} are bound per mole of mitochondrial protein, assuming a molecular weight for all mitochondrial proteins of 60,000. This is a value in great excess of the Ca^{++}-binding capacity of casein or egg albumin, for example. Vasington and Murphy calculated that if the Ca^{++} taken up by mitochondria at the saturation level were in aqueous solution in the intramitochondrial water, then its concentration would approach 0.5 M, an improbably high figure.

Rossi, Greenawalt, and Lehninger examined the anions in Ca^{++}-loaded mitochondria and soon found by isotopic and

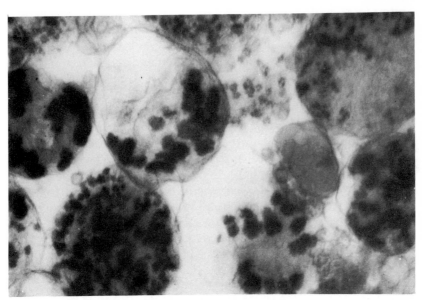

sucrose, M	specific gravity	control mitochondria	calcium-loaded mitochondria	protein and radioactivity in loaded mitochondria
				■ specific activity, cpm per mg protein
0.25	1.02			
0.80	1.10			80,000 60,000 40,000 20,000
1.00	1.14			
1.40	1.176			
1.60	1.20			
1.75	1.22			
2.20	1.28			
2.50	1.34			
3.00	1.37			
				16 12 8 4
				□ protein, mg

Figure 8–1 Properties of mitochondria loaded with Ca^{++} and P_i. (J. W. Greenawalt, C. S. Rossi, and A. L. Lehninger, in press.) The upper figure shows results of equilibrium centrifugation in a density gradient; heavy mitochondria contain CA^{++} and P_i and have specific gravity of 1.39. Such mitochondria have numerous dense osmiophilic granules, as shown in electron micrograph.

other approaches that inorganic phosphate of the suspending medium accompanies Ca^{++} during active accumulation of the latter; no other anions were taken up in comparable amounts. The ratio $Ca^{++}:P_i$ in loaded mitochondria recovered from the medium was about 1.7 in a long series of experiments; this value may be compared with the $Ca^{++}:P_i$ ratio of 1.0 for $CaHPO_4$, of 1.5 for $Ca_3(PO_4)_2$, and of 1.67 for hydroxyapatite ($[Ca_3(PO_4)_2]_3 \cdot Ca(OH)_2$). Actually, the very large amounts of Ca^{++} and P_i taken up far exceeded the solubility products of each of these salts at the pH of the medium. It was therefore necessary to conclude that one of these insoluble phosphates, probably hydroxyapatite, precipitated or crystallized out in the intramitochondrial space.

Electron micrographs of such Ca^{++}-loaded mitochondria showed them to consist of two distinct types. The great majority of the mitochondria contained many large, dense osmiophilic granules in the matrix; the other type was relatively clear of such granules. These two types of mitochondria could be separated by centrifugation in a sucrose density gradient. The type containing the Ca^{++} and P_i, and also the electron-dense granules, were by far the heaviest (specific gravity $= 1.37$). Figure 8–1 shows the results of such a separation and an electron micrograph of the "heavy" mitochondria. X-ray and electron diffraction measurements indicated, however, that the granules are not crystalline. This material may make up 10 to 20 per cent of the dry weight of such Ca^{++}- and P_i-loaded mitochondria.

The ability to accumulate Ca^{++} and P_i is present in mitochondria of liver, kidney, heart, and brain tissue. The accumulations of calcium phosphate in the mitochondria apparently occur at the so-called dense granules of the mitochondria (see Chapter 2), which may contain biochemical mechanisms or structures capable of providing a nidus for precipitation of calcium phosphate.

THE STOICHIOMETRIC RELATIONSHIP OF ACTIVE Ca^{++} AND P_i ACCUMULATION TO ELECTRON TRANSPORT

The experiments of Vasington and Murphy and more refined measurements by Rossi and Lehninger have revealed the stoichiometric relationships between Ca^{++} accumulation, P_i accumulation, and oxygen uptake. The experiment of Figure 8–2 shows that in the early period of Ca^{++} uptake, before the

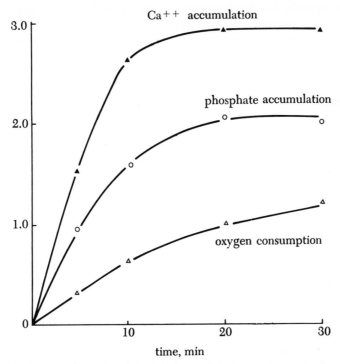

Figure 8–2 Rate of uptake of Ca^{++}, P$_i$, and O$_2$ by rat liver mitochondria. (Rossi and Lehninger, 1963.)

mitochondria become saturated with Ca^{++}, the ratio of atoms of Ca^{++} accumulated to atoms of oxygen taken up is about 4.5 and that the ratio of moles of phosphate accumulated to atoms of oxygen taken up is about 2.8 when pyruvate + malate is the substrate. These ratios are relatively independent of the concentration of Ca^{++} and P$_i$ in the test medium. It is not only clear that Ca^{++} uptake by mitochondria is a relatively rapid and massive process, but it also appears probable that some quantitative and stoichiometric relationship exists between electron transport and the ion accumulations. In particular, it is suggested that there is a relationship of Ca^{++} uptake to the number of phosphorylation sites in the respiratory chain.

In Table 8–2 are shown some representative data collected by Rossi and Lehninger on the stoichiometry of Ca^{++} and P$_i$ accumulation by mitochondria during respiration with different

Table 8–2 Stoichiometry of ion uptake and oxidative phosphorylation in kidney mitochondria*

Substrate	Ca^{++} uptake, $m\mu atoms$	P_i uptake, $m\mu moles$	O_2 uptake, $m\mu atoms$	Accumulation ratios		ADP:O
				Ca:O	P:O	
β-hydroxybutyrate	163	98	33	4.94	2.97	2.88
Succinate	292	208	109	2.70	1.91	1.91
Ascorbate	170	96	97	1.78	0.99	0.99

* Data of Rossi and Lehninger, 1963. The test system contained the substrates shown, Mg^{++}, $Ca^{45}Cl_2$, P_i, ATP, and buffer, pH 7.0. Incubated 10 min at 30°. The ADP:O ratios were measured in a parallel system not containing Ca^{++}.

substrates. It is seen that there is a distinct relationship between the ratio of atoms of Ca^{++} accumulated to atoms of oxygen taken up and the ratio of moles of P_i accumulated to atoms of oxygen, and the number of phosphorylation sites traversed by electron transport between the specific substrate and oxygen. For the case of β-hydroxybutyrate, whose oxidation to acetoacetate normally involves formation of 3 moles of ATP, the Ca^{++}:O accumulation ratio was 4.94 and the P:O accumulation ratio 2.97. On the other hand, for the case of ascorbate, whose oxidation normally proceeds with but a single phosphorylation that occurs between cytochrome c and oxygen, the Ca^{++}:O accumulation ratio was 1.78 and the P:O accumulation ratio was 0.99.

It is clear that there is a simple stoichiometric relationship between the Ca^{++}:O and P:O ratios of ion accumulation to the P:O ratio of oxidative phosphorylation. Approximately 1 molecule of inorganic phosphate and approximately 1.7 molecules of Ca^{++} may be accumulated by the mitochondria from the medium as a pair of electrons traverses each phosphorylation site in the respiratory chain when Ca^{++} is in the medium.

Rossi and Lehninger have found that liver mitochondria take up Ca^{++} in the absence of respiration provided the medium contains a high concentration of ATP or an active ATP-regenerating system in the presence of Mg^{++}. Under these circumstances, Ca^{++} uptake is only slightly inhibited by cyanide, but it is completely inhibited by oligomycin or dinitrophenol, which indicates that Ca^{++} uptake can be driven by ATP in the absence of respiration, presumably through reversal of steps in the oxidative phosphorylation mechanism. ATP hydrolysis takes place as Ca^{++} is taken up in such systems.

ACCUMULATION OF Mg^{++} AND Mn^{++}

Some years ago Green and his colleagues observed a large respiration-dependent uptake of inorganic phosphate in the presence of Mg^{++} by kidney *cyclophorase* preparations; the bound phosphate was called *gel-phosphate*. They concluded that gel-phosphate was an intermediate in oxidative phosphorylation. However, more recent work in Green's laboratory on heart mitochondria has shown that Mg^{++} uptake accompanies P_i uptake in such experiments; Mg^{++} and phosphate accumulated in a ratio of about 1.7. Actually, in most respects accumulation of Mg^{++} and P_i by heart mitochondria resembles the uptake of Ca^{++} and phosphate described above, as shown by Brierley and his colleagues. Hydroxyl ions are also accumulated and H^+ ions discharged, and they suggested that the uptake process could be expressed by the equation:

$$3\,Mg^{++} + 2HPO_4^{=} \rightarrow Mg_3(PO_4)_2 + 2H^+ \qquad (8\text{--}1)$$

However, in two respects the accumulation of Mg^{++} differs from that of Ca^{++}. The ratio of Mg^{++} taken up to oxygen utilized is considerably lower than the corresponding ratio for Ca^{++} uptake in liver; it is only about 0.7 during succinate oxidation, whereas the Ca^{++}:O ratio is about 2.9 in rat liver mitochondria. Secondly, the uptake of Mg^{++} does not require the presence of ATP, whereas Ca^{++} uptake does.

More recently, Chappell and his colleagues have also observed the mitochondrial uptake of Mn^{++} under very similar circumstances, and it now appears most probable that the uptake of Ca^{++}, Mg^{++}, and Mn^{++} by mitochondria is brought about by the same basic mechanism that is associated with the energy-conserving sites in the respiratory chain.

RELATIONSHIPS AMONG INTRAMITOCHONDRIAL Ca^{++}, Mg^{++}, K^+, Na^+, AND Cl^-

Carafoli and Rossi have carried out a complete analysis of the movement of the major cations and anions into and out of

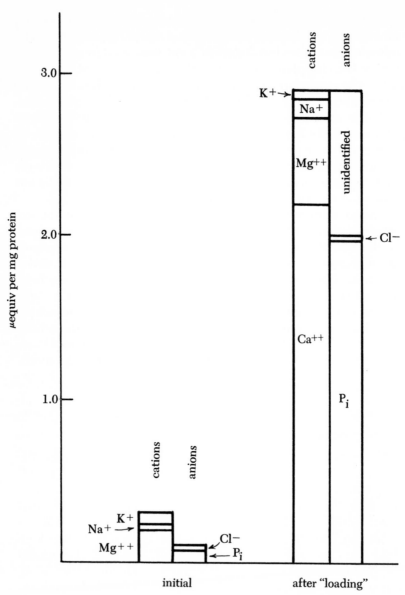

Figure 8–3 Cation and anion content of rat liver mitochondria before and after respiration-linked "loading" with Ca^{++} and P_i (Carafoli, Rossi, and Lehninger, 1963).

rat liver mitochondria during respiration; they did so in order to establish the interrelationships of these movements. The mitochondria were incubated in a medium containing respiratory substrate, phosphate, Cl^-, Na^+, K^+, Mg^{++}, Ca^{++}, and ATP. The results are given in Figure 8–3, which shows the ionic composition before and after the incubation. The fresh mitochondria show the occurrence of K^+ and Mg^{++} as the major cations, with only very low amounts of Na^+ and Cl^-, in general agreement with data in Table 8–1. However, the fully loaded mitochondria, after incubation, showed not only a strikingly large uptake of Ca^{++} and phosphate, but also a significant change in the pattern of Mg^{++}, Na^+, K^+, and Cl^-.

The amounts of Ca^{++} and P_i taken up by the incubated mitochondria represent a 20-fold increase in the total electrolytes of the mitochondrion, expressed in terms of milliequivalents per milligram of protein. In addition, however, there is also a nearly fourfold increase in Mg^{++} content; in fact, it has been found that Mg^{++} is always taken up together with Ca^{++}. A second noteworthy point is that Na^+ and Cl^- are accumulated with Ca^{++} and Mg^{++}, whereas K^+ is lost. To date there have been found no conditions in which there is a separation of these ion movements, suggesting that the ion-transporting mechanisms are all closely linked together.

CHANGES IN MITOCHONDRIAL ION CONTENT
IN THE INTACT CELL

Vallee and his colleagues, as well as Rees, have studied the metal ion distribution in isolated rat liver mitochondria at different stages in the development of carbon tetrachloride poisoning, as well as the spontaneous reversal to the normal liver that occurs after the administration of CCl_4 is terminated. Vallee's results are summarized in Figure 8–4. It is seen that mitochondrial Na^+ and Mg^{++} remain essentially constant throughout the period of poisoning and its remission. On the other hand, it is seen that the Ca^{++} content, normally rather low, increases some 15-fold during the development of the toxic symptoms but recedes to its normal value after cessation of the CCl_4 treatment.

With this dramatic change there is a synchronous but inverse change in mitochondrial K^+, which falls sharply as Ca^{++} rises, with a return to the normal ratio on the recovery of the

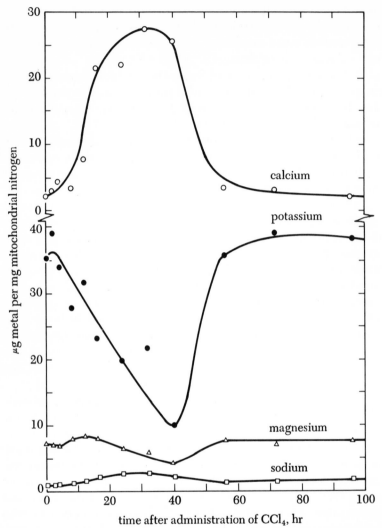

Figure 8–4 Changes in metal-ion concentrations in mitochondria after administration of CCl_4. The inverse relationship of mitochondrial Ca^{++} and K^+ is strikingly shown, as well as the relative constancy of mitochondrial Mg^{++} and Na^+ content. The sum of Na^+, K^+, Mg^{++}, Ca^{++} remains essentially constant. [R. E. Thiers, E. S. Reynolds, and B. L. Vallee, *J. Biol. Chem.*, **235**, 2131 (1960).]

animal. The sum of all four cations is shown to be relatively constant throughout this series of changes. Such changes also occur in mitochondria treated in vitro with carbon tetrachloride. The inverse relationship between Ca^{++} and K^+ seen in these in vivo experiments, as well as in the in vitro experiments of Carafoli and Rossi described above, is rather striking and may be a clue to the mechanism of the mitochondrial ion-transport process.

A second significant point may be noted in comparing the in vivo experiments of Vallee with the in vitro experiments of Vasington and others described above. In the intact organism the accumulation of Ca^{++} during carbon tetrachloride poisoning, although strikingly evident as a 15-fold increase, is still only a very small fraction of the enormous accumulation of Ca^{++} and phosphate seen with isolated mitochondria. To date there is no evidence that mitochondria in the intact cell accumulate such massive quantities of Ca^{++} and other ions as may occur in isolated mitochondria. Perhaps the massive Ca^{++} accumulation seen in vitro is the result of an otherwise normal process that has "gone wild" after the mitochondria are isolated from the normal biochemical checks and balances that exist in the intact cell.

Presumably, the ion-transport mechanisms in mitochondria in the intact cell operate with the same stoichiometric relationships with electron transport as have been observed in vitro; the difference may lie in the extent of ion accumulation. In the intact cell the Ca^{++} concentration may be much lower; moreover, in the intact cell ADP is normally present to act as phosphate acceptor and thus to compete with Ca^{++} for intramitochondrial phosphate. In addition, there may be mechanisms by which Ca^{++} is discharged from mitochondria in the intact cell that may not operate in isolated mitochondria. In any case, the massive accumulation of Ca^{++} by isolated mitochondria has yielded important biochemical information on the relationship between ion transport and oxidative phosphorylation.

MECHANISMS OF ION TRANSPORT IN MITOCHONDRIA

From Table 8–2, approximately 1.7 molecules of Ca^{++} and 1.0 molecule of P_i are accumulated per pair of electron equivalents traversing a single phosphorylation site. It is clear that the accumulation of P_i from the medium is related in an integral

1:1 ratio with the phosphorylation sites, whereas the nonintegral value 1.7 for the Ca:O accumulation ratio appears to be more a reflection of the $Ca:P_i$ ratio in the calcium phosphate salt that precipitates in the mitochondria. This suggests that it is the P_i that is "actively" accumulated by the mitochondria and that Ca^{++} follows passively. Since P_i is also taken up during accumulation of Mg^{++}, Mn^{++}, Ba^{++}, and Sr^{++}, as well as in oxidative phosphorylation, P_i uptake is the common denominator in all these events. The uptake of Ca^{++}, Mg^{++}, or Mn^{++} may be secondary, or "passive," events determined by the permeability of these ions, the specificity of the ion-binding sites, and their propensity to form insoluble phosphates within the mitochondria.

The inorganic phosphate that is taken up during electron transport at the coupling sites may be trapped as inorganic phosphate within the mitochondria when Ca^{++} is present. In this way the phosphate that normally is used to phosphorylate ADP may be diverted into formation of calcium phosphate in the presence of Ca^{++}. This view is supported by the fact that when calcium phosphate formation occurs in mitochondria during electron transport, there is no net formation of ATP from ADP. Actually, Green and his colleagues have observed that phosphate accumulation in the presence of Mg^{++} is diminished when ADP is present as phosphate acceptor. These facts suggests that when phosphate is taken up, it has two possible fates: either accumulation as insoluble salts of Ca^{++}, Mg^{++} or Mn^{++} or combination with ADP to yield ATP. However, further information is required before this view can be accepted. This type of explanation may actually be less appropriate for the case of K^+ accumulation, which apparently occurs in the presence of ADP as phosphate acceptor. Again, more evidence is required on this point.

Finally, it is necessary to point out that the action of oligomycin on Ca^{++} uptake may be an important clue to the intermediate involved in the translocation mechanism. Oligomycin does not block Ca^{++} uptake when it is activated by respiration, but it does when it is activated by ATP directly. Since Ca^{++} binding is blocked by dinitrophenol when it is activated by *either* respiration *or* ATP, it appears likely that some high-energy intermediate *between* the point of action of oligomycin and the energized carrier(s) is responsible for the primary act of ion accumulation or separation. It is very curious and significant that guanidine compounds, which inhibit respiration similarly to oligomycin, have been found by Pressman to be accumulated by mitochondria, along with inorganic phosphate. Thus research on the mechanism of ion accumulation may yield important new information on the mechanism of oxidative phosphorylation. For this reason Vasington's recent finding that Ca^{++} accumulation occurs in submitochondrial systems is of the greatest interest.

CELLULAR ROLE OF ACTIVE ION ACCUMULATION BY MITOCHONDRIA

Relatively little thought has been given to the cellular significance of active ion accumulation by mitochondria. Some authors have, in fact, been rather skeptical that mitochondrial ion accumulation has any quantitative biological significance. However, it seems unlikely that such a dynamic and conspicuous process has no specific function, and in this section a rationalization is offered.

Two avenues of speculation appear to be open. Just as the transport mechanisms of the cell membrane can provide protection for the intracellular environment against fluctuations in the solute composition in the external environment, so it appears possible that the ion-transport systems of the mitochondrial membrane can maintain the *intramitochondrial* milieu constant and favorable in the face of local fluctuations of pH and solute composition of the bathing hyaloplasm. Although these fluctuations must certainly be small and localized, they could be very critical for mitochondrial enzymatic activities such as respiration and phosphorylation. It has long been speculated that the mitochondria of aerobic cells originally arose from bacteria that parasitized the host cell; it is possible that the ion-transport mechanisms of the membrane of such bacteria could have been utilized and selected to favor the permanent life of these "parasites" as mitochondria within the cytoplasm of the host cell.

The second avenue of speculation is not exclusive of that just developed. The mitochondria, thousands of which may occur in a single cell, may be visualized as membrane-bounded cytoplasmic islands the internal contents of which are separated or, in effect, exteriorized from the hyaloplasm, just as the extracellular fluid is separated from the hyaloplasm by the cell membrane. Such islands could conceivably furnish an extension of the transport activity of the cell membrane to bring about more exquisite microscopic control of solute homeostasis in the hyaloplasm. Ion accumulation by mitochondria could not, of course, really rid the intact cell permanently of any net amount of unwanted electrolytes, since the mitochondrial matrices do not communicate with the extracellular phase. However, the mitochondria could serve as temporary "ion-buffering systems" capable of local and transient sequestration of certain ions to control microscopic disparities in solute composition of the hyaloplasm.

In the liver cell the mitochondria make up some 20 per cent of the cell volume, and this could provide a large ion-sequestering capacity, particularly for Ca^{++}. The enormous surface-volume relationship of some mitochondria that is provided by the membrane systems of the cristae would also be of some quantitative significance. In the relatively large aerobic cells of higher animals the diffusion process may become critical for metabolism, since the diffusion path to the interior of large cells may be relatively long. A local ion-uptake process in mitochondria could assist in maintaining homeostasis in any critical diffusion-limited local metabolic or enzymatic process.

That the mitochondrion may play an important role in active transport of the transcellular type, in addition to participating in homocellular ion transport, is strongly suggested by the work of Rhodin and Sjostrand on the spatial disposition of mitochondria in renal tubule cells, as reconstructed from electron microscope observations. Figure 8–5 shows a diagrammatic representation of these findings. The orientation of the mitochondria along the axis of active transport across the epithelial cell barrier very strongly suggests that the mitochondria are involved in transcellular active transport in a directionally polarized manner. A microscopic gradient of ion concentrations in the hyaloplasm along the length of a single mitochondrion is thus conceivable; along it, the ion-transport function of the mitochondrial membrane may act. It is of some relevance that the mitochondria of renal tubule cells have been found to undergo characteristic swelling and deformation in vivo when renal function is disturbed by severe dehydration. This change is reversible.

Finally, it must be added that recent experiments of DeLuca and Rasmussen indicate that the uptake of P_i may be specifically stimulated by parathyroid hormone under certain cir-

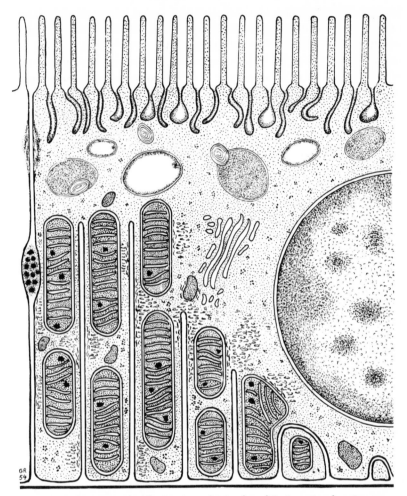

Figure 8–5 Directional polarization of mitochondria in axis of active transport; proximal renal tubule cells. (From Rhodin, Karolinska Institute, Stockholm, 1954.)

cumstances and that mitochondrial Ca^{++} may be discharged by vitamin D. It is hardly necessary to point out the potential physiological significance of the mitochondria in physiological regulation of Ca^{++} and phosphate absorption and transport and in the metabolism of bone-forming cells. Actually, large dense granules, presumably identical with those of isolated, Ca^{++}-

loaded mitochondria described here, have been observed recently in the mitochondria of bone osteoclasts. Furthermore, excitation or stimulation of cells and tissues often results in large changes in Ca^{++} distribution and content, and it is conceivable that the mitochondria play an important role in releasing or sequestering free Ca^{++}.

REFERENCES

Reviews

Lehninger, A. L., "Water uptake and extrusion by mitochondria in relation to oxidative phosphorylation," *Physiol. Rev.*, **42**, 467 (1962).

Mitchell, P., "Chemiosmotic coupling in oxidative and photosynthetic phosphorylation," *Nature*, **191**, 144 (1961).

Robertson, R. N., "Ion transport and respiration," *Biol. Rev. Cambridge Phil. Soc.*, **35**, 231 (1960).

Papers in Chance, B. (ed.), *Energy-Linked Functions of Mitochondria*, Academic, New York, 1963.

Research papers

Bartley, W., and J. E. Amoore, "The effects of Mn^{++} on the solute content of mitochondria," *Biochem. J.*, **70**, 718 (1958).

———— and R. E. Davies, "Active transport of ions by subcellular particles," *Biochem. J.*, **57**, 37 (1954).

Brierley, G. P., E. Bachmann, and D. E. Green, "Active transport of inorganic phosphate and Mg^{++} by beef heart mitochondria," *Proc. Natl. Acad. Sci. U.S.*, **48**, 1928 (1962).

————, E. Murer, and D. E. Green, "Participation of an intermediate of oxidative phosphorylation in ion accumulation by mitochondria," *Science*, **140**, 60 (1963).

DeLuca, H. F., G. W. Engstrom, and H. Rasmussen, "The action of vitamin D and parathyroid hormone in vitro on calcium uptake and release by kidney mitochondria," *Proc. Natl. Acad. Sci. U.S.*, **48**, 1604 (1962).

Gamble, J. L., Jr., "K^+ binding and oxidative phosphorylation in mitochondria and mitochondrial membrane fragments," *J. Biol. Chem.*, **228**, 955 (1957).

————, "Retention of K^+ by mitochondria," *Am. J. Physiol.*, **203**, 886 (1962).

Lehninger, A. L., C. S. Rossi, and J. W. Greenawalt, "Respiration-dependent accumulation of inorganic phosphate and Ca^{++} by rat liver mitochondria," *Biochem. Biophys. Res. Commun.*, **10**, 444 (1963).

Pressman, B. C., "The effects of guanidine and alkylguanidine on the energy transfer reactions of mitochondria," *J. Biol. Chem.*, **238**, 401 (1963).

———— and J. K. Park, "Competition between magnesium and guanidine for mitochondrial binding sites," *Biochem. Biophys. Res. Commun.*, **11**, 182 (1963).

Reynolds, E. S., R. E. Thiers, and B. L. Vallee, "Mitochondrial function and metal content in carbon tetrachloride poisoning," *J. Biol. Chem.*, **237**, 3546 (1962).

Rossi, C. S., and A. L. Lehninger, "Stoichiometric relationships between mitochondrial ion accumulation and oxidative phosphorylation," *Biochem. Biophys. Res. Commun.*, **11**, 441 (1963).

———— and ————, "Stoichiometric relationships between accumulation of ions by mitochondria and the energy-coupling sites in the respiratory chain," *Biochem. Z.*, **338**, 698 (1963).

Sallis, J. D., H. F. DeLuca, and H. Rasmussen, "Parathyroid hormone stimulation of phosphate uptake by rat liver mitochondria," *Biochem. Biophys. Res. Commun.*, **10**, 266 (1963).

Scott, R. L., and J. L. Gamble, Jr., "Effect of mercurial compounds on K^+ binding by mitochondria," *J. Biol. Chem.*, **236**, 570 (1961).

Thiers, R. E., E. S. Reynolds, and B. L. Vallee, "The effect of carbon tetrachloride poisoning on subcellular metal distribution in rat liver," *J. Biol. Chem.*, **235**, 2130 (1960).

Vasington, F. D., "Ca^{++} uptake by mitochondrial subfragments and its dependence on electron transport," *J. Biol. Chem.*, **238**, 1841 (1963).

———— and J. V. Murphy, "Ca^{++} uptake by rat kidney mitochondria and its dependence on respiration and phosphorylation," *J. Biol. Chem.*, **237**, 2670 (1962).

9

ENERGY-COUPLED CHANGES
OF VOLUME AND STRUCTURE

We have seen that the respiratory chain of mitochondria is the mainspring for regeneration of ATP, its most conspicuous function, and that it also provides energy for ion accumulation in mitochondria in a process that is parallel to ATP formation or may replace it. These two processes thus represent two different modalities of respiratory energy transformation, chemical and osmotic. We shall now consider a third energy-transforming activity associated with the respiratory chain, namely, the changes in volume and structure of the mitochondrion in different respiratory states.

It has already been mentioned that mitochondria in unfixed living cells undergo changes in shape and volume. There is now good evidence that some of these changes are determined by the activity of the respiratory chain. For example, Frederic has shown that mitochondria in living fibroblasts undergo immediate changes in conformation when respiratory inhibitors such as dinitrophenol and cyanide are introduced into the culture medium. Also, Packer has observed respiration-dependent light-scattering changes in suspensions of Ehrlich ascites tumor cells that correspond to swelling and shrinking of the mitochondria within the cells. We shall now consider the biochemistry and biophysics of these volume changes of mitochondria, which can be readily studied in vitro.

PASSIVE AND ACTIVE VOLUME CHANGES

Changes in volume of isolated mitochondria in vitro associated with respiration were first studied systematically by Raaflaub, by MacFarlane and Spencer, and by Harman and Feigelson in 1952 and 1953. Raaflaub studied volume changes by measuring the turbidity of suspensions of mitochondria, a function of light scattering. He was the first to suggest that mitochondria could undergo two types of volume change: (1) a *passive* change responsive to the osmotic pressure of the suspending medium and (2) an *active* change requiring respiration or high-energy compounds. Raaflaub showed that liver mitochondria behave like simple osmometers when suspended in mannitol solutions of varying concentration, behavior to be expected of an organelle surrounded by a semipermeable membrane. Such volume changes in response to osmotic pressure of the medium have since been studied in more detail by Tedeschi and other investigators, who have shown that isolated liver mitochondria obey osmotic law rather exactly in solutions of sucrose, a relatively slowly penetrating solute, if one assumes an osmotic "dead space" of some 40 per cent of the volume. Volume changes in response to osmolality of the medium are very rapid and have a low temperature coefficient, as expected for a diffusion-controlled process.

Raaflaub also first showed that certain substances related to oxidative phosphorylation profoundly affect the volume of mitochondria in vitro out of all proportion to their osmolal concentration. Very low concentrations of phosphate or succinate caused swelling of mitochondria suspended in isotonic mannitol. Swelling so induced could be prevented by ATP. Raaflaub accordingly suggested that water movements in mitochondria might be active, that is, coupled to the respiratory chain. Tapley later showed that agents capable of uncoupling phosphorylation also had characteristic effects on mitochondrial swelling, some causing swelling and some inhibition.

Parallel experiments of Harman, of MacFarlane and Spencer, and of Davies and his colleagues on suspensions of respiring mitochondria in complex media containing respiratory substrates, adenine nucleotides, Mg^{++}, and phosphate showed that maintenance of a low mitochondrial water content required active, phosphorylating respiration. If adenine nucleotides or substrates were omitted, the mitochondria would swell two- or threefold. Water was extruded again from swollen mitochondria if phosphorylating respiration was reinstituted by addition of substrates and adenine nucleotides. It is the "active" type of mitochondrial volume change that is of most interest in the following discussion.

SWELLING AND CONTRACTION CYCLES

After the earlier work described above, Chance and Packer studied structural changes occurring in intact respiring mitochondria coincident with characteristic changes in respiratory state. The conditions were such that they could make continuous measurements on a fast time scale not only of light scattering by the mitochondria but also of the oxidation-reduction state of the respiratory carriers by means of the double-beam spectrophotometer. This approach permitted study of the relationship of structural changes to respiration under conditions in which the changes were fully reversible and thus comparable to those occurring in the intact cell.

When rat liver mitochondria were kept in state 4, i.e., in the presence of excess substrate and oxygen but deficient in ADP, the mitochondria underwent a structural change, presumably swelling, registered as a decrease in optical density at a neutral wavelength that is isosbestic for the respiratory carriers, as shown in Figure 9–1. In this state respiration is very low and cytochrome b is essentially fully reduced. The swelling occurs at a relatively low rate compared with the rate of reduction of cytochrome b. When ADP is now added, there is a very rapid change to a more oxidized state of cytochrome b and respiration is greatly stimulated. The turbidity of the mitochondria immediately increases, although at a somewhat lower rate than the oxidation of cytochrome b. This is termed a *swelling-contraction cycle*. Throughout a series of such cycles respiration was found to remain tightly coupled and fully responsive to ADP.

Packer has found that uncoupling agents, such as dinitrophenol, accelerate contraction; it is interesting that Frederic

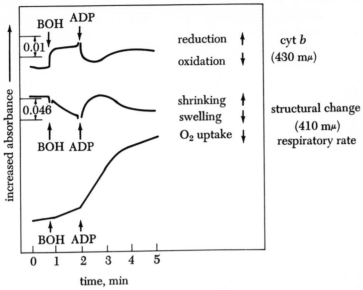

Figure 9–1 Low-amplitude structural changes of mitochondria associated with changes in respiratory state. (After Packer, 1960.) Addition of substrate (BOH) causes slight increase of respiration, reduction of cytochrome *b*, and swelling of mitochondria (respiratory state 4). Addition of ADP as shown causes large increase in respiration, oxidation of cytochrome *b*, and shrinking (state 3). As ADP is exhausted, state 4 returns.

observed mitochondria in the intact fibroblast to contract when dinitrophenol was added. The studies of Packer thus provide a description of the integration of electron flow, phosphorylation, and structural state of the mitochondria under reversible conditions similar to those in the intact cell.

In most of Packer's studies the light-scattering changes studied usually corresponded to mitochondrial volume changes of the order of a few per cent or less and thus have been termed small-amplitude or phase I changes. However, mitochondria may be allowed to undergo much larger changes in volume, designated as large-amplitude or phase II cycles (see Figure 9–2). Intensive study of the properties of large-amplitude mitochondrial swelling and contraction, particularly in the labora-

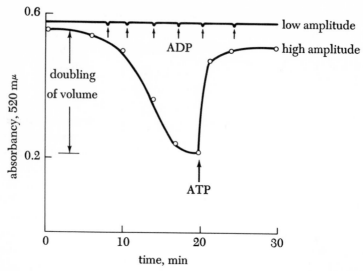

Figure 9–2 Comparison of magnitude of phase I and phase II swelling-
contraction cycles. Note that full phase II cycle (high amplitude)
is slow, with lag period, whereas phase I changes (low amplitude) have time constants more nearly comparable with those
of respiratory changes. Phase II changes lead to irreversible
damage.

tories of Lehninger, Hunter, and Chappell, has permitted some
dissection of the biochemical and enzymatic features of these
changes, as well as their mechanistic relationships to the respiratory chain. These will now be outlined.

ACTIVE SWELLING OF MITOCHONDRIA

Role of respiration. Mitochondria do not swell under anaerobic
conditions but are most susceptible to swelling during respiration in the absence of ADP (or ATP), as shown by Lehninger,
Hunter, and Chappell. Lehninger and his colleagues demonstrated that cyanide, antimycin A, or Amytal completely prevented water uptake by mitochondria; and Chappell and
Greville showed that swelling of aged mitochondria required
addition of respiratory substrates. It was also shown by the
latter and by Hunter that electron flow through any of the three
phosphorylation sites sufficed to confer susceptibility to swell-

ing. In contrast to passive swelling, the active swelling stimulated by respiration has a high temperature coefficient, which is consistent with a chemical or enzymatic process as the rate-limiting step.

Swelling agents. Active swelling of mitochondria is greatly stimulated by the so-called swelling agents. The physiologically occurring swelling agents are inorganic phosphate, Ca^{++}, free fatty acids, thyroxine and other thyroactive compounds, ascorbic acid, reduced and oxidized glutathione (but not all thiols or disulfides), ferrous ions, and four different polypeptide hormones: oxytocin, vasopressin, insulin, and somatotrophin, each of which has at least one disulfide linkage. Inorganic phosphate itself is a requirement for coupled respiration, and it seems likely that its swelling activity is related to some step involving phosphate uptake in oxidative phosphorylation. The swelling caused by Ca^{++} may be related to the fact that Ca^{++} is readily accumulated by mitochondria and that it is also a potent uncoupling agent. Similarly, the swelling activity of free fatty acids may be related to their uncoupling activity.

It is remarkable that no less than five different hormones have intense swelling activity, often at extremely low concentrations approaching physiological levels. The mitochondrial swelling induced by thyroxine has been implicated in the physiological action of this hormone. It is of some significance that surveys of many thyroactive compounds carried out by Tapley and by Lehninger and their colleagues have shown an excellent correlation between thyroactivity and swelling potency.

Although electron microscopic studies of tissues of hypo-, hyper-, and euthyroid rats by Greenawalt have shown no striking changes in volume or shape of mitochondria in most tissues, it must be pointed out that statistical analysis of thin-sectioned tissues can permit detection of only relatively large changes in mitochondrial volume. However, in thyrotoxic tissues Greenawalt and his colleagues have observed pronounced changes in shape, size, and in membrane conformation of mitochondria (Chapter 2). The physiological consequences of thyroxine-induced swelling probably involve changes in permeability and transport phenomena. For example, work of Sokoloff has shown that availability of mitochondrial ATP for protein synthesis is increased by thyroxine.

The strong swelling activity of oxytocin, vasopressin, and insulin were shown by Lehninger and Neubert to resemble the action of oxidized glutathione; the disulfide linkage appears to be the important functional group in this activity. Since the disulfide hormones may be up to 10^7 times more active than oxidized glutathione, the amino acid sequence and the conformation of the peptide chains must also be major determinants of the swelling activity of the hormones. The swelling action of all the active disulfide compounds is enhanced by small amounts of GSH and other thiols; this finding is reminiscent of the fact that thiols enhance the rate of interchange reactions between dissimilar disulfides

$$RSSR + R'SSR' \overset{-SH}{\rightleftharpoons} 2RSSR' \tag{9-1}$$

It is of some interest that mitochondrial swelling initiated by GSSG–GSH, by ascorbate, and by Fe^{++} differs from that induced by other agents in that it is accompanied by formation of lipid peroxides and may proceed to actual lysis of the mitochondria. Apparently, the swelling induced by these agents causes exposure of the double bonds of the unsaturated fatty acids of membrane phospholipids to oxygen and their subsequent autoxidation.

Whether the swelling action of the disulfide hormones is physiological remains to be proved. Schwartz and Rasmussen have shown that these hormones bring about permeability changes in certain membranes, presumably by disulfide-thiol interchange reactions between hormone and membrane protein as shown in Figure 9–3, to cause alterations in the tertiary or quaternary structure of membrane proteins and thus in membrane permeability. Lehninger and Neubert have suggested that this action of disulfide hormones may also occur in the mitochondrial membrane. Even if the mitochondria are not the primary physiological target for all the disulfide hormones, mitochondria are very useful models for simple in vitro study of these effects, particularly since all biological membranes appear to have basically similar molecular architecture and permeability characteristics.

In addition to the so-called physiological swelling agents, other substances are known to cause mitochondrial swelling; some of them may be diagnostic of the biochemical events in swelling. Among these are the alkylating agent iodoacetamide and heavy metals such as Ag^+ and Hg^{++}, which suggest that —SH groups of the membrane, in addition to —SS— groups, are

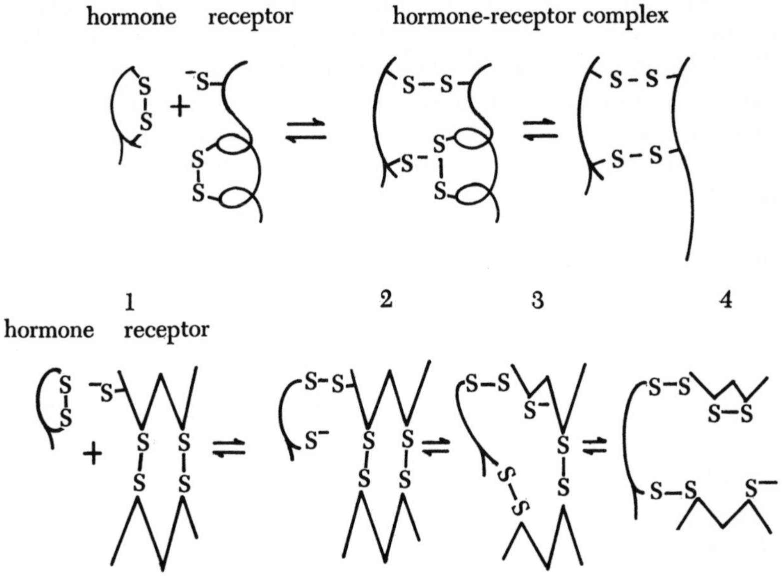

Figure 9–3 A hypothesis illustrating propagation of a series of thiol-disulfide interchanges to produce separation of fibrillar elements in a protein diffusion barrier. [I. L. Schwartz, H. Rasmussen, M. A. Schoessler, L. Silver, and C. T. O. Fong, *Proc. Natl. Acad. Sci. (U.S.)*, **46**, 1296 (1960).]

critical in swelling. It has been found that there are two classes of —SH groups in the membrane; one class is immediately reactive with Ag^+, whose titration causes immediate swelling. Riley and Lehninger have shown that swelling of mitochondria caused by oxidized glutathione is accompanied by disappearance of this class of labile —SH groups, indicating that a thiol-disulfide interaction has occurred between GSSG and membrane.

Neubert and Lehninger showed that the cyclic peptide antibiotics gramicidin D and S and tyrocidine are extremely potent swelling agents that are active in concentrations as low as 10^{-12} M; they also uncouple phosphorylation and stimulate ATPase activity. The amino acid sequence and chain conformation of these polypeptides must play an important role in this activity, as is the case for the polypeptide hormones described above. However, there are no immediately apparent similarities between the amino acid composition and sequence of these antibiotics and of the polypeptide hormones.

Swelling is also caused by phoridzin, long known to interfere with renal tubular transport of glucose. On the other hand, ouabain, a potent inhibitor of Na^+ and K^+ transport in the cell membrane, has no effect on mitochondrial swelling or contraction.

Inhibition of swelling. Active water uptake by mitochondria is prevented not only by blocking respiration or phosphorylation, as shown above, but also by certain other agents associated with the action of the respiratory chain, such as ATP, Mg^{++}, and Mn^{++}, as well as by dinitrophenol and oligomycin. Ethylenediamine tetraacetate and other metal-chelating agents also block swelling, as do spermine and spermidine and certain antihistamine drugs.

ACTIVE CONTRACTION OF MITOCHONDRIA

Role of ATP. As was mentioned above, swollen mitochondria shrink or contract again if phosphorylating respiration is induced. However, after extreme large-amplitude swelling, respiration and phosphorylation may become inactivated, and the mitochondria then fail to contract. However, Lehninger showed in 1959 that ATP alone sufficed to cause extrusion of water from nonrespiring, thyroxine-swollen mitochondria, provided that the medium is low or free of sucrose, mannitol, or other polyhydroxylic solutes often used in suspending media in such tests. ADP, AMP, and nucleoside 5'-triphosphates other than ATP were inactive. The K_m for ATP was found to be substantially less than 30 μM. The action of ATP is enhanced by MG^{++} or Mn^{++} and also by small amounts of bovine serum albumin.

Direct weighing of mitochondrial pellets has revealed that hundreds of molecules of water may be extruded per molecule of ATP added (Figure 9–4). ATP is hydrolyzed to ADP and phosphate during contraction; the hydrolysis slows down and may cease after contraction is complete. As many as 2000 moles of water may be extruded per mole of ATP hydrolyzed. It is not certain, however, that hydrolysis is necessary for contraction; it is possible that it is the binding of ATP that brings about the contractile changes, as has been postulated in the case of muscle contraction.

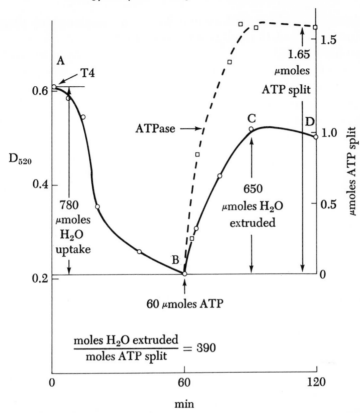

Figure 9–4 Quantitative relationship between ATP and water extruded. In this case about 400 moles water were extruded per mole of ATP hydrolyzed. [A. L. Lehninger, J. Biol. Chem., **234**, 2192 (1959).]

Inhibition of mitochondrial contraction. Just as swelling is inhibited by certain agents that inhibit respiration, so the contraction of swollen mitochondria induced by ATP is characteristically sensitive to certain reagents. However, agents that inhibit swelling do not necessarily inhibit contraction, and vice versa. For example, dinitrophenol inhibits swelling but does not inhibit ATP-induced contraction. Most diagnostic of an enzymatic association between mitochondrial contraction and the energy-coupling mechanisms of the respiratory chain is the finding that such specific inhibitors of oxidative phosphorylation as oligomycin and potassium atractylate block ATP-induced contraction completely at concentrations that are known to just block phosphorylating electron transport. Gramicidin D, gramicidin S, and tyrocidin not only promote swelling but are also extremely potent inhibitors of ATP-linked contraction, being effective at concentrations as low as 10^{-12} M. Also inhibitory are azide and the thiocyanate ion.

Some inhibitors of mitochondrial contraction stimulate ATP hydrolysis and others inhibit hydrolysis; oligomycin, azide, and atractylate inhibit ATPase, whereas gramicidins D and S and tyrocidin stimulate ATPase activity. The mechanistic relationship of swelling and contraction to oxidative phosphorylation and ATPase activity is a jigsaw puzzle, the elements of which are shown in Table 9–1.

Sucrose and many other polyols such as glucose, raffinose, inulin, and mannitol inhibit contraction; glycerol and ethylene glycol are not inhibitory. Since mitochondria are universally isolated from sucrose media, the inhibitory action of sucrose on these mechanochemical changes and on oxidative phosphorylation seems a paradox. However, the inhibition of contraction by sucrose is readily reversible; mitochondria swollen in a sucrose medium can be washed free of sucrose and are then capable of contraction with ATP.

Lehninger has made the suggestion that sucrose is effective in preserving mitochondrial structure during isolation because it reversibly "freezes" mitochondrial structure by inhibiting the swelling and contraction mechanisms linked to phosphorylation. However, another explanation is that once the slowly permeable sucrose enters the mitochondria, the internal water cannot be

Table 9–1 Effects of inhibitors on respiration, phosphorylation, ATPase activity, swelling, and contraction

	Oxygen uptake	Phospho-rylation	ATPase activity	Swelling	Contraction by ATP
Cyanide	Inhibits		Inhibits	Inhibits	No effect
Antimycin A	Inhibits		Inhibits	Inhibits	No effect
Amytal	Inhibits		Inhibits	Inhibits	No effect
Dinitrophenol	No effect	Uncouples	Stimulates	Inhibits	No effect
Gramicidin	No effect	Uncouples	Stimulates	Stimulates	Inhibits
Oligomycin	Inhibits	Inhibits	Inhibits	Inhibits	Inhibits

extruded by ATP unless sucrose also leaves. Contracted mitochondria are less permeable to sucrose than swollen mitochondria; initiation of contraction by ATP could thus "lock" sucrose
molecules inside, together with the water.

RELATIONSHIP BETWEEN WATER TRANSPORT
AND ION TRANSPORT

ATP causes contraction of swollen mitochondria even after
the capacity for oxidative phosphorylation and for active accumulation of K^+ and Ca^{++} have been inactivated by aging of
the swollen mitochondria. The contraction mechanism can thus
be experimentally dissociated from ion transport and ATP formation, but it is still dependent on some process normally
shared with the other two functions, since oligomycin still inhibits ATP-linked contraction of aged mitochondria.

Contraction of extremely swollen mitochondria by ATP is not
influenced by either the concentration or the species of cations
and anions in the suspending medium, within limits. K^+ may be
replaced in the medium by Na^+, Li^+, NH_4^+, and Rb^+, and Cl^-
may be replaced in the medium by $SO_4^=$, Br^-, F^-, I^-, acetate$^-$,
NO_3^-, and ClO_4^-, with no effect on water extrusion by ATP.
The contraction is also insensitive to ouabain, an inhibitor of ion
transport. Finally, it has been observed that ATP-dependent
structural changes sensitive to oligomycin can be observed to
take place in well-washed fragments of the mitochondrial membranes produced by treatment with digitonin or by sonic vibration. Therefore, the structural changes occurring during contraction appear to be inherent in the membrane itself and do not
appear to require the soluble contents of the mitochondrial
matrix, nor are they secondary to active ion transport.

MORPHOLOGICAL CHANGES
IN SWELLING AND CONTRACTION

Relatively little is known of the specific morphological
changes that occur in mitochondrial swelling and contraction.
The reversible, low-amplitude cycles studied by Packer and
others are not accessible to direct electron microscope study at
present because of the almost hopeless statistical problem of
evaluating very small changes in average mitochondrial vol-

umes from diameters of cut sections of mitochondria. However, with large-amplitude cycles the changes may be visualized more successfully. Some studies by Greenawalt and Lehninger on thyroxine-induced swelling of rat liver mitochondria and its reversal by ATP have shown good agreement among optical, gravimetric, and electron microscopic measurement of mitochondrial volume.

For a doubling of volume as indicated by gravimetric and optical measurement, an average increase in diameter of about 40 per cent was observed in electron micrographs, compared to the expected 45 per cent increase if the mitochondria are assumed to be perfect spheres. Figure 9–5 shows the conformation of freshly isolated, of swollen, and of ATP-contracted rat liver mitochondria. It may be noted that in the swollen mitochondria the two membranes have separated at the periphery of the mitochondrion; presumably water (and solutes) have entered this compartment. It is also seen that the cristae have become "inflated," exposing more of their membrane surface. The ATP-contracted mitochondria are remarkably similar to untreated mitochondria. Weinbach and his colleagues have reported similar findings and have established conditions for ATP-linked contraction of fully swollen mitochondria that also bring about full restoration of electron transport and oxidative phosphorylation. Under appropriate conditions, then, both small-amplitude and large-amplitude swelling are fully reversible changes.

From measurements of electrical resistance and capacitance of the mitochondrial membrane, as well as the membrane charge density as measured by electrophoresis, it appears that the mitochondrial membrane does not simply stretch during swelling, but rather exposes more charge-bearing surface, apparently by unfolding or inflation of the cristae.

It is remarkable that there is wide variability of maximum swelling amplitude among mitochondria of different cell types. Packer has shown that mitochondria from many tissues, including brain mitochondria, undergo low-amplitude cycles. On the other hand, whereas liver and kidney mitochondria can undergo two- or threefold reversible volume increases in vitro, brain mitochondria cannot swell more than 1 or 2 per cent of their volume. Heart mitochondria are intermediate. It appears possible that the specific arrangement or conformation of the cristae in brain mitochondria prevent large increases in volume.

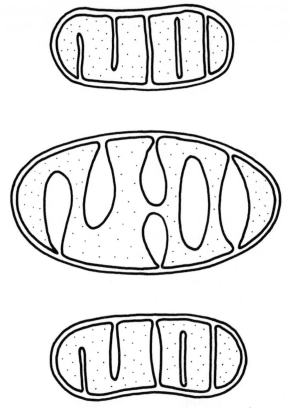

Figure 9–5 Top drawing shows intact mitochondrion with normal density of matrix. Middle drawing shows inflation of cristae and dilution of matrix which occur during swelling. Bottom drawing shows mitochondrion after contraction by ATP; it retains some inflation of cristae.

THERMODYNAMIC ASPECTS
OF THE SWELLING-CONTRACTION CYCLE

Lehninger has measured the actual dimensional and volume changes of the mitochondria following contraction induced by ATP, as well as the amounts of ATP hydrolyzed and bound. The maximum energy yield from the sum of the ATP hydrolyzed and bound that could have been employed in the contractile process was determined by establishing the osmotic pressure increment in a solution of a nonpermeant solute (sucrose) that was experimentally found to produce exactly the same level of water extrusion by passive means as was produced by a given concentration of ATP during the active process. Such data permitted the approximation that under the best experimental conditions tested, some 20 per cent of the energy of hydrolysis and binding of ATP had been converted into mechanical energy of contraction.

It is a fundamental identifying characteristic of mechanochemical systems, or "engines," that they are not necessarily reversible. Although input of a given increment of chemical energy produces a specific increment of conformational change, input of a given increment of mechanical change in the system does not necessarily cause a corresponding increment of a chemical change. It has already been shown (Figure 9–4) that when swollen mitochondria are contracted by ATP, the latter is hydrolyzed during contraction but hydrolysis ceases when contraction is complete. This finding satisfies at least one of the criteria for a mechanochemical coupling.

SPECIFIC REQUIREMENTS FOR CONTRACTION
AND ENZYMATIC MECHANISMS

Recent research, particularly in Lehninger's laboratory, has revealed that contraction of swollen mitochondria in the presence of ATP and Mg^{++} requires the presence of certain other specific substances under appropriate experimental conditions. These required factors may be listed:

1. Long-chain unsaturated fatty acids, such as oleate or linoleate
2. α-Glycerophosphate
3. Phosphatidyl inositol
4. C factor I (catalase)
5. C factor II (glutathione peroxidase)
6. C factor III (an unidentified lipid or lipoprotein)

No single set of conditions in which all of these components must be added together to restore contraction of swollen mitochondria by ATP has been found, but each of the factors has been shown to be required when the mitochondrial system has been suitably modified. Identification of these factors thus may provide new clues to the mechanism of the contraction and, by extension, of oxidative phosphorylation. The role of some of the factors is described below.

ROLE OF FATTY ACIDS AND PHOSPHOLIPIDS

One of the most significant enzymatic changes occurring during large-amplitude swelling and contraction involves phospholipids of the mitochondrial membrane, as shown by work of Wojtczak and Lehninger. When mitochondria are allowed to swell in the presence of thyroxine or Ca^{++}, free fatty acids are formed enzymatically in the mitochondria from a heat-stable precursor in the membrane, presumably a phospholipid. Because the ability to phosphorylate is lost when these fatty acids accumulate, they have been collectively termed *uncoupling factor* or *U factor*; it will be recalled that fatty acids are potent swelling and uncoupling agents. Bovine serum albumin, which binds fatty acids tightly, can prevent thyroxine-or Ca^{++}-induced swelling; it therefore appears that it is the formation and accumulation of endogenous fatty acids that actually cause swelling induced by thyroxine or Ca^{++}.

When ATP is added to thyroxine-swollen mitochondria to contract them again, the free fatty acids formed during the swelling phase disappear again, at a rate synchronous with the rate of contraction (Figure 9–6). The fate of these fatty acids was traced by adding a small amount of C^{14}-labeled oleate to swollen mitochondria, followed by addition of ATP. The labeled oleate disappeared during contraction, but it could be recovered again in the phospholipids of the membrane. Chromatographic separation of the lipids revealed that the oleate was incorporated into the phosphatidic acid fraction, and also into cardiolipin.

Wojtczak and his colleagues have found that when mitochondria are swollen by high concentrations of phosphate, they require for contraction, in addition to ATP and Mg^{++}, two other components: oleate and α-glycerophosphate. These compounds are building blocks in the enzymatic synthesis of phosphatidic acid and of cardiolipin. Furthermore, when each of these precursors was labeled with C^{14} and then added in turn to swollen mitochondria, it was found to be incorporated into the phosphatidic acid fraction of the membrane lipids during the ATP-induced contraction. The rate of incorporation was again found to be synchronous with the rate of contraction. Most striking

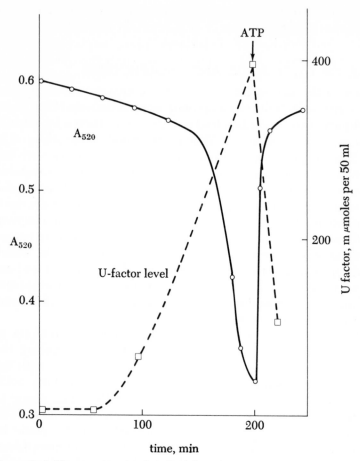

Figure 9–6 Changes in mitochondrial free fatty acids ("U factor") during swelling-contraction cycle. [After L. Wojtczak and A. L. Lehninger, *Biochim. Biophys. Acta,* **51**, 451 (1961).]

was the finding that sucrose and oligomycin, which characteristically block ATP-induced contraction, also block the enzymatic incorporation of these building blocks into cardiolipin.

On the other hand, these investigators found that inorganic phosphate was not rapidly incorporated into phosphatidic acid during ATP-induced contraction. These observations may therefore define a specific function of phosphatidic acid or cardiolipin in mitochondrial membrane changes. By extension, it also appears that phosphatidic acid or cardiolipin has a specific function in the mechanism of oxidative phosphorylation; indeed, other investigators had earlier observed that this phospholipid fraction is rapidly labeled during oxidative phosphorylation in intact mitochondria.

Recent work by Vignais and Vignais has revealed that phospholipids other than phosphatidic acid may be specifically involved in mitochondrial contraction. They have found that mitochondria aged in the cold for three days swell readily but do not contract again on addition of ATP $+ Mg^{++}$. Addition of a mitochondrial protein fraction containing the "contractile" protein of Ohnishi and Ohnishi restored the ability to contract. The activity of this protein was lost following extraction with lipid solvents. The active component was found to be phosphatidyl inositol, which is active at a level of 10^{-6} M. Many other lipids and fatty acids have been tested, but none possess such activity. It is of some significance that phosphatidyl inositol has also been implicated in the mechanism of active transport by recent work in a number of other laboratories.

CONTRACTION FACTORS AND THE ACTION
OF CATALASE AND GLUTATHIONE PEROXIDASE

Lehninger and his colleagues found that mitochondria swollen with reduced glutathione failed to contract when ATP was added, particularly at low mitochondrial concentrations. This failure was traced to the fact that reduced glutathione caused detachment of a heat-labile factor, apparently protein in nature, from the mitochondria into the suspending medium, from which it could be recovered. When this factor was added in some excess to a suspension of glutathione-swollen mitochondria, the ability of ATP to bring about the contraction of the latter was restored. The concentration of the contraction factor (designated C factor) was found to determine the equilibrium extent of contraction; within limits, the level of contraction was found to be proportional to the amount of C factor added, as shown in Figure 9–7. C-factor activity has been found in sonic extracts of mitochondria of all tissues tested, as well as in erythrocytes, some bacteria, and some plant tissues. It appears to be associated with membrane structures capable of energy-linked or active swelling and contraction changes.

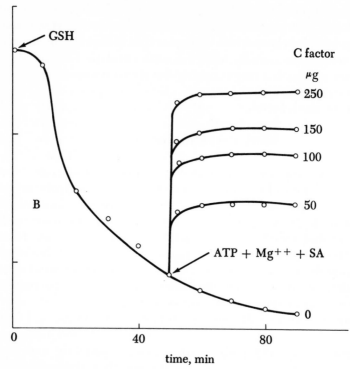

Figure 9–7 Effect of contraction factor on water extrusion from glutathione-swollen mitochondria. Increasing equilibrium levels of contraction are produced by increasing additions of C factor. [A. L. Lehninger and G. S. Gotterer, *J. Biol. Chem.*, **235**, PC8 (1960).]

Neubert, Wojtczak, and Lehninger have shown that C-factor activity of extracts of rat liver mitochondria can be resolved by chromatographic methods into three forms, designated C factors I, II and III; each has been greatly purified. C factor I is the most active, and it has the absorption spectrum of a simple protein. C factor II has lesser activity per milligram of protein and gives the spectrum of a hemoprotein, with a Soret peak at 403 to 405 mμ. Some 25 different highly purified proteins and enzymes were tested for C-factor activity, but in no case could activity be detected. However, crystalline catalase obtained from different sources unexpectedly showed considerable C-factor activity; on the other hand, no other iron-containing protein tested, including hemoglobin, myoglobin, cytochrome c, horse-radish and milk peroxidases, and ferritin, was active. It was soon shown by Neubert and his colleagues that C factor II of rat liver mitochondria is actually identical with catalase. Further study of other enzymes acting on peroxides showed that C factor I is in turn identical with the enzyme glutathione peroxidase, which catalyzes the reaction

$$2GSH + H_2O_2 \rightarrow GSSG + 2H_2O \qquad (9\text{--}2)$$

Other types of peroxidases tested were devoid of activity.

Identification of C factors I and II as these enzymes at first suggested that they merely perform a protective function by removing hydrogen peroxide that may be formed during swelling and that may be toxic to ATP-induced contraction. However, this explanation is not correct, since added hydrogen peroxide does not inhibit either swelling or contraction of mitochondria, nor does it seem likely that these enzymes participate in formation or removal of lipid peroxides.

Neubert and his colleagues postulated that catalase and GSH peroxidase may participate in an as yet unrecognized manner in electron transport, which in turn controls swelling and contraction. Earlier work by Chance showed that unidentified reductants and oxidants for catalase and peroxidase are continuously formed during electron transport. Among these reductants may be thiols, which are known to be important functional groups in electron transport and oxidative phosphorylation, as we have seen before. Whatever the outcome of these investigations, they may reveal the true cellular role of catalase, a perennial biochemical mystery.

COMPARATIVE BIOCHEMISTRY OF CONTRACTION IN MITOCHONDRIA AND IN THE MYOFIBRIL; MITOCHONDRIAL ACTOMYOSIN

Lehninger has pointed out that the contractile systems of the mitochondrion and of the myofibril share a number of common properties that are relatively unique to these structures. They may be summarized briefly:

1. Both systems have ATPase activity in which mechano-chemical coupling occurs.

2. The ATPase activity may be latent and can be stimulated by dinitrophenol.

3. The ATPase activity is inhibited by oligomycin.

4. Both systems catalyze an exchange between the oxygen atoms of water of the medium (labeled with O^{18}) and the oxygen atoms of inorganic phosphate; this exchange is not a common property of all ATP-linked phosphate-transferring enzymes.

5. Both systems possess two classes of thiol groups that control ATPase activity in a biphasic manner. Titration of the first class of −SH groups stimulates ATPase activity; further titration with Ag^+ blocks the second class of −SH groups, resulting in inhibition of ATPase activity.

These and other similarities suggest that these two specialized ATPase systems, which are involved in energy transformation in such apparently diverse structures as the mitochondrion and myofibril, may have a common evolutionary origin and some common denominators of molecular design.

There is now some new experimental evidence for this relationship. Very recently Ohnishi and Ohnishi, as well as Neifakh and Kazakova, by extraction of mitochondria with KCl solutions of high ionic strength, were able to separate a protein that was similar in many respects to the actomyosin of skeletal muscle; it showed ATPase activity, possessed viscosity and dissociation properties similar to those of muscle actomyosin, and showed the superprecipitation phenomenon. It was also dissociable into fractions corresponding to actin and myosin.

Recent work in Lehninger's laboratory has confirmed some of these findings, although the protein appears to be far from homogeneous. Moreover, it was found that mitochondrial *contractile protein* is a contraction factor. Rat liver mitochondria extracted with 0.6 *M* KCl do not contract when ATP is added alone, but addition of contractile protein restores contraction. However, at least some of this effect has been found to be given by a specific lipid adhering to the contractile protein, namely, phosphatidyl inositol. Nevertheless, the nature of mitochondrial contractile protein deserves further study.

CELLULAR FUNCTION OF MECHANOCHEMICAL CHANGES

Mitochondrial swelling and contraction in vitro were at first regarded as a laboratory curiosity. However, there is now significant evidence that these changes take place in the intact cell, as we have seen. One function of this activity may be in the active transcellular movement of water in cells such as those of the renal tubule, since it has been found that dehydration of animals or changes in their ion intake will result in swelling of mitochondria in situ; restoration of a normal intake restores normal mitochondrial form. Whether swelling and contraction in the intact cell is a rather slow process or a rapid, pulsating phenomenon is not yet clear, but movies of intact cells suggest that the latter type of change occurs.

Another possible cellular function of mitochondrial swelling and contraction is to bring about changes in permeability to extramitochondrial metabolites and intramitochondrial ATP. It appears likely that when the external ATP/ADP ratio is high, mitochondria remain in a contracted, less permeable state; the access of oxidizable substrates and the "leakage" of intramitochondrial ATP may be diminished. When the external ATP concentration declines, ATP is lost from mitochondria and the permeability to substrates may increase, leading to oxidation and formation of more ATP.

Thus the swelling-contraction cycle may be another of the many cybernetic mechanisms permitting self-adjustment of respiration and phosphorylation in the intact cell. Because these mechanochemical changes are brought about by intermediate reactions of oxidative phosphorylation, they may give some important clues to molecular relationships between the mechanical changes and the enzymes of the respiratory chains. For example, recent work has implicated phosphoproteins of mitochondria as intermediates in oxidative phosphorylation as we have seen; similarly, Judah has found characteristic changes in the phosphoprotein phosphorus content during swelling and contraction.

COMPARATIVE ASPECTS
OF MECHANOCHEMICAL CHANGES

From the standpoint of comparative cytology and biochemistry it is most significant that other cells and membrane-bounded organelles also show energy-linked water uptake and extrusion cycles. Abrams has demonstrated that protoplasts of *Streptococcus faecalis* undergo swelling and contraction associated with glycolysis. The membrane of the protoplast contains an ATPase similar to that of the mitochondrial membranes.

The erythrocyte membrane also contains enzymatic mechanisms involved in water uptake and extrusion, in addition to an ATPase requiring K^+ and Na^+. Nakao and his colleagues have shown that a change of shape that may be similar to the change of shape in mitochondria can be induced in erythrocytes by addition of ATP. Furthermore, recent work by Packer and others on chloroplasts of spinach leaves has demonstrated a light-dependent water uptake by these organelles, which contain the enzymatic equipment for absorption of light energy and for photosynthetic electron transport and coupled phosphorylation. ATP also brings about light-scattering changes in chloroplasts.

It must now be concluded that the respiratory assemblies in the mitochondrial membrane that are responsible for coupling ATP synthesis to electron transport are polymodal energy-transducing systems that can convert oxidation-reduction energy into chemical or phosphate bond energy, into the osmotic energy of active transport, and into the mechanical energy of contraction. The following chapter will consider possible mechanisms for accounting for swelling and contraction and for ion translocations.

REFERENCES

Reviews

Chappell, J. B., and G. D. Greville, "The influence of the suspending medium on the properties of mitochondria," in "Methods of separation of subcellular structural components," *Biochem. Soc. Symp. (Cambridge, Engl.),* **23** (**1963**), 39.

Lehninger, A. L., "Water uptake and extrusion by mitochondria in relation to oxidative phosphorylation," *Physiol. Rev.,* **42,** 467 (1962).

——, "Respiration-linked mechanochemical changes in mitochondria," in M. Kasha and B. Pullman (eds.), *Horizons in Biochemistry,* Academic, New York, 1962.

Research papers

Ahmed, K., and J. D. Judah, "Mitochondrial phosphoprotein metabolism," *Biochim. Biophys. Acta,* **71,** 295 (1963).

Greenbaum, A. L., and S. E. Dicker, "The effects of mammalian posterior lobe hormones on the swelling of liver and kidney mitochondria," *Biochim. Biophys. Acta*, **74**, 519 (1963).

Hunter, F. E., Jr., J. M. Gebicki, P. E. Hoffsten, J. Weinstein, and A. Scott, "Swelling and lysis of rat liver mitochondria induced by ferrous ions," *J. Biol. Chem.*, **238**, 828 (1963).

Lehninger, A. L., "A heat-labile factor required in extrusion of water from mitochondria," *J. Biol. Chem.*, **237**, 946 (1962).

────── and D. Neubert, "Effect of oxytocin, vasopressin, and other disulfide hormones on uptake and extrusion of water by mitochondria," *Proc. Natl. Acad. Sci. U.S.*, **47**, 1929 (1961).

Neifakh, S. A., and T. B. Kazakova, "Actomyosin-like protein in mitochondria of mouse liver," *Nature*, **197**, 1106 (1963).

Neubert, D., and A. L. Lehninger, "The effect of oligomycin, gramicidin and other antibiotics on reversal of mitochondrial swelling by ATP," *Biochim. Biophys. Acta*, **62**, 556 (1962).

────── and ──────, "The effect of thiols and disulfides on water uptake and extrusion by rat liver mitochondria," *J. Biol. Chem.*, **237**, 952 (1962).

──────, G. V. Foster, and A. L. Lehninger, "Effect of temperature on uptake and extrusion of water by isolated rat liver mitochondria," *Biochim. Biophys. Acta*, **60**, 492 (1962).

──────, T. H. Rose, and A. L. Lehninger, "Assay and cellular distribution of mitochondrial contraction factor," *J. Biol. Chem.*, **237**, 2025 (1962).

──────, A. B. Wojtczak, and A. L. Lehninger, "Purification and identification of mitochondrial contraction factors I and II," *Proc. Natl. Acad. Sci. U.S.*, **48**, 1651 (1962).

Ohnishi, T., and T. Ohnishi, "A contractile protein of mitochondria," *J. Biochem. (Tokyo)*, **51**, 380 (1962); "Extraction of actin- and myosin-like proteins from liver mitochondria," *J. Biochem. (Tokyo)*, **52**, 230 (1962).

Packer, L., "Light scattering changes correlated with photosynthetic phosphorylation in chloroplast fragments," *Biochem. Biophys. Res. Commun.*, **9**, 355 (1962).

──────, "Metabolic and structural states of mitochondria. I, II," *J. Biol. Chem.*, **235**, 242 (1960); **236**, 214 (1961).

Schwartz, I. L., H. Rasmussen, M. A. Schoessler, L. Silver, and C. T. O. Fong, "Relation of chemical attachment to physiological action of vasopressin," *Proc. Natl. Acad. Sci. U.S.*, **46**, 1288 (1960).

Shaw, W. V., T. J. Lannon, and D. F. Tapley, "The effect of analogs of thyroxine and 2,4-dinitrophenol on the swelling of mitochondria," *Biochim. Biophys. Acta*, **36**, 499 (1959).

Sokoloff, L., S. Kaufman, P. L. Campbell, C. M. Francis, and H. Gelboin, "Thyroxine stimulation of amino acid incorporation into protein. Localization of stimulated step," *J. Biol. Chem.*, **238**, 1432 (1963).

Vignais, P. V., P. M. Vignais, C. S. Rossi, and A. L. Lehninger, "Restoration of ATP-induced contraction of pre-treated mitochondria by contractile protein," *Biochem. Biophys. Res. Commun.,* **11,** 307 (1963).

Vignais, P. M., P. V. Vignais, and A. L. Lehninger, "Restoration of ATP-induced contraction of 'aged' mitochondria by phosphatidyl inositol," *Biochem. Biophys. Res. Commun.,* **11,** 313 (1963).

Weinbach, E. C., H. Sheffield, and J. Garbus, "Restoration of oxidative phosphorylation and morphological integrity to swollen, uncoupled mitochondria," *Proc. Natl. Acad. Sci. U.S.,* **50,** 561 (1963).

Wojtczak, L., and A. L. Lehninger, "Formation and disappearance of an endogenous uncoupling factor during swelling and contraction of mitochondria," *Biochim. Biophys. Acta,* **51,** 442 (1961).

———, P. Wlodawer, and J. Zborowski, "ATP-induced contraction of rat liver mitochondria and synthesis of mitochondrial phospholipids," *Biochim. Biophys. Acta,* **70,** 290 (1963).

10

THE ULTRASTRUCTURE OF
THE MITOCHONDRIAL MEMBRANE
AND THE RESPIRATORY ASSEMBLY

In preceding chapters we have seen that the mitochondrial membrane system not only serves as a structural envelope but also contains the highly organized assemblies of respiratory enzymes that are responsible for formation of ATP, for the osmotic work of active transport, and for the mechanochemical energy coupling involved in shape and volume changes. We shall now consider the ultrastructure of the mitochondrial membrane as deduced from chemical analysis and from electron microscopic and other physical methods, as well as the molecular and enzymatic architecture of the respiratory assemblies that may be presumed to be units of structure of the mitochondrial membrane.

CHEMICAL COMPOSITION
OF THE MITOCHONDRIAL MEMBRANE

A number of mitochondrial membrane preparations have been analyzed in some detail; these include the Keilin-Hartree particles, the ETP particles of Green, and the cholate particles described by Ball and Cooper and other workers, each of which is derived from heart mitochondria. From rat liver mitochondria, the digitonin fragments of Cooper and Lehninger have also been studied. Such membrane preparations show remarkable similarity in enzymatic composition, as has already been pointed out. They ordinarily contain 35 to 40 per cent lipids, largely phosphatides, and 60 to 65 per cent protein; the minor variations that have been observed are probably due to differences in conditions of the chemical or physical methods used to disrupt structure.

Lipid composition. The lipid composition of mitochondria from rat liver and beef heart has been determined in studies from several laboratories. In general, nearly all of the mitochondrial lipid is present in the membrane fraction, especially in beef heart mitochondria. Over 90 per cent of the membrane lipid is phospholipid; the remainder is largely composed of triglycerides, diglycerides, and cholesterol. Rat liver mitochondria contain considerable phosphatidyl ethanolamine, phosphatidyl choline, inositol phosphatides, cardiolipin, and phosphatidyl serine, but little or no plasmalogen or sphingomyelin. On the other hand, beef heart mitochondria are quite rich in plasmalogens; they contain both ethanolamine and choline derivatives.

Both types of mitochondria contain significantly large amounts of cardiolipin, in fact, nearly all the cardiolipin of the intact cell, in contrast to microsomes, which contain little or none. Phosphatidic acid is present in vanishingly small amounts in most preparations. Although lysophosphatides have been observed in chloroform-methanol extracts of intact mitochondria and of digitonin fragments, it is likely that they arise by hydrolysis of the parent lipids during extraction of the mitochondria. Actually, lysophosphatides are known to cause swelling of mitochondria and also uncoupling of phosphorylation.

The fatty acid composition of the lipids of rat liver mitochondria and microsomes has also been determined. Liver mitochondrial lipids contain palmitic acid (17.8 per cent of total), stearic (14.9 per cent), oleic (11.9 per cent), linoleic (23.4 per cent) and arachidonic (17.0 per cent) acids as major components, as determined by Getz and his colleagues. In general, as compared with whole liver, liver mitochondria contain less palmitic and oleic acid but a rather higher proportion of linoleic, arachidonic, and docosahexaenoic acids. The cardiolipin fatty acids are almost entirely comprised of linoleic acid. However, mitochondria from other tissues or species do not always contain linoleic acid in such large amounts.

Undoubtedly, the great bulk of the membrane lipids serves a purely structural function in the lipid bilayer core of the membranes. However, certain lipids in the membrane have been identified as having quite specific functions in electron transport, translocation mechanisms, and swelling and contraction. For example, phosphatidic acid and/or cardiolipin, as well as phosphatidyl inositol, have been shown to be involved in the mechanism of mitochondrial contraction, as has been described in Chapter 9. Lecithin may have a specific function in the action of cytochrome oxidase and in D-β-hydroxybutric dehydrogenase, as indicated by work in Green's laboratory. The possible occurrence of small amounts of lipo-amino acids and lipopeptides in mitochondria is a question of some interest, since such lipids could be involved in the biosynthesis of membrane proteins. They have not been detected to date, however.

The characteristic content and ratio of lipids in the mitochondrial membrane are presumably related to the necessity for maintenance of a thermodynamically stable lipid bilayer as a core of the membrane for support of the assemblies of respiratory enzymes, as will be developed below. It appears quite significant that virtually all of the lipids of the mitochondrial membrane are extractable with chloroform-methanol. This indicates that there is little or no covalent bonding between the lipids and protein elements, a fact that attests to the high degree of stabilization of lipids and proteins in the membrane structure. Work in Green's laboratory has suggested that added labeled phospholipids in the medium may exchange with phospholipids of the mitochondrial membrane to a significant degree, but in view of the fact that mitochondrial and hyaloplasmic lipids are different in composition and turnover, further work is required to verify this effect and its specificity.

PROTEINS

It has been a common experience that the proteins and enzymes of mitochondrial membrane fragments are difficult to extract in soluble native form and free of adhering lipid, a fact that has greatly impeded study of enzymes of electron transport and oxidative phosphorylation. There is some evidence that the lipids of the membrane are involved in maintaining the insoluble and firmly attached nature of the membrane proteins; extraction of membrane fragments with acetone or detergents such as cholate often causes "loosening" or solubilization of specific enzymes from the membrane.

Use of cholate in solubilizing and fractionating membrane proteins has been highly developed by Green and his colleagues to isolate cytochromes *a, b,* and *c* and other enzymes, as well as to separate the so-called structural protein of the membrane. Cholate does not truly extract the protein in a permanently water-soluble, monodisperse form, since when cholate is removed from such preparations, the proteins promptly become insoluble again, often as polymers.

Criddle and his colleagues have postulated that hydrophobic bonding endows the membrane proteins and enzymes with the capacity to polymerize and to form insoluble polymolecular complexes with each other and with certain lipids. Crane has shown that cytochrome *c* combines with phosphatidyl ethanolamine to form a stable, ether-soluble complex, termed lipocytochrome *c,* in which the ϵ-amino groups of the lysine residues of cytochrome *c* combine electrostatically with the lipid molecules. Presumably, the membrane structure is stabilized by such lipid-protein interactions and by hydrophobic bonding.

Structural protein.   Criddle and his colleagues have isolated from beef heart mitochondria treated with a mixture of cholate, deoxycholate, and sodium dodecylsulfate the monomeric form of what they term structural protein of the mitochondrial membrane, free of flavoproteins and cytochromes. Since this protein comprises about 55 per cent of the total membrane protein, they suggest it is the main structural protein of the membrane; the membrane is therefore suggested to be made up of recurring identical protein molecules similarly to the protein sheath of viruses.

Structural protein is polymeric and insoluble in water at neutral pH but can be made soluble by anionic detergents and alkali. The monomeric form predominates in such solutions, but insoluble polymers and aggregates form when the systems are restored to neutral pH or when the detergent is removed. The monomeric form has a molecular weight of some 22,000, but accurate measurements of sedimentation and electrophoretic behavior are complicated by the tendency to polymerize. Amino acid analysis shows that some 41 per cent of the residues are nonpolar; the combined aspartate and glutamate content is 16 per cent. These data indicate that the structural protein is only slightly more hydrophobic than most proteins, but presumably the amino acid sequence and tertiary structure are such that a preponderance of nonpolar groups is present at critical areas on the surface.

In virus proteins, which are composed of recurring identical monomers, the N-terminal or C-terminal amino acid residues of the units are identical. Similar analysis of mitochondrial structural protein has been complicated by incomplete reactions with the specific reagents used for end-group analysis. Leucine and lesser amounts of tyrosine were found to be split off by carboxypeptidase, whereas no success attended efforts to identify N-terminal amino acids.

Structural protein has been found to combine with pure cytochromes a, b, or c to form water-soluble complexes in a 1:1 molar ratio under conditions that differ somewhat in each case. The combination of structural protein with cytochrome b was shown to cause a substantial change in the oxidation-reduction potential of the latter. It is presumed that the bonding in such complexes is essentially hydrophobic. Furthermore, it was shown that structural protein combines with phospholipids. Thus the structural protein can combine with the two other major molecular elements of the membrane: the electron carriers and the phospholipids.

The investigations of Criddle and his colleagues still leave unanswered many questions regarding the homogeneity and identity of structural protein that must be answered with more rigor than has been possible to date. Nevertheless, the findings are exceedingly promising and significant. The propensity of each of the cytochromes and of the flavoproteins, as well as the structural proteins, to exist in monomeric and polymeric forms is suggestive of a strong tendency for these molecules to arrange themselves in very stable, insoluble macromolecular assemblies of lamellar nature.

Other protein components of the membrane. Mention has already been made of mitochondrial actomyosin, which can be extracted from intact mitochondria with 0.6 M KCl and precipitated by dilution to 0.15 M KCl. Although few data are available for the size, shape, and homogeneity of this protein or protein complex, it is remarkable that rather large amounts of it occur in mitochondria and that it possesses, at least on preliminary examination, so many attributes of myofibrillar actomyosin. This protein also acts as a contraction factor for mitochondria. Presumably, it is also a component of the mitochondrial membrane.

Another protein component of the mitochondrial membrane is the phosphoprotein described earlier. To date, this has not been isolated in native form, but considerable evidence is available, from work of Kennedy, Boyer, and Wadkins, that it contains phosphorylated histidine and serine residues. Since the phosphorus content diminishes during swelling and increases during ATP-linked contraction and since it appears likely that phosphoprotein is also concerned in ion-translocation mechanisms in the mitochondrion, mitochondrial phosphoprotein may have its special significance in its ability to serve as a polyelectrolyte in the membrane that is capable of enzymatic gain and loss of charged groups. Existing data do not exclude the possibility that structural protein and mitochondrial phosphoprotein are identical; the former is known to contain both histidine and serine residues.

Finally, it is necessary to mention that sialic acid has been found to occur in mitochondria as well as in other membrane systems, presumably linked to proteins. Its significance is not yet known, but Thompson and McLees have found that the negatively charged groups conferring the characteristic electrophoretic mobility on the mitochondrial membrane have a rather low pK, in the same region as those of sialic acid. Thompson and McLees have also shown that the charge density of the membrane does not change during swelling of mitochondria, suggesting the membrane does not stretch but instead unfolds new surface.

The electron carriers and respiratory assemblies. The chemical, physical, and catalytic properties of the flavoproteins and cytochromes, which are firmly embedded in the mitochondrial membranes, have already been described in detail—in particular, their propensity to engage in hydrophobic bonding to form insoluble polymers or complexes with each other and with structural protein. It has also been pointed out that the electron carriers occur in simple molar ratios, a fact that suggests they occur in specifically organized recurring "assemblies" having the nature of biochemical and molecular "machines." It is very likely the respiratory assemblies are more or less regularly spaced in the membrane structure, since stepwise fragmentation of the membranes by sonic methods yields pieces in which the assemblies remain intact and in which the amount of the respiratory carriers per milligram of protein, as well as the lipid content, remains essentially constant even in the smallest fragments.

It is now quite clear that the catalytically active electron carriers and coupling enzymes must comprise a large fraction of the total membrane protein. Spectroscopic and chemical analysis in the laboratories of Ball, Green, Chance, and Lehninger indicates that some 25 per cent or more of the total membrane protein may be composed of these enzymes in the form of the respiratory assemblies. This fact strongly suggests that the mitochondrial membrane is not merely a relatively inert skin, but rather is an extremely complex structure consisting of recurring multienzyme systems.

Such a picture also implies that the physical and chemical properties of the membrane such as permeability and conformation may be dictated by the complex enzymatic reactions and equilibria that occur in the membrane, a prediction fully borne out by the research on water and ion movements in mitochondria that has already been described. The ultimate arrangement and orientation of the individual enzyme molecules in this continuous sheet of highly ordered structure therefore becomes a matter of paramount significance in describing the molecular architecture and function of the membrane.

MEMBRANE ULTRASTRUCTURE

Before the advent of electron microscopy, considerable evidence had been adduced that most biological membranes have essentially similar chemical and physical characteristics and that the core of such membranes is a lipid bilayer system. This evidence, which has been summarized by Davson and Danielli, remains rather compelling and is supported by more recent experimentation. The major lines of evidence include the following considerations. Most biological membranes contain from 30 to 40 per cent lipid (largely phospholipid) and 60 to 70 per cent protein; these ratios are stoichiometrically consistent with a structure possessing a lipid bilayer of about 60 Å thickness coated on each side with at least a monolayer of protein molecules. The lipid bilayer is presumed to contain a "neat" or smectic phase, that is, the hydrocarbon chains are oriented inward to make a continuous phase, whereas the polar groups of the phospholipids are on the outer surfaces. The amount of phospholipid in the erythrocyte membrane, for example, has been calculated to be sufficient to provide a double layer of lipid molecules over the entire surface.

Another point is that the permeability coefficient (i.e., flux of solute per unit area of membrane) of various nonelectrolytes through natural membranes is approximately proportional to their olive oil–water partition coefficients. In effect, lipid-soluble solutes penetrate fastest, a fact that is consistent with occurrence of a continuous lipid phase in the membrane. Tedeschi and Harris have conclusively shown that the mitochondrial membrane also shows such permeability behavior. Biological membranes also possess very high electrical resistance and capacitance, properties to be expected of structures containing a continuous barrier of a dielectric such as would be provided by a smectic lipid phase. Pauly and his colleagues have recently established that the mitochondrial membrane also shows high electrical resistance. On the other hand, surface tension measurements on biological membranes are consistent with occurrence of a protein coat.

Another major line of evidence on the constitution of biological membranes may be mentioned, namely, the revealing studies of Schmitt, Finean, Robertson, and others on the myelin sheath. The sheath is composed of the cell membrane of the Schwann cell wrapped concentrically around a nerve fiber, a rather unique membrane conformation with repeatedly recurring layers admirably suited to examination by X-ray scattering, polarization optics, and electron microscopy. Such observations on the myelin sheath strongly support occurrence of a lipid bilayer of about 55 Å as the core of the myelin membrane and also yield information on the limiting dimensions of the protein coats on each side of the core.

ELECTRON MICROSCOPY OF MITOCHONDRIAL MEMBRANES BY POSITIVE CONTRAST

For over a decade osmium tetroxide and potassium permanganate have been widely used as fixatives for electron microscopic examination of cell ultrastructure, particularly of membranes and granules. These agents, which are quite electron-dense, are characteristically deposited in such structures and stain them "positively," whereas the surrounding material, which does not take the stain, remains electron-lucid. This type of staining is called positive contrast, and presumably it depends on a chemical or physical affinity of the stain for a specific chemical or physical structure in the object taking the stain. Each of these stains gives positive contrast to the membrane, but in a somewhat different way.

There has not been complete agreement in interpretation of such findings, but the diagram in Figure 10–1 illustrates the dimensions of the mitochondrial membranes after staining by osmium and by permanganate, as well as a representation of the molecular organization according to the views of Sjöstrand.

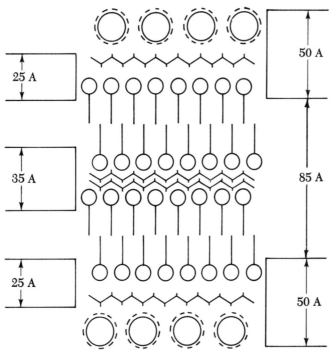

Figure 10–1 Relative location of osmium-dense (at right) and KMnO$_4$-dense lines (at left) in mitochondrial membrane in relation to membrane structure. [F. Sjöstrand, *Radiation Research*, **Suppl. 2**, 375 (1960).]

It is seen that osmium tetroxide (at the right of the diagram) yields two dense lines, of about 50 Å each, separated by a lucid space of 85 Å; these dimensions are invariant characteristics of the surrounding membrane of mitochondria of all cell types. To the left is shown the pattern given by permanganate, which yields three dense lines separated by electron-lucid lines of 25 Å.

Sjöstrand feels that the two membrane elements are normally fused, as shown in his molecular representation. When mitochondria swell, the inner permanganate line undergoes subdivision. Robertson and other investigators find that the inner $KMnO_4$ lines are rarely fused and that a space exists between the membranes, which can be "shrunk" with hypertonic sucrose. Figure 10–2 gives a schematic representation prepared by Finean for comparison. The evidence adduced by these investigators, as well as by Robertson and by Stoeckenius, cannot be described in detail here, but it is a fair conclusion that the mitochondrial membranes stain in a very characteristic manner and spacing with osmium and with permanganate.

The question that is not completely resolved is the molecular basis for the staining and, with it, the actual disposition of the

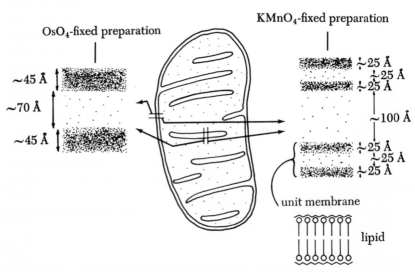

Figure 10–2 Relationship between osmium-dense and $KMnO_4$-dense lines. (After J. B. Finean, *Chemical Ultrastructure in Living Tissues*, Charles C Thomas, Springfield, Ill., p. 86.)

lipid and protein molecules in the membrane structure. Although the occurrence of a lipid bilayer as the core is a near certainty, perhaps the major outstanding questions are the thickness and disposition of the protein layers of the membrane and whether the protein is unfolded or globular, particularly the protein in immediate contact with the lipid bilayers.

Robertson has proposed that all biological membrane systems are composed of so-called unit membranes of specific and constant thickness and composition each of which shows two thin, dense lines with permanganate separated by a light space of 25 Å. The total thickness of each pair of lines is 75 Å, as shown in Finean's schematic diagram (Figure 10–2). Robertson has assumed that each unit membrane contains a lipid bilayer of about 50 Å coated on each side with an unfolded protein monolayer of about 10 to 15 Å, to comprise a total of about 75 Å. Robertson suggested that such unit membranes may exist as single units, as in the cell membrane, or as paired or compound membranes, as in the surrounding mitochondrial membrane or cristae.

This concept has been valuable in analyzing and systematizing complex membrane structures, but it now appears probable, particularly from work of Sjöstrand and his school, that there is in fact significant differentiation of different types of biological membranes that is visible in high-resolution electron micrographs of osmium-stained material. Sjöstrand's electron micrographs of mitochondrial cristae show that each of the paired membranes possesses distinctly thicker osmium-dense lines, with evidence of a granular fine structure, than does the plasma membrane.

Actually, such a structural differentiation is perhaps to be expected, since the cristae contain the highly organized respiratory assemblies and the plasma membrane is devoid of these structures, although it probably possesses other types of organized enzyme systems that are less elaborate. Robertson has also recognized that the unit membrane may differ in thickness in different cell membranes, and he suggests the differences to be caused by the characteristic lipids and proteins of each type.

NEGATIVE STAINING OF MEMBRANES

More recently there has been growing interest in the use of negative-contrast staining to visualize membrane structure, particularly of mitochondrial membranes. In negative staining, application is made of an electron-dense substance that is chemically inert and presumably does not combine with any component of the membrane structure, but rather surrounds the structure and reveals its outline or profile. The substances used for this purpose are usually phosphotungstate or uranyl acetate. Negative staining has been especially successful in visualizing the structure of isolated virus particles.

Fernández-Morán has recently applied the negative staining method, combined with new high-resolution techniques, to the problem of the ultrastructure of beef heart mitochondrial membranes. He has discovered that the negatively stained images show the membrane to contain many spherical or ellipsoidal particles of about 70 to 90 Å in diameter, which he has called elementary particles (Figure 10–3). The elementary particles are seen to be connected by narrow stalks to the electron-lucid core of the membrane; in most of the images, both sides of this core are coated with elementary particles. At first, Fernández-Morán indicated that these particles are found in both the outer membrane and the cristae, but more recently he has stressed their occurrence in cristae. Such elementary particles were reported by Fernández-Morán to occur also in erythrocyte membranes and in the myelin sheath.

These observations have now been confirmed in a number of other laboratories. Stoeckenius has observed these particles in mitochondria of *Neurospora;* Parsons and also Greenawalt have observed them in rat liver mitochondria; and D. S. Smith has observed them in the cristae of mitochondria of insect flight muscles. While Stoeckenius and Parsons could detect no repetitive pattern in their distribution, Smith has found, in surface images of the cristae, that the elementary particles are arranged in recurring clusters or rosettes.

Smith also finds that the negatively stained membrane has distinct fine structure, as shown in Figure 10–4. He has suggested the elementary particle and its stalk comprise one-half of a symmetrical dumbbell structure, with the second particle buried in the membrane. Smith estimates that there are about 4000 particles per square micron of membrane surface.

The negative staining method has also revealed other aspects of mitochondrial structure. Horne and Whittaker have shown (Figure 10–5) that negative staining reveals the outlines of the cristae of brain mitochondria to be wormlike structures that

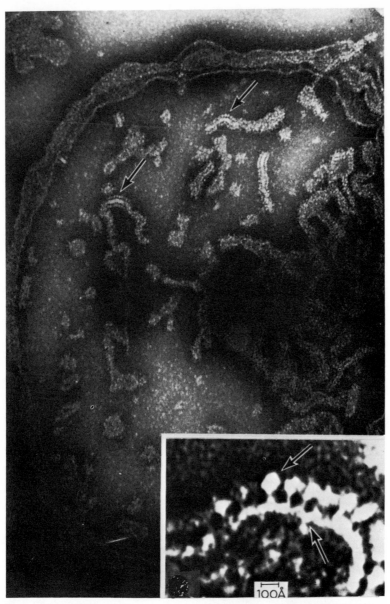

Figure 10–3 Electron micrograph of portion of a beef heart mitochondrion embedded in a thin layer of phosphotungstate. Note characteristic paired arrays of elementary particles in profiles of fragmented cristae (× 120,000). The enlargement in lower right corner (× 600,000) shows attachment of elementary particles to cristae by stalks. (Photograph provided by Dr. H. Fernández-Morán.)

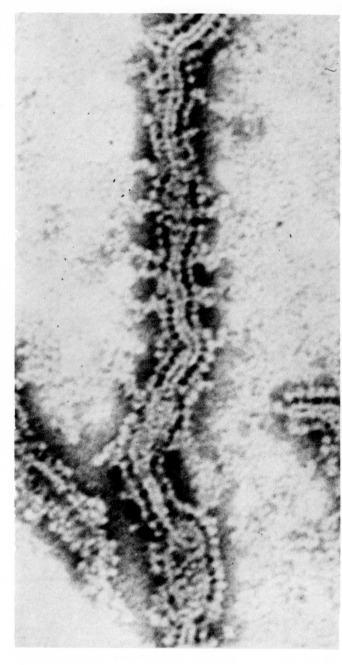

Figure 10—4 High-resolution electron micrograph of phosphotungstate-stained profile of mitochondrial membrane. The globular particles appear to be paired in a dumbbell configuration, attached by stalks, sc that the core of the membrane appears to be made up of two rows of discrete particles. [D. S. Smith, J. Cell. Biol., **19**, 135 (1963).]

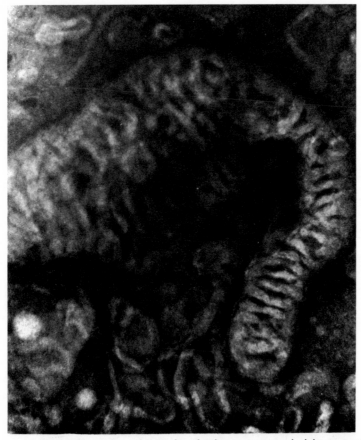

Figure 10–5 Conformation of mitochondrial cristae revealed by negative staining with phosphotungstate. [R. W. Horne and V. P. Whittaker, Z. *Zellforsch.*, **58**, 9 (1962).]

are clearly invaginations of the inner surface of the surrounding membrane system; in some pictures an actual cristal orifice can be seen. Parsons, as well as Greenawalt, has observed long, narrow, ribbonlike structures coated with elementary particles in lysed mitochondria (Figure 10–6). Parsons has concluded that these structures are actually cristae; however, Greenawalt and other investigators feel that they are too long, narrow, and numerous to be cristae. Sjöstrand has recently expressed the view that the elementary particles as observed following nega-

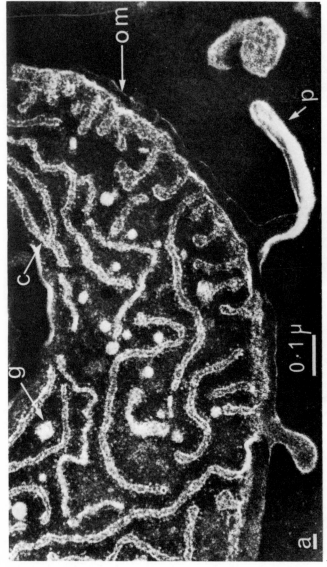

Figure 10–6 A negatively stained rat liver mitochondrion. *om* is the outer membrane, *p* a projection of the outer membrane, *g* a dense granule, and *c* indicates structures that Parsons has concluded are cristae (see text). [D. F. Parsons, *Science*, **140**, cover (1963).]

tive staining are probably artifacts. He does, however, support the conclusion that the membrane surface is coated with particles. On study of frozen-dried cytomembrane surfaces (Figure 10–7), he has found regularly arranged particles with an average diameter of 40 to 45 Å. He has suggested the possibility that such particles are globular micelles of lipids.

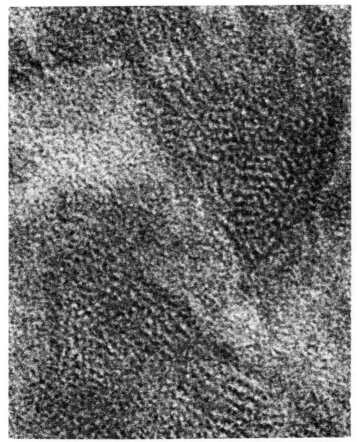

Figure 10–7 Electron micrograph of surface of cytoplasmic membrane in mouse pancreas exocrine cell, showing regular arrangement of granular elements; these have a diameter of about 40 to 45 Å. No fixative was used; the specimen was frozen and dried. [Photograph provided by Dr. F. Sjöstrand; cf. Sjöstrand, Nature, **199**, 1263 (1963).]

CONSTRUCTION OF LIPID BILAYERS

That it may be possible in the not too distant future to reconstruct in vitro membrane systems bearing ordered arrays of enzymes or enzyme systems is suggested by recent successes in the construction of stable phospholipid bilayers and in the fuller understanding of the physical principles involved in their formation and stabilization. Rudin and Mueller and their colleagues have recently shown that stable lipid bilayers having physical properties remarkably similar to those of natural membranes may be formed from crude mixtures of brain lipids. A drop of a chloroform-methanol solution of the brain lipids is placed in a small aperture in a plastic septum between two compartments containing KCl solution. As the lipid solvent diffuses out of the droplet into the aqueous phase, the oriented phospholipid molecules in the two solvent interfaces of the droplet approach each other and finally join in a rather stable bilayer across the aperture.

Such bilayers are of the neat, or smectic, type described earlier. They have the approximate thickness of the lipid bilayer of natural membranes and also show high electrical resistance, self-sealing properties, and other attributes of natural membranes.

Thompson and Huang have refined the method of Rudin and Mueller and have perfected more accurate means of measuring the optical, electrical, mechanical, and permeability properties of lipid bilayers. They have studied formation of bilayers from highly purified lipids of known composition in an effort to determine the basic molecular prerequisites for the formation of self-stabilizing bilayer systems. Thompson and his colleagues have found that such stable bilayers cannot be formed from any phospholipid or neutral lipid; rather, it is necessary to have certain combinations of specific lipids in order to obtain a stable system.

The simplest stable system is composed of the combination of egg lecithin and n-tetradecane, which may be replaced by methyl oleate or by cholesterol plus n-decane. The properties of this simple system are in surprising agreement with those of natural membranes, as is seen in the data of Table 10–1.

Thompson and his colleagues believe that the structure and stability of lipid bilayers may in principle be governed by

Table 10–1 Comparison of properties of natural membranes and of a phospholipid bilayer membrane*

Property	Natural membrane, 20–25°	Phospholipid bilayer membrane, 36°
Thickness of lipid layer, Å	60–80	61 ± 10
Electrical resistance, ohms per cm^2	10^2–10^5	$(0.25$–$4) \times 10^6$
Electrical capacitance, μf per cm^2	0.5–1.3	0.75
Surface tension, dynes per cm	0.03–3.0	0.5
Water permeability, μ per min per atm	0.1–3.0	0.16
Breakdown voltage, mV	100–300	200 ± 20

* After Thompson, 1963.

the same considerations that lead to stable secondary, tertiary, and quaternary structures of protein molecules. Their stability is determined by the nature and the ratio of the lipid building blocks, their electrical charges, and their space-filling properties. The lipid bilayers are stabilized largely through Van der Waals dispersion forces between methylene groups of adjacent hydrocarbon chains. Although these forces are very weak taken singly, they become formidably large when repeated many times in three dimensions along the close-packed hydrocarbon chains.

Thompson has pointed out that the different types of component lipids may be to membrane structure what amino acids are to protein structure, that is, the secondary, tertiary, and quaternary structure of membranes are determined by the structure and space-filling properties of the building blocks, their ratio, and their two-dimensional patterns. Actually, such lipid bilayers represent one of only two or three thermodynamically stable conformations of phospholipid-water systems, as shown by Luzzati and Husson. In addition to the lamellar array represented by the bilayer, there are rectangular and inverted micellar forms; the latter do not provide a continuous hydrocarbon phase and are less likely to be found in natural membranes.

THE ULTRASTRUCTURE OF THE RESPIRATORY ASSEMBLY

We have seen that respiratory assemblies composed of complete sets of electron carriers and coupling enzymes are arranged in the mitochondrial membrane at apparently regularly spaced intervals and that these make up 25 per cent or more of the total membrane protein, as isolated after physical or chemical disruption of the membranes. It is possible to calculate, from the known content of the carriers, how many assemblies are present in a single mitochondrion. Estabrook and Holowinsky estimate that in a single liver mitochondrion some 17,000 molecules of cytochrome a are present and in the case of heart mitochondria, as many as 50,000. If each respiratory assembly contains one molecule of cytochrome a, then about 17,000 respiratory assemblies are present in each mitochondrion; however, if the assemblies are not monomeric, their number must be correspondingly less. It will be recalled that cytochrome oxidase may be a complex containing six molecules of cytochrome a.

Presumably, the assemblies are largely located in the membranes of the cristae, which we have already seen to have much more surface than the outer envelope. Furthermore, the respiratory rate of mitochondria appears to correlate with profuseness of cristae and reaches its acme in the mitochondria of flight muscle of insects.

In Table 10–2 are listed the components and molecular weights of a *minimum respiratory assembly*, which is assumed to contain one molecule each of NADH dehydrogenase, succinate dehydrogenase, and cytochromes a, b, c, and c_1. It may be noted that there is some uncertainty about the molecular weight of the NADH dehydrogenase, the largest component, but the value given is that of Singer's enzyme, which appears to be most "native." From these considerations the basic minimum respiratory assembly must be thought of in terms of a total particle weight of about 1,350,000.

In Figure 10–8 is shown an early representation of the respiratory assembly and its arrangement in the membrane proposed by Lehninger on the basis of Robertson's structure of the cell unit membrane. It was proposed that the assembly is part of the protein monolayer of the membrane. However, an alternative representation is that it is not part of the basic monolayer but is attached laterally. This arrangement would perhaps be

Table 10–2 Components of the respiratory assembly*

Electron-transferring enzymes		Mol. wt.
NADH dehydrogenase		1,000,000
Succinate dehydrogenase		200,000
Cytochrome b		28,000
Cytochrome c_1		40,000
Cytochrome c		12,000
Cytochrome a monomer		70,000
	Subtotal	1,350,000
Coupling factors:		
Site I 2 × 30,000		60,000
Site II 2 × 30,000		60,000
Site III 2 × 30,000		60,000
	Subtotal	180,000
Auxiliary enzymes tightly bound to respiratory fragments:		
D-β-hydroxybutyrate dehydrogenase		60,000
α-glycerophosphate dehydrogenase		60,000
Fatty acyl-CoA dehydrogenases		60,000
Electron-transferring flavoprotein		60,000
Pyridine nucleotide transhydrogenase		60,000
	Subtotal	300,000
	Minimum assembly weight	1,350,000
	Maximum assembly weight	1,830,000

* The "minimum assembly" is one containing only the electron carriers; the "maximum assembly" also contains the coupling factors and other tightly bound dehydrogenases present in mitochondrial membrane.

more consistent with Sjöstrand's finding that the membranes of the cristae are somewhat thicker than the outer membrane.

The representation of Lehninger has certain advantages, particularly since it permits a simple orientation of active sites of the component enzymes with respect to the plane of the membrane, a feature that is consonant with the vectorial or directional properties of ion transport and mechanochemical events in the membrane.

Recently, following the discovery of the so-called elementary particles, Green and Fernández-Morán and their colleagues have proposed that these particles are themselves the respira-

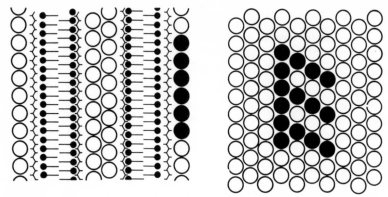

Figure 10–8 Schematic representation of a respiratory assembly in the mitochondrial membrane. The assembly is indicated by black circles; it includes three sets of coupling enzymes arranged laterally to account for oxidative phosphorylation of ADP. The open circles indicate the structural protein of the membrane. [A. L. Lehninger, *Sci. Am.*, **204**, 73 (Sept. 1961).]

tory assemblies in which the carriers are arranged in an approximately spherical array, the whole being attached to the membrane by a stalk. As supporting evidence they showed that respiratory particles isolated from heart mitochondria are approximately the same size as elementary particles and are also spherical in shape when stained negatively. The diameters of such isolated particles were, however, significantly larger than the particles seen in intact membranes, and the negative-contrast images are perhaps not clear enough to justify a firm conclusion yet.

Actually, there appears to be a discrepancy in the matter of the size of the respiratory assemblies and the particle weight of the elementary particles. If the latter are spheres with a diameter of 90 Å, they have a particle weight considerably less than the minimal molecular weight of 1,400,000 of the respiratory assembly (Table 10–2). The calculations of Green and his colleagues also make use of molar ratios of the carriers and molecular weights that are not in full agreement with those observed in other laboratories.

It must also be emphasized, in carrying out such calculations, that it is not at all certain that the respiratory chain is truly monomeric, particularly since active cytochrome oxidase is believed to be a pentamer or hexamer. In the latter case the number of the other cytochromes and the flavoproteins must be correspondingly increased. Furthermore, other enzymes tightly associated with the respiratory particles such as D-β-hydroxybutyrate dehydrogenase, fatty acyl-CoA dehydrogenases, and α-glycerophosphate dehydrogenase may also be part of the basic respiratory assembly; in that case also the respiratory assembly would have a much larger particle weight than the elementary particles visualized by negative contrast (Table 10–2). Further experimental details of Green's work are therefore awaited with much interest and should make possible a more certain evaluation of his proposal.

More recently, Chance has proposed a rather different idea of the significance of the elementary particles. He has suggested that they are not complete assemblies, but rather that each elementary particle contains a single electron carrier component and possibly some additional protein components. He has suggested that adjacent elementary particles, each containing a specific carrier, interact with each other by translational diffusion limited by the length and flexibility of the stalk, which acts somewhat like the swinging arm of the lipoic acid moiety of α-keto acid dehydrogenases referred to in Chapter 3.

VECTORIAL PARAMETERS OF THE STRUCTURE
OF THE RESPIRATORY ASSEMBLY

A completely satisfactory representation of mitochondrial membrane structure and of the arrangement of enzyme molecules in the respiratory assembly must take account not only of the size and shape of the component enzymes but also of two other features of the respiratory assembly. It has been stressed in earlier chapters that the assembly is a machine not only for making ATP but also for bringing about ion translocation and the conformational changes in the membranes involved in swelling and contraction. Actually, there is evidence that all three of these activities are vectorial or directional in nature, a fact that must have a structural basis, that is, it must derive from the asymmetric organization of the individual enzymes or the whole assembly in the membrane.

These directional properties of the respiratory assembly provide a basis for Mitchell's concept of anisotropy of location of respiratory enzymes in the mitochondrial membrane and for the concept of vectorial enzyme action in membranes as distinguished from the scalar or nondirectional action of soluble enzymes in solution. Although many if not all enzymatic reactions are probably asymmetrical at the active site of the enzyme, this vectorial characteristic cannot be expressed in a bulk directional movement unless the rotational and translational diffusion of enzyme molecules can be constrained in a barrier in such a manner as to achieve specific orientation of the active sites.

For these reasons definition of the geometry and dimensions of the respiratory assembly is a far more complex matter than simply packaging a set of enzymes to achieve respiration and phosphorylation, and it would appear that the proposals for the structure of the respiratory assembly outlined above fall short of accounting satisfactorily for all known properties of the assembly.

In Figure 10–9 are shown some schematic representations of respiratory assemblies that are considered to provide the appropriate asymmetry of organization required by the considerations just outlined. The first shows the arrangement proposed by Mitchell, which accounts for asymmetric discharge of H^+ and OH^- ions during electron transport. The second shows a representation of a membrane ATPase, also capable of asymmetric discharge or uptake of H^+ and OH^- (or the phosphoryl group). The third shows a modification of these, proposed by Lehninger, that allows for asymmetric formation of ATP and for asymmetric formation of H^+ and OH^- at each of the coupling sites; it is an extension of a proposal made originally by Davies and Ogston.

None of these representations as schematized accounts for the directional changes in membrane conformation that lead to water movements. However, Figure 10–10 gives some schematic representations that should be visualized as being superimposed on those of Figure 10–8 in order to account for the three main types of vectorial enzyme action of the respiratory assemblies. In one representation, the conformation of the assembly is proposed to change as a function of the phosphate potential (i.e., the ratio [ATP] / [ADP] [P_i]) or of the oxidation-reduction state, either by shifts in quaternary structure or in tertiary structure of the component molecules.

It is of some interest that the tertiary configuration of some flavoproteins and cytochromes is known to change as a func-

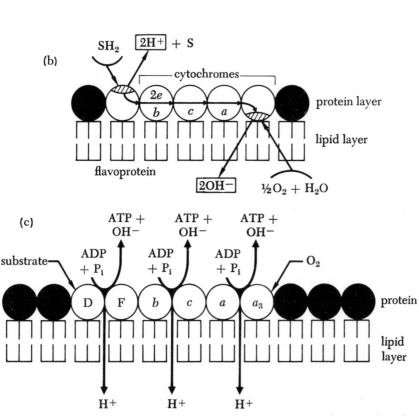

Figure 10–9 Schematic representations of ion-transport mechanisms based on asymmetric arrangement of active sites of ATPases or electron carriers in the membrane structure, permitting separation of H^+ and OH^+ across a membrane relatively impermeable to H^+. (a) indicates an asymmetric ATPase capable of creating a pH gradient. In (c) such an ATPase is shown to be responsible for oxidative phosphorylation of ADP, with concomitant separation of H^+ and OH^-. In (b) separation of H^+ and OH^- is brought about by asymmetric and opposite arrangement of flavoprotein and cytochrome oxidase in membrane, as SH_2 is oxidized to S by oxygen.

229

(a) changes in conformation of coupling enzymes

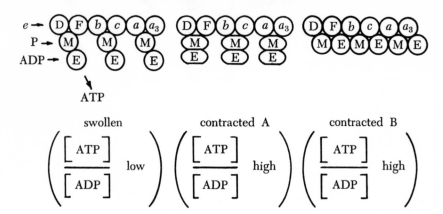

$$\left(\dfrac{\left[\text{ATP} \right]}{\left[\text{ADP} \right]} \;\; \text{low} \right) \quad \left(\dfrac{\left[\text{ATP} \right]}{\left[\text{ADP} \right]} \;\; \text{high} \right) \quad \left(\dfrac{\left[\text{ATP} \right]}{\left[\text{ADP} \right]} \;\; \text{high} \right)$$

swollen   contracted A   contracted B

(b) changes in conformation of carrier molecules

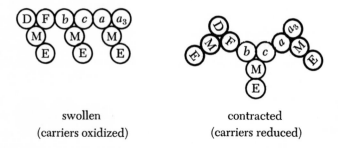

swollen   contracted

(carriers oxidized)   (carriers reduced)

(c) changes in conformation of structure protein or contractile protein

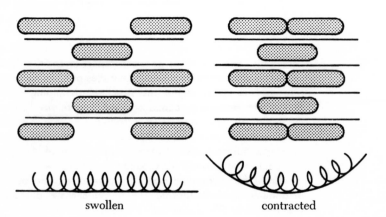

swollen   contracted

tion of oxidation-reduction state. Another representation is suggested in a recent paper by Cole; in this arrangement, contractile actomyosin-like molecules could be attached laterally to the surface of the membranes. Such an arrangement might give asymmetry of conformational changes as a function of phosphate potential. The coupling enzymes or "mitochondrial actomyosin" may be the contractile elements in such a system.

From these considerations the structure and conformation of the respiratory assembly is clearly one of the most challenging and complex problems in contemporary molecular biology, and its solution may also yield the secrets of the mechanism of oxidative phosphorylation, of active ion transport, and of the active contractility of membranes.

REFERENCES

Reviews

Ball, E. G., and C. D. Joel, "The composition of the mitochondrial membrane in relation to its structure and function," *Intern. Rev. Cytol.*, 13, 99 (1962).
Davson, H., and J. F. Danielli, *The Permeability of Natural Membranes*, Cambridge, London, 1952.

Figure 10–10 Schematic representations of some possible molecular mechanisms for the active changes in dimensions or conformation of mitochondrial membranes.

In (a) it is suggested that the coupling enzymes may undergo changes in tertiary structure (A) or packing arrangement (B) as a function of the ATP/ADP ratio.

In (b) the carrier molecules may undergo changes in conformation or packing arrangement as a function of oxidation-reduction state; there is some evidence that the tertiary structure of cytochrome c and of some flavoproteins undergoes changes as a function of oxidation state.

In (c) are shown two representations of changes in packing arrangement of structural protein or contractile protein (such as mitochondrial actomyosin). These changes might be a function of the ATP/ADP ratio.

Structural changes such as these must be visualized as being superimposed on transport activities of the kind shown in Figure 10–9.

Engström, A., and J. B. Finean, *Biological Ultrastructure*, Academic, New York, 1958.

Fernández-Morán, H., "Cell-membrane ultrastructure," *Circulation*, **26**, 1039 (1962).

Lehninger, A. L., "Water uptake and extrusion by mitochondria in relation to oxidative phosphorylation," *Physiol. Rev.*, **42**, 467 (1962).

Robertson, J. D., "The ultrastructure of cell membranes and their derivatives," *Biochem. Soc. Symp. (Cambridge, Engl.)*, **16**, 3 (1959).

Robertson, R. N., "Ion transport and respiration," *Biol. Rev. Cambridge Phil. Soc.*, **35**, 231 (1960).

Articles in *The Interpretation of Ultrastructure, Symp. Intern. Soc. Cell Biol.*, Academic, New York, 1961, Vol. 1.

Research papers

Blair, P. V., T. Oda, D. E. Green, and H. Fernández-Morán, "Studies on the electron transfer system. LIV. Isolation of the unit of electron transfer," *Biochemistry*, **2**, 756 (1963).

Cole, A., "A molecular model for biological contractility: Implications in chromosome structure and function," *Nature*, **196**, 211 (1962).

Criddle, R. S., R. M. Bock, D. E. Green, and H. D. Tisdale, "Physical characteristics of proteins of the electron transfer system and interpretation of the structure of mitochondria," *Biochemistry*, **1**, 827 (1962).

Estabrook, R. W., and A. Holowinsky, "Studies on the content and organization of the respiratory enzymes of mitochondria," *J. Biophys. Biochem. Cytol.*, **9**, 19 (1961).

Getz, G. S., W. Bartley, F. Stirpe, B. M. Notton, and A. Renshaw, "The lipid composition of rat liver mitochondria, fluffy layer, and microsomes," *Biochem. J.*, **83**, 181 (1962).

Horne, R. W., and V. P. Whittaker, "The use of the negative staining method for the electron-microscopic study of subcellular particles from animal tissues," *Histochemie*, **58**, 1 (1962).

Huang, C., L. Wheeldon, and T. E. Thompson, "The properties of lipid bilayer membranes separating two aqueous phases; formation of a membrane of simple composition," *J. Mol. Biol.*, in press.

Lehninger, A. L., "Energy transformation in the cell," *Sci. Am.*, May, 1960.

Luzzatti, V., and F. Husson, "Liquid-crystalline phases of lipid-water systems," *J. Cell Biol.*, **12**, 219 (1962).

MacFarlane, M. G., G. M. Gray, and L. W. Wheeldon, "Fatty acid composition of phospholipids from subcellular particles of rat liver," *Biochem. J.*, **77**, 626 (1960).

Mueller, P., D. O. Rudin, H. T. Tien, and W. C. Wescott, "Reconstitution of excitable cell membrane structure *in vitro*," *Circulation*,

26, 1167 (1962); also, "Methods for the formation of single bimolecular lipid membranes in aqueous solution," *J. Phys. Chem.,* **67,** 534 (1963).

Parsons, D. F., "Mitochondrial structure: Two types of subunits on negatively stained mitochondrial membranes," *Science,* **140,** 685 (1963).

——, "Negative staining of thinly spread cells and associated virus," *J. Cell Biol.,* **16,** 620 (1963).

Pauly, H., and L. Packer, "The relationship of internal conductance and membrane capacity to mitochondrial volume," *J. Biophys. Biochem. Cytol.,* **7,** 603 (1960).

——, ——, and H. P. Schwan, "Electrical properties of mitochondrial membranes," *J. Biophys. Biochem. Cytol.,* **7,** 589 (1960).

Pease, D. C., "Demonstration of a highly ordered pattern upon a mitochondrial surface," *J. Cell Biol.,* **15,** 385 (1962).

Smith, D. S., *J. Cell. Biol.,* in press.

Stoeckenius, W., "Some observations on negatively stained mitochondria," *J. Cell Biol.,* **17,** 443 (1963).

Thompson, T. E., "The properties of bimolecular phospholipid membranes," in M. Locke (ed.), *Cellular Membranes in Development,* Academic, New York, in press.

—— and B. McLees, "An electrophoretic study of suspensions of intact mitochondria and of fragments of mitochondrial membranes," *Biochim. Biophys. Acta,* **50,** 213 (1961).

11

BIOGENESIS OF MITOCHONDRIA

Since the first recognition of mitochondria as distinctive intracellular granules, the question of their origin and biogenesis has intrigued cytologists and aroused much speculation. The question looms even larger today, now that we have at hand an abundance of information on the enormous molecular complexity of mitochondrial structure and function. The dramatic contemporary developments in genetic biochemistry and the molecular definition of the gene-enzyme relationship may make possible some first approaches to the genetics of cell structure and the biogenesis of cell organelles.

THEORIES OF BIOGENESIS OF MITOCHONDRIA

The theories that have been proposed may be classified into three categories:

1. De novo synthesis of mitochondria from submicroscopic precursors present in the hyaloplasm.

2. Formation from other membranous structures of the cell.

3. Growth and division of preexisting mitochondria.

All three ideas were first proposed early in the history of mitochondria, largely on the basis of microscopic examination of
living or fixed cells, sometimes in different stages of their life
cycles, with little reference to biochemical and metabolic considerations. The experimental evidence in most cases was highly
circumstantial. Nevertheless, it now appears possible to assess
each of these theories critically, not only on the basis of microscopic observations, but particularly in the light of current
knowledge of the biochemistry of cell organization and metabolism.

THE THEORY OF DE NOVO SYNTHESIS

Although many speculations have been made that mitochondria arise de novo, presumably from soluble components of the
hyaloplasm not visible in the light or electron microscope, the
first rigorous experimental test of this theory was made in 1914
by Beckwith, whose work was repeated many years later by
Harvey. In these experiments fertilized eggs of the sea urchin
and other organisms were centrifuged, with formation of a
"pellet" of mitochondria and yolk at the heavy end of the cell,
a zone of clear "protoplasm" in the middle, and a layer of lipids
at the light end of the cell, containing no visible mitochondria.
The eggs were then allowed to divide. In some of the eggs
cleavage so occurred that the yolk and mitochondria appeared
in one daughter cell and the lipid layer in the other. Although
many eggs died, some developed into larvae, whether they
arose from the lipid-rich end of the egg cell, which was apparently devoid of mitochondria at the time of division, or from the
end of the egg rich in mitochondria. The presence of mitochondria was assessed after staining with dyes such as methyl green
or Janus green.

Since mitochondria were found in the cells of the larvae arising from both types of cell, it was concluded by Beckwith, and
by Harvey in turn, that the mitochondria were not essential for
development and that mitochondria were formed de novo from
clear protoplasm and lipids in those daughter cells rich in lipid
but originally containing no mitochondria as determined by
the methods used.

Although the experiment was well contrived, it was later
found that the optical and staining methods employed apparently were unable to visualize mitochondria in the lipid-rich

daughter cells. Lansing, on repeating the experiments in 1952–1953 with the electron microscope and staining by osmium tetroxide, was able to recognize large numbers of mitochondria in the lipid-rich cells in which Beckwith and Harvey had seen none by the conventional optical methods they used. Lansing's work has since been confirmed. Presumably, the mitochondria failed to take the Janus green stain in the lipid-rich cells in the earlier experiments.

Despite this turn of events, a number of investigators have since presented other observations thought to support de novo formation of mitochondria. Some of these observations were made from time-lapse moving pictures of living cells under phase contrast, but the uncertainties introduced by the limited focal depth and by changes in refractile properties of the streaming cytoplasm prevent acceptance of such observations. Increasing attention has been paid to the possibility that mitochondria may be assembled from preexisting elements of the cytoplasm of a somewhat higher degree of organization than simple, soluble proteins or lipids, perhaps from organized granular aggregates seen in the "ground substance" of the hyaloplasm, such as the so-called microbodies, as suggested by Rouiller. However, recent work by Baudhuin and Beaufay shows the microbodies to have an enzyme content very different from that of mitochondria.

Actually, a number of biochemical considerations mitigate against de novo synthesis of mitochondria from components of the cytoplasm. For example, most enzymes specifically characteristic of mitochondria have been found to be completely absent in the soluble cytoplasm. Among these are cytochromes a, b, c, and c_1, the succinate and NADH dehydrogenase flavoproteins, D-β-hydroxybutyrate, choline, and α-glycerophosphate dehydrogenases, among many others.

Unless complete de novo synthesis of fully functional mitochondria occurs instantaneously, one might reasonably expect to find at least some of the many specific enzymes from which mitochondrial membranes are presumably assembled preexisting in the cytoplasm. Although it is true that some enzymes present in mitochondria are also present in the cytoplasm, such as malate and isocitrate dehydrogenases, it is probable that these are different molecular forms, i.e., so-called isozymes, having rather different functions in the two cytoplasmic compartments. There is, in addition, immunological evidence that stands against the idea of de novo synthesis from the cyto-plasmic proteins.

It is conceivable, of course, that phospholipids of the soluble cytoplasm may be utilized as building blocks for mitochondrial membrane biosynthesis, but mitochondria have the capacity to synthesize at least some of the stages in lipid biosynthesis. As will be seen below, recent work of Luck appears to exclude de novo synthesis of mitochondria as being a major bulk mech-anism, at least in *Neurospora crassa* cells.

BIOGENESIS OF MITOCHONDRIA
FROM OTHER MEMBRANE SYSTEMS

Much experimental work, again of a circumstantial nature, has been cited as supporting the biogenesis of mitochondria from other membrane systems of the cell. In fact, every mem-brane system of the cell has been proposed at one time or an-other as the precursor of mitochondria.

One of the major theories is that of Robertson, who has pro-posed that mitochondria may be formed from the plasma mem-brane by a double infolding and pinching-off process. Figure 11–1 shows how the double-membrane system of mitochondria may arise from the single "unit membrane" of the cell envelope. At one stage in this process, a "tail" or connection with the plasma membrane is suggested, although such connections have not been unequivocally observed. Geren and Schmitt earlier suggested that mitochondria of the axons of the squid are formed from the plasma membrane of the Schwann cell, on the basis of some very suggestive electron micrographs. In no case, however, has a convincing time-sequence study showing all stages of such a process been carried out.

A variant of the idea that mitochondria may arise from the plasma membrane has been suggested by Gey and other workers; it is that mitochondria arise by morphological differ-entiation of pinocytotic vesicles, which are themselves in turn formed by pinching off of the plasma membrane during pinocy-tosis, or the engulfing of external fluid by the plasma mem-brane. This possibility perhaps should not be discounted, but such a process must explain how the double-membrane system of the mitochondria is formed from the single-membrane vesicle. Presumably the pinocytotic vesicles are precursors of the *lysosomes*, which contain certain specific hydrolytic en-

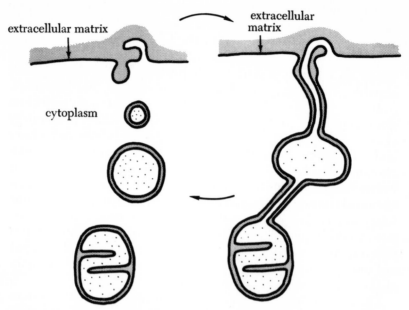

Figure 11–1 Suggested mechanism of origin of membrane systems of mitochondrion from single unit cell membrane. (After Robertson, 1961.)

zymes and which also appear to be devices for absorption and disposal of foreign proteins and enzymes; the lysosomes usually appear in the mitochondrial fraction.

Actually, among the various theories for formation of mitochondria from other membranous structures, the idea that they arise from the cell membrane is theoretically an admissible one, since the mitochondrial membranes are capable of some of the functions found in cell membranes. The plasma membrane contains molecular devices for translocating ions, although these appear to differ in fundamental respects from those of mitochondria. Furthermore, it is evidently endowed with mechanochemical or contractile activity, and, in the case of bacterial cell membranes, it may also contain respiratory activity. Nevertheless, convincing evidence for formation of mitochondria from the plasma membrane remains to be presented.

It has also been proposed that the endoplasmic reticulum may be a precursor of mitochondria. At one time Chantrenne and Brachet proposed that microsomes are precursors of mitochondria, which were believed to arise through a series of stages that could be differentiated on the basis of their enzyme content. These authors have since abandoned this view, which was based on the use of earlier cell fractionation techniques not capable of resolving mitochondria, microsomes, and lysosomes.

It may be noted, however, that the endoplasmic reticulum does contain a rudimentary nonphosphorylating respiratory chain comprised of NAD and NADP-cytochrome reductases and cytochrome b_5 but these components are not found in mitochondria. Furthermore, the lipid distribution in microsomes is rather different from that in mitochondria. Although these biochemical considerations do not necessarily exclude endoplasmic reticulum as the precursor of mitochondria, such a transformation would require a very considerable amount of biochemical differentiation to take place. The differentiation would consist not only of loss of specific microsomal enzymes but also gain of the specific mitochondrial enzymes.

The nuclear membrane has also been proposed as the system of origin of mitochondria, the basis of the proposal being electron microscopic studies of nerve cells, amoebae, and trypanosomes and from work on plant cells. The evidence from such observations is indeed very suggestive and perhaps more convincing than the evidence for formation of mitochondria from other membrane structures, but again it is quite circumstantial. Little biochemical information is at hand for comparison of the chemical and enzymatic features of the nuclear membrane with those of mitochondria.

Ehret and Powers have suggested that the nucleolus may be the site of origin of mitochondria, on the ground that in *Paramecium* species these two organelles appear to be very similar structurally, as revealed by electron micrographs. In other cell types, however, there appears to be little evidence of similarity. Nevertheless, there are biochemical aspects of some interest in such a relationship. Work of Allfrey and Mirsky has clearly shown that isolated nuclei of thymus and other cells respire and are able to phosphorylate internal or endogenous nucleotide, processes that presumably occur in the nucleolus, in which the turnover of RNA is very high.

Nuclear respiration has a number of interesting common denominators with mitochondrial respiration, as well as some significant differences; for example, nuclear respiration and phosphorylation are not sensitive to the same inhibitors as are the mitochondrial processes. Isolated nuclei also are capable of ion transport. These biochemical and functional relationships are thus very suggestive; and together with other evidence described later, the theory that mitochondria originate from the nucleus must be given further consideration.

The Golgi apparatus has often been postulated to be the site of origin of mitochondria, and indeed of other membrane systems of the cell. This idea has not yet been fully developed and also deserves further consideration, particularly since the function of the Golgi apparatus in the cellular economy is still not certain. Finally, recent work in Sjöstrand's laboratory indicates that during development of immature retinal rod cells, there is a large increase in the number of mitochondria. From serial sections it has been found that the new mitochondria arise from a point in the cell removed from the nucleus or cell membrane, apparently from simple, smaller vesicles with a single membrane.

BIOGENESIS BY GROWTH AND DIVISION

The bulk of the experimental evidence on the biogenesis of mitochondria favors the concept that preexisting mitochondria may grow and divide. This process would require acquisition of biochemical precursors from the cytoplasm and their assembly by the action of mitochondrial enzymes to the level of new, additional membrane structure and enzyme assemblies. The large mitochondria would then divide by a fission process. Such a picture was first proposed, in principle, by Altmann and other earlier investigators, who considered mitochondria to undergo a genetically linked division cycle. Among the items of evidence that may be cited in support of this hypothesis is the careful study of Frederic, who observed by time-lapse cinematography under phase contrast the number and distribution of mitochondria in cells at different stages of cell division. He found that the mitochondria of the parent cell underwent a passive, equal distribution in the daughter cells. Some time after cell division was complete, the original number of mitochondria was restored in each daughter cell by a process of lengthening and division.

Electron micrographs have frequently shown mitochondria in an extended dumbbell configuration, suggesting beginning of a division. For example, such mitochondria have been observed to be rather common in liver cells of thyrotoxic animals by Greenawalt. The propensity of mitochondria to undergo lengthening or end-to-end aggregation, which was mentioned in Chapter 2, may also be related to mitochondrial growth and division.

Ingeniously designed experiments reported by Luck provide important evidence for a process of mitochondrial growth and division in *Neurospora crassa*. Luck allowed a choline-requiring mutant of *Neurospora* to grow on a medium containing radioactive choline. In the growth process the labeled choline was incorporated into the phosphatidyl choline of the mitochondrial membrane. Such labeled cells were then placed in a medium containing nonradioactive choline and allowed to grow through the logarithmic growth period.

Since *Neurospora* cultures of this type represent a homogeneous population characterized by relatively synchronous growth, it was possible to harvest cells in nearly homogeneous states over three mass-doubling cycles. From cells harvested at specific time intervals, the mitochondria were isolated and the distribution of label in individual mitochondria was determined by a quantitative radio-autographic technique. In this experiment three labeling patterns in the mitochondria of the daughter cells could have been expected depending on the mechanism of biogenesis of the mitochondria.

1. All mitochondria of the daughter cells might be labeled relatively equally and the average grain count per mitochondrion could decrease as a function of growth. This pattern would be consistent with mitochondrial division.

2. Both labeled and unlabeled mitochondria might be found, with the labeled ones decreasing in proportion during growth, but with the grain count per labeled mitochondrion remaining the same. This pattern would be consistent with de novo synthesis of mitochondria from essentially nonlabeled precursors.

3. An intermediate pattern, in which the label would not be randomly distributed in all mitochondria and the proportion of labeled mitochondria would decrease less rapidly than in case 2, with the grain count per mitochondrion decreasing, remaining the same, or even increasing slightly. This pattern would be consistent with formation of mitochondria from labeled precursors, particularly from other labeled membrane structures.

After performing necessary control experiments, Luck found that when such *Neurospora* cells with labeled mitochondria had doubled in mass, the average grain count for all mitochondria had diminished to almost exactly one-half. Secondly, he found, on counting the grains of radioactivity in some 300 mitochondria at each stage, that the radioactivity was randomly distributed among all the mitochondria over a total of three mass-doubling cycles. From these experiments Luck concluded that the mitochondrial mass increases by a continuous addition of new choline-containing lipids and other precursors to existing mitochondria, followed by division, in a completely random manner. It is thus clear that the preexisting labeled mitochondrial membrane lipid is transmitted uniformly to all progeny.

Luck presented some evidence that the methods used for isolating mitochondria did not cause randomization of label between labeled and unlabeled mitochondria, and he was also able to exclude occurrence of very rapid fusion-and-fission cycles. However, the control experiments were perhaps unable to exclude all possible types of complicating events. Although Luck's conclusion may be valid only for *Neurospora* cells, it appears very unlikely that different cell types have fundamentally different mechanisms for biosynthesis of mitochondria. Luck's experiment may be accepted for the time being as perhaps the most rigorous test yet devised for the mechanism of mitochondrial biogenesis.

THE EVOLUTIONARY ORIGIN OF MITOCHONDRIA

The question of how and in what types of cell mitochondria first arose during the course of evolution may give further insight into the mechanisms of formation of mitochondria that have just been discussed. This question may be approached by considering the comparative occurrence of mitochondria in different cell types, particularly in microorganisms.

Mitochondria have been found in all aerobic cells of higher animals and plants, as well as in the higher Protists, including algae, protozoa, and fungi. The cells of all these forms are relatively large and sometimes contain enormous numbers of mitochondria. However, there is a sharp division when we contemplate the lower Protists, which include the bacteria and the blue-green algae, since, in general, the latter possess no mitochondria, at least as far as has been examined. The lower Protists are usually very small cells of about the same dimensions as mitochondria of higher cells, and they therefore cannot contain mitochondria of the same dimensions as seen in larger cells. In the true bacteria the respiratory enzymes and phosphorylation systems are present in the plasma membrane of the cell rather than in cytoplasmic granules, at least in the few organisms that have been examined, which include *Micrococcus lysodeikticus* and *Bacillus megaterium.* However, some of the true bacteria may attain relatively large size, and it would be of the greatest interest to determine whether such larger bacteria contain true mitochondria, in view of metabolic considerations.

Vanderwinkel and Murray have demonstrated that respiratory activity in a few microorganisms is located in the *mesosomes,* small vesicular structures with a complex folded membrane system. Giesbrecht has also recently presented microscopic evidence that some bacteria may in fact contain a few small "mitochondria." In the evolution of higher cells it would appear that at some point the simpler, smaller bacterial cells evolved into larger and more complex forms by addition of new structural envelopes or membranes that may have taken over some of the functions of the cell membrane in the smaller bacteria.

It has also been suggested that mitochondria of higher cells may have evolved from microorganisms that originally parasitized the cytoplasm of a large host cell. Over the course of evolution such parasites may have become permanent "residents" who adjusted their life cycle to that of the host cells. Many intracellular parasites are, of course, known today; examples are the malarial parasites and the Rickettsiae.

It seems not impossible that such intracellular parasites may have become nonpathogenic in the course of evolution of the host cell and achieved a truly symbiotic relationship with it. It is remarkable that bacteria are about the same size as mitochondria, that they contain phosphorylating respiratory chains in their surrounding membrane, as do the mitochondria, and that they show remarkably similar swelling-contraction cycles and ion-transport activities. Furthermore the sialic acid recently found in mitochondria may be a vestige of the more elaborate mucopolysaccharide wall of the bacterial cell.

The basis of metabolic symbiosis may lie in the possibility that a very large cell, such as in mammalian tissues, which might have a several thousandfold larger volume than a bacterium, might not be able to survive if its phosphorylation processes and respiratory chains were limited to the outer plasma membrane, as is the case in simple bacteria. The energy requirement of the large cytoplasmic mass could not be adequately supplied with ATP from respiratory assemblies in the plasma membrane alone, either because of the relatively long diffusion paths or because the plasma membrane could not possibly contain enough respiratory assemblies to manufacture the amounts of ATP required.

Bacterial parasites in the cytoplasm might be able to provide additional respiratory assemblies to manufacture additional ATP in the interior cytoplasm and so make up the deficit. However, it is necessary to point out that a parasitic bacterium can not be useful to a host cell unless the ATP it manufactures becomes available to the surrounding cytoplasm. Normally, bacteria make ATP but retain it within the cell; it is not secreted. The bacterial membrane might, however, have acquired the property, which mitochondria do have, of making possible transfer of high-energy phosphate from internal ATP to external ADP via adenylate kinase or ATP-ADP exchange enzymes in the membrane.

It is of some interest that the Rickettsiae, which parasitize cells of some insects and higher animals, catalyze oxidations of the Krebs cycle and also oxidative phosphorylation. These organisms have never been cultivated successfully in a synthetic medium, suggesting they are quite dependent on factors that may be provided by the cytoplasm of the host cell. In fact, there is some evidence that the Rickettsiae are unable to catalyze glycolysis and possibly require a cytoplasmic medium in which the products of glycolysis are provided for them.

BIOGENESIS OF MITOCHONDRIA
IN FACULTATIVE CELLS

One fruitful line of investigation currently yielding interesting information on the biogenesis of mitochondria is the series of studies on facultative yeasts, which are capable of either anaerobic or aerobic life. It is now well known that aerobically grown yeast cells contain mitochondria that are readily isolated and show about the same type of respiratory organization and phosphorylation capacity as in higher mammalian cells. However, Ephrussi and Slonimski showed some years ago that anaerobically grown yeast cells contain no cytochrome a or b, which are synthesized only in response to the presence of oxygen, suggesting they are induced enzymes.

Linnane and his colleagues have recently examined with the electron microscope the cytoplasm of *Torula utilis* yeast cells grown under aerobic and anaerobic conditions, and they have carried out correlative biochemical and enzymatic studies. The aerobic cells contained mitochondria with the usual structural features. On the other hand, the anaerobically grown cells contained no mitochondria, but the cytoplasm of such cells was found to contain a previously undescribed membrane system that is not present in aerobic cells. This membrane system consists of a number of single *unit membranes* some of which are closely adjacent and parallel to each other, resembling superficially the organization of the myelin sheath. Some of the unit membranes are dispersed through the cytoplasm in a manner resembling the endoplasmic reticulum, but they differ from the latter in that they are disposed as single rather than double unit membranes and they contain no adhering granules (i.e., ribosomes). Some of the pictures clearly show that this membrane system is continuous with the nuclear envelope.

Linnane and his colleagues isolated from such anaerobic cells a particulate membrane fraction that presumably originated from the single cytoplasmic membranes. This fraction was found to have no aerobic oxidative capacity and contained no cytochrome a, but it did have very small amounts of cytochromes b and c. It is very significant, however, that these fragments were found to contain both succinate and NADH dehydrogenases capable of reducing ferricyanide, suggesting that the cytoplasmic membrane of the anaerobic cells contained some but not all of the components of the respiratory chain. When anaerobic *T. utilis* cells were aerated, the reticular membranes lined up in parallel arrays and fused to form what appeared to be rudimentary mitochondria with a few cristae; this process was accompanied by formation of cytochromes b and c and by appearance of respiratory activity.

A similar experimental approach has been taken in France by Yotsuyanagi, who has studied genesis of mitochondria in yeast. Although his findings are not entirely identical with those of Linnane, there seems little doubt that this experimental approach will yield information of the greatest significance. Furthermore, experiments like those of Ephrussi and his colleagues on the genetic basis of cytochrome formation in such yeasts may also reveal the cytogenetic mechanisms involved in morphogenesis of mitochondria.

METABOLIC TURNOVER
OF MITOCHONDRIAL STRUCTURE

In the experiments of Luck described above the mitochondrial mass approximately doubled as the total mass of the *Neurospora* cells doubled, with the increase in mitochondrial mass coming via growth of existing mitochondria; in these fast-growing cultures it is possible that mitochondrial growth and division are approximately synchronous with cell growth and division. It is of some interest, however, to consider the "turnover time" of mitochondria in cells with a much longer division time, as in the tissues of higher animals.

Fletcher and Sanadi have reported some interesting isotopic experiments on the rate of turnover of specific components of mitochondria in the livers of normal rats. The rats were given S^{35}-labeled methionine and C^{14}-labeled acetate in single doses to bring about biological in situ labeling of the proteins and lipids of mitochondria. The mitochondria were then isolated from groups of rats at intervals of 7 days and the metabolic replacement curves of the S^{35} in cytochrome c, insoluble membrane protein, and soluble protein were measured, as well as the metabolic decay curves of the total lipid C^{14}. It was found that the half-period of decay or regression was approximately the same for each of the four entities measured, indicating that the lipids, the soluble and insoluble proteins, and one specific enzyme component, cytochrome c, were replaced at about equal rates.

A second important finding was that the half-life for replacement of these mitochondrial components was about 10.3 days. Since the figures were not corrected for reutilization of labeled breakdown products, the half-life may have been even shorter. This figure compares with the half-life of total liver proteins of about 5 to 6 days.

Since the life span of DNA in intact adult rat liver, which is a measure of the lifetime of the liver cell, is very long, of the order of some 150 days, it is probable that at least the major components of mitochondria are replaced several times in the lifetime of the liver cell. The figures deduced by Fletcher and Sanadi are in agreement with those of Lund and his colleagues, who found by electron microscopic studies that depletion of mitochondria from mouse kidney in vivo, caused by administration of a foreign protein, is followed by essentially complete regeneration in about 10 days.

On the other hand, it appears possible that in some stable cells the mitochondria may also be very stable. Davison and his colleagues in London have found that the sulfatides of rat brain mitochondria, labeled during early growth of the rat by incorporation of S^{35}, turn over very slowly indeed; the half-time for replacement of S^{35} was about two years and was very similar to that of the labeled sulfatides in myelin sheath lipids. These results suggest that brain mitochondria grow and divide only very slowly and may be stable for the lifetime of the cell. They are also consistent with the view that sulfatides of mitochondria may be extremely stable, metabolically speaking, in comparison to the proteins and the other lipids of mitochondria.

BIOSYNTHETIC MECHANISM IN MITOCHONDRIA

Building-block molecules for synthesis of mitochondrial structure may be provided by the surrounding cytoplasm or by action of mitochondrial enzyme systems. Presumably, these building blocks are assembled in a synchronous manner into the characteristic proteins and lipids of the membranes and matrix by the action of biosynthetic enzymes. Some of these enzymes are present in the hyaloplasm or in extramitochondrial structures, and some are intrinsically located in the mitochondria per se; it is possible that construction of new mitochondrial material requires interplay of enzymes and precursors located in both mitochondria and extramitochondrial structures. Since lipids and proteins are the most prominent components of mitochondria, we may now consider whether isolated mitochondria can carry out biosynthesis of their own lipids and proteins by action of self-contained enzyme systems. Traditionally, the mitochondria have been regarded primarily as sites of oxidative activity, but recent work indicates they are also capable of considerable biosynthetic activity.

BIOSYNTHESIS OF LIPIDS IN MITOCHONDRIA

In the last few years the view has developed that biosynthesis of fatty acids and oxidation of fatty acids proceed by different pathways and by the intervention of different sets of enzymes located in different parts of the cell. Oxidation of fatty acids occurs in mitochondria by the pathways described in an earlier chapter, with acetyl-CoA as the basic unit removed at each turn of the spiral. However, fatty acid synthesis is known to take place by condensation of malonyl-CoA residues primarily, so that only the two methyl-terminal carbon atoms of the fatty acid chain arise from acetyl-CoA and all the other carbons arise from two adjacent carbon atoms of malonyl-CoA, the third being lost by decarboxylation.

The synthesis of fatty acids takes place through acyl thioesters not of CoA, but of an enzyme-bound —SH group. It has been rather generally held that fatty acid synthesis by this mechanism occurs by action of an extramitochondrial enzyme system and that the mitochondria are capable of only limited chain elongation of fatty acids, such as the conversion of C_{16} to C_{18} acids. More recently, however, Hülsmann has shown that beef heart mitochondria are in fact capable of quite rapid biosynthesis of long-chain fatty acids, and it is a very significant finding that this synthesis was found to occur via the malonyl-CoA route rather than by the reverse action of the enzymes catalyzing fatty acid oxidation. Hülsmann has also shown that mitochondria are capable of forming malonyl-CoA, the necessary precursor for fatty acid synthesis, through the reaction

$$\text{acetyl-CoA} + \text{oxalacetate} \rightleftharpoons \text{malonyl-CoA} + \text{pyruvate} \qquad (11\text{–}1)$$

Hülsmann has found that mitochondria from several cell types are capable of quite high rates of fatty acid synthesis, and in fact he suggests that earlier conclusions that fatty acid synthesis is normally extramitochondrial may be erroneous and that the mitochondria may in fact be a major site of cellular fatty acid synthesis.

Recent work also indicates that isolated mitochondria are capable of carrying out the enzymatic assembly of at least portions of some of the phospholipids. The respiration-dependent incorporation of inorganic phosphate into the total phospholipids of isolated mitochondria was first observed by Friedkin and Lehninger; and since their work, incorporation of phosphate into specific lipids such as lecithin and inositol phosphatides has been observed by several investigators. Furthermore, incorporation of other labeled building blocks such as long-chain fatty acids, serine, phosphorylcholine, phosphatidic acid, glycerophosphate, and glycerol, has also been observed in isolated respiring mitochondria. Although a completely systematic survey of all the enzymes required in biosynthesis of all the complex lipids of mitochondria has not yet been reported, Wilgram and Kennedy have found that some of these enzymes are localized outside the mitochondria. For example, the enzyme catalyzing the last stage in biosynthesis of phosphatidylcholine is almost entirely localized in the microsomes, or endoplasmic reticulum.

Thus, although mitochondria can carry out the total synthesis of fatty acids, as well as the incorporation of inorganic phosphate and other building blocks they are not capable of carrying out alone the complete synthesis of some of the major phosphatides. These findings thus indicate that endoplasmic reticulum and other cell structures must also participate in biosynthesis of mitochondrial membrane lipids.

BIOSYNTHESIS OF PROTEINS IN MITOCHONDRIA

It has already been pointed out that mitochondrial proteins rapidly become labeled when isotopic amino acids are administered to intact animals. The recent developments in the study of protein biosynthesis have implicated the ribosome as the central and basic site of amino acid incorporation and protein formation, and since the ribosomes of the ergastoplasm have ordinarily been considered to be purely extramitochondrial in occurrence, it has been doubted by many investigators that isolated mitochondria are capable of de novo synthesis of mitochondrial proteins without intervention of the ribosomes.

More recently, however, evidence has accumulated that proteins may be synthesized at sites other than ribosomes attached to the endoplasmic reticulum. For example, isolated nuclei are capable of quite rapid protein synthesis, and it has been shown that nuclei of some cells actually contain ribosomes. To date, however, there has been no unequivocal demonstration of the occurrence of ribosomes within mitochondria in sections of intact tissue.

It has been found in several laboratories that isolated, respiring liver and heart mitochondria do incorporate labeled amino acids into mitochondrial membrane proteins without the addition of either ribosomes or the so-called soluble pH 5.0 fraction of hyaloplasm that is known to furnish the amino acid–activating enzyme required in ribosomal protein synthesis. Work and Roodyn and their colleagues showed that the incorporated amino acids could not be found in any significant quantity in certain specific mitochondrial enzymes, such as cytochrome *c* and malate dehydrogenase, in relatively short incubation periods. Rather, the isotopic amino acid was chiefly incorporated into a crude protein fraction rich in phospholipid and RNA and possessing succinoxidase activity; presumably, this was derived from the mitochondrial membrane.

Controlled disruption of the mitochondrial membranes with detergents revealed that most of the isotopic incorporation occurred in the structural protein fraction, which may comprise, as we have seen, some 50 per cent or more of the membrane protein. It is striking that all mitochondrial proteins, including cytochrome *c*, become rapidly labeled in in vivo experiments, but only the structural protein becomes labeled in in vitro experiments, a finding that suggests that membrane proteins and enzyme proteins may be formed by different mechanisms.

Kroon has recently made the interesting discovery that the rate of incorporation of radioactive amino acids into mitochondrial proteins is very much greater when digitonin fragments of mitochondria are used than is the case for intact mitochondria. In fact, digitonin fragments of mitochondria were found to be far more active in incorporating amino acids than even ribosomes. It appears that mitochondria may have a rather intense ability to synthesize protein. However, this capacity may be kept under some check by permeability barriers or crypticity of certain enzymes. Conversely, it is possible that digitonin removes some inhibitor of protein synthesis in mitochondria.

Other studies by Truman and Korner have shown that the soluble fraction of mitochondrial proteins contains an amino acid–activating enzyme, and thus the enzymatic capability for forming amino acyl derivatives of sRNA. However, it is not yet known whether the mitochondria contain sRNA, the normal amino acid donor in ribosomal protein synthesis. Isolated mitochondria have long been known to contain RNA, but this has been traditionally regarded as adventitious and contributed by adhering microsomes.

Roodyn has pointed out that the mitochondrial RNA is probably not attached to ribosomes, which have a characteristic RNA:protein ratio of 1.0. It is of some interest in this connection that oxidative phosphorylation in liver and other mitochondria is uncoupled by crystalline ribonuclease, suggesting a function of RNA or a polynucleotide in oxidative phosphorylation. This view is directly supported by Pinchot's finding that a polynucleotide is necessary for oxidative phosphorylation in *Alcaligenes faecalis* extracts. Chèvremont and his colleagues have recently presented evidence that DNA may also be present in mitochondria in certain stages of cell division. These findings on mitochondrial nucleic acids deserve much more work, since they may be of extreme importance not only in biosynthesis of mitochondrial proteins but also in relation to the question of the mechanism of origin and division of mitochondria.

Hendler has suggested that protein synthesis is accompanied by concerted synthesis of phospholipids and that the two syntheses may be mutually dependent. He has found that amino acid incorporation into hen oviduct protein is inhibited by phospholipase A, lysolecithin, and deoxycholate, and he has also found that it can be greatly stimulated by addition of cytidine triphosphate, which is a necessary component in the biosynthesis of some phospholipids. Since the mitochondrial membrane consists of a highly organized lamellar structure of phospholipids and structural proteins, it appears very attractive to consider that membrane synthesis must occur by concerted synthesis of both the lipid and protein components, in such a manner that each serves as the structural template for the other, to form a thermodynamically stabilized end product. That the synthesis of membrane proteins occurs by a route and mechanism that may differ from the synthesis of soluble or ribosomal protein is also indicated by recent work of Phillips.

If the synthesis of biological membranes occurs by a special concerted mechanism of the kind described above, possibly each membranous structure of the cell, including the mitochondrion, may have the enzymatic capacity to "spin off" new membrane in such a manner that preexisting membrane serves as the template for its own assembly from specific proteins and lipids. The enzyme molecules comprising the respiratory assemblies may be synthesized by some more specific, possibly ribosomal process and later attached to the mitochondrial membrane in a secondary process. Of great significance in this connection is the work of Pette and Bücher and their colleagues, who have demonstrated that the ratios of specific activities of certain mitochondrial enzymes involved in the electron-transport chain and in the Krebs cycle are approximately constant in mitochondria of different tissues and species, suggesting that these enzymes are synthesized in specific molar ratios and in possibly synchronous or genetically related processes.

From these findings it is now clear that mitochondria may have the capacity to synthesize at least some of their own membrane lipids and proteins in vitro, and it appears quite possible that some elements of morphogenesis of mitochondrial structure may be amenable to study in vitro. Perhaps this area will constitute a new chapter in the molecular biology of the mitochondrion.

REFERENCES

Reviews

Ephrussi, B., "Interplay of heredity and environment in the synthesis of respiratory enzymes in yeast," *Harvey Lectures*, Ser. 44, 45 (**1948–1949**), (1950).

Moulder, J. W., *The Biochemistry of Intracellular Parasitism*, University of Chicago Press, Chicago, 1962.

Novikoff, A. B., "Mitochondria (chondriosomes)," in J. Brachet and A. E. Mirsky (eds.), *The Cell*, Academic, New York, 1960, Vol. II, p. 299.

Rouiller, C., "Physiological and pathological changes in mitochondrial morphology," *Intern. Rev. Cytol.*, 9, 227 (1960).

Research papers

Baudhuin, P., and H. Beaufay, "Examen au microscope électronique des fractions purifiées d'organites cytoplasmiques de foie de rat," *Arch. Intern. Physiol. Biochim.*, 71, 119 (1963).

Chèvremont, M., E. Baeckeland, and S. Chèvremont-Canhaire, "Contribution cytochimique et histo-autoradiographique à l'étude du metabolism et de la synthèse des acids désoxyribonucléiques dans des cellules animals cultivées *in vitro*. II," *Biochem. Pharmacol.*, 4, 67 (1960).

Davison, A. W., and J. Dobbing, "Metabolic stability of body constituents," *Nature*, 191, 844 (1961).

Fletcher, M. J., and D. R. Sanadi, "Turnover of rat liver mitochondria," *Biochim. Biophys. Acta*, 51, 356 (1961).

Giesbrecht, P., "Über organisierte Mitochondrien und andere Feinstrukturen von Bacillus Megaterium," *Zentr. Bakteriol., Parasiten., Abt. I(a) Ref.,* **179,** 538 (1960).

Hülsmann, W. C., "Fatty acid synthesis in heart sarcosomes," *Biochim. Biophys. Acta,* **58,** 417 (1962).

Klingenberg, M., and D. Pette, "Proportions of mitochondrial enzymes and pyridine nucleotides," *Biochem. Biophys. Res. Commun.,* **7,** 430 (1962).

Kroon, A. M., "Amino acid incorporation into the protein of mitochondria and mitochondrial fragments from beef heart," *Biochim. Biophys. Acta,* **69,** 184 (1963).

Linnane, A. W., E. Vitols, and P. G. Nowland, "Studies on the origin of yeast mitochondria," *J. Cell Biol.,* **13,** 345 (1962).

Luck, D. J. L., "Genesis of mitochondria in *Neurospora crassa,*" *Proc. Natl. Acad. Sci. U.S.,* **49,** 233 (1963).

Pette, D., M. Klingenberg, and T. Bücher, "Comparable and specific proportions in the mitochondrial enzyme activity pattern," *Biochem. Biophys. Res. Commun.,* **7,** 425 (1962).

Robertson, J. D., "Cell membranes and the origin of mitochondria," *Regional Neurochem., Proc. 4th Neurochem. Symp.,* Pergamon, Oxford, 1961, p. 497.

Roodyn, D. B., "Protein synthesis in mitochondria. III," *Biochem. J.,* **85,** 177 (1962).

Schatz, G., "The isolation of possible mitochondrial precursor structures from aerobically grown baker's yeast," *Biochem. Biophys. Res. Commun.,* **12,** 448 (1963).

Truman, D. E. S., and A. Korner, "Initial stages in the incorporation of amino acids into proteins in rat-liver mitochondria," *Biochem. J.,* **85,** 154 (1962).

Wilgram, G. F., and E. P. Kennedy, "Intracellular distribution of some enzymes catalyzing reactions in the biosynthesis of complex lipids," *J. Biol. Chem.,* **238,** 2615 (1963).

Yotsuyanagi, Y., "Études sur le chondriome de la levure. I, II," *J. Ultrastruct. Res.,* **7,** 121, 141 (1962).

INDEX

INDEX